# Contributors

Sir William M. Henderson, DSc, FRCVS, FRSE, FRS.
  Former Secretary to the Agricultural Research Council.
Professor R. L. Bell, PhD, CEng, FIM, FInstP.
  Director, National Institute of Agricultural Engineering, Wrest Park, Silsoe, Bedford.
P. M. Biggs*, DSc, FRCVS, FRCPath, FIBiol., FRS.
  Director, Houghton Poultry Research Station, Huntingdon, Cambridgeshire.
Sir Kenneth L. Blaxter, DSc, FRSE, FRS.
  Director, Rowett Research Institute, Bucksburn, Aberdeen.
J. B. Brooksby*, CBE, DSc, FRCVS, FRSE, FRS.
  Former Director, Animal Virus Research Institute, Pirbright, Surrey.
K. N. Burns, BSc(VetSc), MRCVS.
  Scientific Adviser in Veterinary Medicine to the Secretary, Agricultural Research
    Council.
G. W. Cooke, CBE, PhD, FRSC, FRS.
  Former Chief Scientific Officer, Agricultural Research Council.
E. E. Croker, Chief Personnel Officer, Agricultural Research Council.
Professor D. J. Finney, CBE, ScD, FRSE, FRS.
  Honorary Director, Unit of Statistics, University of Edinburgh.
L. Fowden, PhD, FRS.
  Director, Rothamsted Experimental Station, Harpenden, Herts.
J. C. Hawkins, BSc, NDA, FIAgrE.
  National Institute of Agricultural Engineering, Wrest Park, Silsoe, Bedford.
Professor W. Holmes, BSc(Agric), DSc, FIBiol.
  Department of Agriculture, Wye College, Ashford, Kent.
J. W. B. King, PhD, FIBiol., FRSE.
  Director, Animal Breeding Research Organisation, Edinburgh.
W. B. Martin*, PhD, MRCVS, DVSM.
  Director, Animal Diseases Research Association, Moredun Institute, Edinburgh.
Professor J. M. Payne*, PhD, MRCVS.
  Director, Institute for Research on Animal Diseases, Compton, Berkshire.
Professor W. F. Raymond, CBE, MA, FRSC.
  Deputy Chief Scientist, Ministry of Agriculture, Fisheries and Food, London.
Ralph Riley, DSc, FRS.
  Secretary to the Agricultural Research Council.
J. A. F. Rook, DSc, FRSE.
  Second Secretary to the Agricultural Research Council. (Former Director, Hannah
    Research Institute, Ayr, Scotland.)
D. Rudd-Jones, PhD, FIBiol.
  Director, Glasshouse Crops Research Institute, Littlehampton, West Sussex.
D. W. F. Shannon†, PhD, DMS.
  Director, Poultry Research Centre, Roslin, Midlothian.
F. Yates, CBE, ScD, FRS. (Former Head of the Statistics Department)
  Rothamsted Experimental Station, Harpenden, Herts.

---

*Contributor to the essay on Animal Diseases
†Contributor to the essay on Animal Husbandry

# Agricultural Research Council, 1931–1981

## Preface

British agriculture is a success story. During the last forty years our farmers have achieved a more rapid transformation of our agriculture than was ever previously experienced. In the 1930s we depended for about two-thirds of our food on imports from overseas. Now two-thirds of the kinds of food that can be grown in our climate, or just over half of our total requirements, are home-produced on less land, by much less labour, and for a larger population. Average cereal yields are double those of forty years ago and root crops yield about 50% more than they did in the 1930s. Our farms provide for 40% more cattle, four times as many pigs, twice as many hens, and more sheep, than they did in 1939. Annual milk yields per cow, and eggs per hen, are more than 50% greater than in pre-war days.

These changes have been greatly aided by improved economic conditions for farming, beginning in the war and continued as national policy in the post-war period, and the necessary capital investment has been forthcoming to enable this increase in productivity to be brought about. But they would not have taken place without scientific knowledge on how to manage our land, crops and livestock for high productivity. The advance of agriculture was helped by better varieties and an understanding of how efficiently to use fertilisers and protect crops against pests and diseases. Similarly, by the use of scientific knowledge about reproduction, nutrition and disease, many of the factors have been removed or diminished that formerly limited livestock productivity. Developments in agricultural engineering have been of equally great importance and the way our land is worked, our crops are grown and harvested, and our livestock are kept, has changed out of all recognition in the last fifty years. More recently the contribution of science to food technology has increased and my Council is committed to the extension of this by further research.

The improvement in our farming owes a great debt to our excellent Advisory Services, and the Universities and Agricultural Colleges have contributed to the high competence of present-day farmers to deal with technological change. But little would have been possible without the research done during the last fifty years in agricultural science and engineering. The Agricultural Research Council was set up in 1931 and during the last fifty years it has guided the many components of our system that provide for research and development in agriculture. The nucleus of Institutes and University groups existed before the ARC was formed. Since 1931 the Council has skilfully developed other scientific areas that were needed, and has enabled the Agricultural Research Service to become the comprehensive, competent and stable entity that we see today. Because of its great achievements for the improvement of British agriculture, I am proud to be associated with the Council as its Chairman.

No organisation is stronger than its components and here I must praise all of those public-spirited people who have, during the last fifty years, given their energy, understanding and time to the Council's affairs. It is not just a matter of attending meetings: the health of the Agricultural Research Service is constantly in their minds and they help by visiting Institutes and Units and provide advice on the many special problems that arise in managing and developing the Service. Council's strength has lain over these fifty years in the corporate wisdom of its members. They include scientists, farmers, industrialists and administrators and, in my experience, Council is always able to debate effectively scientific, technical or administrative matters. I would like to thank particularly those Council members who are my colleagues in this Jubilee year, for I see at first hand all that they do for the Agricultural Research Service and therefore for the scientific development of agriculture.

Our research has been generously supported by Government funds over the fifty years that we are now reviewing, and my Council is grateful for the support it has received. The economic and social return from this investment by governments has been very considerable, and I am confident that the funds entrusted to us have been well and, from the national point of view, profitably spent. In this we have enjoyed the fullest collaboration with the Ministry of Agriculture, Fisheries and Food. I must also emphasize that the Council has had a long, useful and happy association with the Department of Agriculture and Fisheries for Scotland. This association has enabled agricultural research on both sides of the Border to work as a single integrated endeavour.

The ultimate value of Council lies, of course, in the scientific work which it sponsors, guides and administers. Therefore one important feature of its Golden Jubilee must be an assessment of the gains in scientific information that have accrued in the last fifty years. This is provided by the twelve essays in this volume which deal with most important aspects of agricultural science and engineering. Their authors are distinguished scientists who are, or have been, associated with the Agricultural Research Service. The first part of the volume describes the history of Council since its formation in 1931, and the establishment of the Institutes and Units which now make up the Service. We were fortunate indeed that Sir William Henderson, Secretary to the Council from 1972 to 1978, was persuaded to write this history. I must thank him for providing an account that is fascinating to read, which is thorough and comprehensive, and yet conveys much of the vigour of Sir William's personality. His deep knowledge and understanding of the affairs of Council and the Service, and his profound belief in the value of our work for farming and the need to maintain the highest standards in science and administration, all come out clearly in his chapters.

It is appropriate that I should pay tribute to Sir William's own contribution to Council's affairs since this does not emerge clearly from what he has written! He has, of course, described the conditions under which he took up his duties and the difficult situation he immediately encountered in establishing the commissioning of work by the Ministry of Agriculture, Fisheries and Food which ultimately became responsible for over half of the funding of the research done in England and Wales. He also played a major rôle in establishing the Joint Consultative Organisation which advised its three sponsors, the Ministry of Agriculture, Fisheries and Food, the Department of Agriculture and Fisheries for Scotland, and the ARC, on the priorities which should be ascribed to different topics in our work. Sir William also saw the need to establish broad priorities in the new areas that represent the growing points of agricultural science. To achieve this he set up Council's Priorities Working Party which has had a major rôle in establishing the Council's initiative in several new fields of research, and, has attracted some increase in the funds available for such work. Sir William strove continuously to promote the interests and welfare of working scientists so that they could give of their best. At the same time he was always available to guide his staff with his acute mind and to listen to the views of individuals. His warm personality and keen interest in all scientific work made him a welcome visitor everywhere and greatly strengthened the Service.

This assessment of Sir William's rôle at a critical time in the Council's history does not preclude an expression of my appreciation of the present Secretary, Dr Ralph Riley, who took office only a few weeks after I became Chairman. His experience in research has been of great value to me and to Council during the last two years.

Finally I must pay tribute to the very many workers, past and present, in the Agricultural Research Service upon whose dedication the success of our work has been built. They include scientists who have opened new vistas and who have achieved international recognition. There have also been very many who, by their devotion on farms, in workshops, offices and libraries have enabled agricultural research to be pursued with resolution by those in the front lines of our programmes in the field, animal house, glasshouse or laboratory. The future will continue to provide great challenges to our staff. The frontiers of the battles against diseases of plants and animals are never static. Increases in the prices of energy and nutrients will require changes in methods and the research to back them up; welfare and environmental considerations will make new demands. If the present quality of the teams, on Council, and in the whole Service, can be maintained, I foresee an even greater contribution in the next fifty years to the efficiency of agriculture, and to food production, from the new research that will be done.

PORCHESTER

## Acknowledgement

The Council wishes to thank the Directors of Institutes and Units of the Agricultural Research Service for their help in compiling Appendix 6. Nearly all of the illustrations in this Volume came from Institutes; Directors and staff who supplied the many photographs, from which the selection was made, are thanked for their help.

The thanks of the Agricultural Research Council are also due to Dr. George Cooke, CBE, who acted as General Editor of this Volume. They also thank Mr. Laurence Porter, OBE, who assisted Sir William Henderson in the preparation of the historical survey; Mrs. Eveline Docherty, MBE, who typed and retyped the manuscript; and Mrs. Marion Lewis who assisted the General Editor in manifold ways.

# BRITISH AGRICULTURAL RESEARCH

and

# THE AGRICULTURAL RESEARCH COUNCIL

A Personal Historical Account

Sir William Henderson

*Secretary to the Council*
1972–1978

# Chapter 1

# 1700–1931

## The Foundations of Agricultural Research

The publication of this volume is in celebration of 50 years of agricultural research in Great Britain under the aegis of the Agricultural Research Council. Although the following historical review has been written to provide an account of that period, it has to include some reference to the antecedents and to the contemporary development of other organisations if the work and influence of the Council are to be seen in correct perspective. In describing the rôle of the Council and the development of the present research structure which, for convenience, is referred to as the Agricultural Research Service, the approach has been to attempt to identify the succession of episodes, the influence of which had their effect on the Council's policy. Less attention than is merited is given to the work of the individual Institutes and Units. This applies even more so to the Directors and the Headquarters' personnel responsible for the effective functioning of the system. This account is in no way, therefore, a history of the research establishments except to record where and when they appeared in the train of events of which this chronicle is composed. Althought mention is made throughout the text of the personages most immediately involved, this citation is far from complete. A number of tables and appendices have, therefore, been prepared which list those whose contribution certainly deserves mention. There are many others who are neither listed nor mentioned whose contribution was equally important. No offence is intended. Those who, because of the positions they held and the parts that they played, were first mentioned relatively early in their careers, tended to acquire recognition which altered their style of address or added to their post-nominals. The procedure adopted is as follows: in general, the first mention uses the form of address then extant but without post-nominals; any subsequent change in the form of address as the result of an honour conferred by the Sovereign is recorded. Thereafter, the highest title received is used. In the various appendices, names are given under the highest rank attained with titles as at the latest date. In the exceptional case of a person being mentioned only once, or because of being so well known, or due to the context, these criteria have not always been strictly observed.

### The Gifted Amateurs

There is a long tradition in Great Britain in all branches of science and technology by which contributions to knowledge by observation or experiment may come from gifted amateurs as well as from those trained in a particular discipline. This is the story of progress in agriculture starting from the first attempts at the domestication of our plants and animals but the current period can be considered to have begun during the 18th century. A most significant change had largely taken place at that time, namely, the replacement of the medieval open-field system by enclosed holdings. It thus became possible to grow crops on larger acreages and rear livestock in larger numbers in a much more planned and controlled manner. Two prominent examples of gifted amateurs of that early period were born in the same year but in very different backgrounds. One was Charles Townshend, second Viscount Townshend (1674–1738) of Rainham, Norfolk who, because of his activities which now merit reference, came to be known as "Turnip" Townshend. The other was Jethro Tull (1674–1741), the Berkshire farmer who introduced the concept of precision of placing with reference to the plant and the soil and who saw the necessity to discriminate between crops and weeds. Townshend, after a very active political career during the reigns of Queen Anne, George I and George II, retired to his Norfolk estate and devoted himself to the improvement of agriculture, especially on enclosed land. A particular interest was the establishment of the turnip as a field crop which hitherto had been grown solely as a garden vegetable. The contemporary inspiration of Tull which led to his designing and developing specific implements such as the seed drill and the horse-drawn hoe for the furtherance of the productivity of arable crops complemented Townshend's contributions. Fodder crops for livestock had thus become available just at the right time to enable Robert Bakewell (1726–1795) and his contemporaries more effectively to encourage and develop their practices of livestock improvement by selection and breeding within a flock or herd gathered to contain the best individuals of a local type. The personal success of Bakewell produced the Leicester breed of sheep which was followed by the development of many British breeds of farm livestock that subsequently dominated animal production to an extraordinary extent. All the following breeds have been recognised, recorded in their studbooks and supported by their breed socieities for more than 100 years, and in some cases at least recognised for more than 200 years:

Cattle :  Shorthorn, Hereford, Ayrshire, Aberdeen Angus.
Pigs :    Tamworth, Large White, Berkshire, Large Black.
Sheep :   Leicester, Southdown, Cheviot, Oxford Down, Hampshire Down, Clun,
                Border Leicester, Scottish Blackface, Romney Marsh.
Horses : Thoroughbred, Clydesdale, Suffolk, Shire, Hackney.

## The Agricultural Societies and the Boards of Agriculture

The initiatives of Townshend, Tull, Bakewell and their contemporaries stimulated a desire for the dissemination of information, and many agricultural societies were formed in the second half of the 18th century for the purpose of demonstrating new methods and new techniques. A Board of Agriculture was established in 1793 as a part of this movement with Arthur Young, a contemporary of Bakewell as its first Secretary. A decline in interest in agriculture following the end of the Napoleonic wars led to the disappearance of this Board. A subsequent Board of Agriculture which continues today as the Agricultural Departments, was not established until 1889. There was, however, much else happening in spite of the demise of the first Board of Agriculture. In 1838 "The English Agricultural Society" was formed which, in 1840, became the Royal Agricultural Society of England. The principal interest of the Society was the promotion of advances in agricultural education and knowledge.

## Animal Disease and Veterinary Medicine

A recurrent theme in agricultural progress is the effect of disease, especially in animal production. The losses caused by the diseases of horses (glanders, epizootic lymphangitis and mange) and by the diseases of cattle (rinderpest, pleuropneumonia, tuberculosis and foot-and-mouth disease) reached such serious proportions in the 18th century that the demand for effective veterinary intervention led to the establishment of veterinary schools, firstly in Lyon, France, in 1762, thereafter in Denmark, Germany, Austria and Hungary and in London in 1781 (The Royal Veterinary College). Repeated outbreaks of rinderpest in cattle which first occurred in Great Britain in 1714 led, in 1865, to the establishment of a State Veterinary Service. The measures which were then introduced involving the slaughter of diseased animals, and severe restrictions on movement and importation of animals led to the disappearance of the disease from this country in 1877. It will be seen later how, up to the present day, the control of animal disease is repeatedly identified as being of the highest priority.

## More Amateurs and some Professionals

The tradition of the individual contributing towards agricultural innovation is still continued. The private livestock breeder not only improves strains within breeds but also, on occasion, seeks to evolve new breeds. Improvement in the design of agricultural implements still receives a valuable contribution from farmers.

The story with regard to plants has a number of differences. During the last few centuries, many collections of plants were built up and introductions into Britain were very numerous, especially among the ornamentals. Mention has been made of "Turnip" Townshend and there were many other selectors and improvers but it was not until the end of the nineteenth century and into the beginning of the twentieth century that plant breeding became established with the production of greatly improved varieties of the principal arable crops. The early plant breeders who contributed most in the history of their science in this country were William Bateson (1861–1926), Rowland Harry (later Sir Rowland) Biffen (1874–1949) and E. S. Beaven, a contemporary of Bateson. It is interesting to note that the parentage of Biffen's famous Yeoman wheat included the variety "Browick", introduced about 1890. This had been derived from a mixed stock from a selection made in 1844 by Robert Banham of Browick, Norfolk, from the field crops on his farm.

## The First of the Agricultural Research Institutes

The start of organised agricultural research with the creation of specific institutes for this purpose dates from the last century with the generally recognised starting point being the experiments by John Bennet Lawes (Plate 1) in the fields of Rothamsted Manor from the 1830s with the formal establishment of the Rothamsted Experimental Station in 1843. Joseph Henry Gilbert (Plate 2) was Lawes' collaborator and together they continued their classic experiments by which the names of the principal fields at Rothamsted became, perhaps, as well known to agriculturalists at least as those of the many battle fields in our history. Indeed, there may be many for whom Broadbalk (Plate 3), Hoosfield and Park Grass are more familiar than, say Chalgrove, Roundway Down and Rowton Heath, scenes of Civil War contests.

In 1889 Lawes established the Lawes Agricultural Trust with part of the proceeds of the sale some years earlier of his fertilizer business. The Trust fund was for the permanent maintenance of the Experimental Station and although in no way approaching the sum now required for current expenditure, it has provided the Station with a most valuable degree of independence in that it has been sufficient for the purchase of land and for the construction of certain buildings. The history of the Woburn Experimental Farm for which the Lawes Agricultural Trust has also been responsible since 1926 provides another example of the way in which the action of individuals has been so successfully combined with that of official bodies for the maintenance of a working research enterprise over many decades.

*Plate 1* Sir John B. Lawes, Bt, FRS, the founder of Rothamsted Experimental Station.

The Agricultural Holdings Act (England) 1875 gave an outgoing tenant the right to compensation for the value of unexhausted manures including the manurial value of purchased feedingstuffs. The results of the experiments conducted by Lawes and Gilbert provided some relevant evidence but the Royal Agricultural Society of England stressed the need for additional investigations. In 1876 the then Duke of Bedford, (the ninth Duke), a Vice-President, offered the Society the possession of Crawley Mill Farm, and later some additional land to a then total extent of 52.6 hectares. Other small parcels added since 1962 increased this area to 76.9 hectares. Lawes and Dr. J. C. A. Voelcker, Consulting Chemist to the Society, were asked to design suitable

*Plate 2* Sir Joseph H. Gilbert, FRS, who worked with Sir John Lawes from 1843 to 1900.

*Plate 3* The Broadbalk Experiment on growing wheat continuously began at Rothamsted in 1843; a harvest scene in the late Nineteenth Century.

experiments, the cost of which was to be paid by the Duke. The tenancy and financial arrangements were continued by the tenth and the eleventh Dukes of Bedford for 36 years. The Society was successful in an application to the Development Commission for a grant for the Woburn experiments for 1912–13. This arrangement continued until 1921 when adverse financial circumstances led the Society to give up the tenancy. Since 1884, Dr. J. A. Voelcker, on the death of his father, had filled the appointments of consulting Chemist to the Society and Director of the Woburn Farm. As a private individual he took over the tenancy of the farm from the Society and continued the experiments which had long since been increased in their scope from the original remit to determine residual manurial values. The Ministry of Agriculture now provided the funds but with the stipulation that the work be supervised. This function was provided by the Lawes Agricultural Trust Committee which finally took over the tenancy from Voelcker in 1926. This type of combination of committee activities, reinforced by the dedication of individual champions of their causes, is not an unusual feature of the history of many agricultural research institutes.

## The Development Commission

The Development Commission was established under the Development and Road Improvement Funds Act (1909). Its function was to advise the Treasury on making grants or loans for the development of rural and coastal areas, including grants for agricultural research. These advances were made from the Development Fund. The Board of Agriculture and Fisheries and the Department of Agriculture for Scotland also supported research. With the creation of the Development Fund, however, this became the largest single source of government support for agricultural research. Further reference is made to the Development Commission in describing the creation of the Agricultural Research Council in 1931.

## The Beginnings of Agricultural Research in the Universities and Colleges

Agricultural research has always been part of the programme of the Universities, not only in Departments of Agriculture but progressively over the years in the departments of the sciences relevant to agriculture. This was also true of other educational establishments such as Colleges of Agriculture, some of which have become incorporated into their neighbouring University. The State Agricultural Departments developed their own research competence in addition to providing grants-in-aid to independent institutions. There is little to record for the end of the nineteenth century except that Wye College of Agriculture and the University College of Reading were engaged on soil studies and in 1894 the Ministry of Agriculture established a veterinary laboratory in rooms adapted for the purpose in Whitehall Place. This was the forerunner of the Central Veterinary Laboratory sited at New Haw, Weybridge, since 1917.

## The Beginnings of Animal Disease Eradication

Much more was being achieved in the late nineteenth century on the Continent of Europe especially in microbiology as can be exemplified by citing Pasteur, Koch and Ehrlich. Plant virology was born when in 1892 Iwanowsky discovered the filterability of the agent causing the mosaic disease of tobacco and 1897 was the starting date for animal virology through Loeffler and Frosch's filtration of the virus of foot-and-mouth disease. On the other hand this same period was one of great achievement on the part of the British State Veterinary Service in that sheep pox was eradicated in 1866, rinderpest in 1877, bovine pleuropneumonia in 1896 and rabies, for the time being, in 1902. An interesting point about the success of these campaigns of disease-eradication was that the approach was perforce, somewhat empirical. The measures which led to the eradication of rinderpest were devised long before the aetiology of the disease was understood and the viral cause determined. Bovine pleuropneumonia was eradicated in the same year as Nocard and Roux of the Pasteur Institute cultured the causative mycoplasma. Many of the measures for the control and eradication of foot-and-mouth disease were enforced in 1892, five years before it was shown that the agent responsible was a filter-passing virus.

## Local Support for Research

### The Long Ashton Research Station

One of the very strong components in the present agricultural research service is the participation of farmers and growers in the community of interest that can be identified with a specific Institute. This has two dimensions, one of which is the very specific and executive responsibility of a Board of Governors or a Governing Body as exemplified by the first of these in this context, namely, the Committee of the Lawes Agricultural Trust. The other stems from the keen interest of the farmer and the grower in finding solutions to their problems. Their identification with a specific Institute may have a strong regional basis which reflects the growing of certain produce in favoured localities. This is especially true in the horticultural sector of the industry. In connexion with the Institutes now under the aegis of the Agricultural Research Council the priority for the industry's participation must go to the fruit growers and cider makers in the West of England. The chief initiator was Robert Neville Granville who had been experimenting in cider making at his farm at Butleigh Court, near Glastonbury, since 1893 under the sponsorship of the Bath and West and Southern Counties Society aided by small grants from the Board of Agriculture. This assistance, to which were added grants from the County Councils of Devon, Gloucester, Hereford, Somerset, Worcester, and Monmouth provided the finance required for the founding in 1903 of the National Fruit and Cider Institute at Long Ashton to study the problems of cider orchards and cider making. In 1912 it became the Department of Agriculture and Horticulture of the University of Bristol. Since the 1930s it has been known as the Long Ashton Research Station, and it ranks second in the chronological order of the Institutes in the Agricultural Research Service.

### The John Innes Horticultural Institute, now the John Innes Institute

The third oldest Institute in the Agricultural Research Service is the John Innes Institute, founded in 1910 under the will of John Innes of Merton in Surrey. At least a third of the Institutes have, in their history, moved from one location to another but in terms of major removals, the record goes to the John Innes Institute. On the third occasion it found itself in the fortunate position of having to occupy a new site with the opportunity of designing new buildings for its current and future requirements. The Institute was established at Merton Park, which site it occupied from 1910 until 1946. It then became re-established at Bayfordbury in Hertfordshire. In 1967 the Institute again moved, this time, to its present site in Colney Lane, Norwich, in close association with the University of East Anglia. These moves and the occupation of the present buildings with their excellent facilities for research again exemplifies the contribution of the individual. The John Innes Charity, in spite of its diverse objectives, fully maintained the Institute until about thirty years ago and it funded the construction of the Institute's new laboratories and glasshouses, the housing of the John Innes "Special Collection" of rare books on horticulture, and the unique facilities for scientific conferences and staff recreation. The Special Collection deserves mention. Many of the books were acquired by William Bateson, the first Director of the Institute. When the Institute was at Merton Park, these books were kept in Bateson's office. After Bateson's death in 1926, the collection was incorporated into the Library of the Institute. The library facilities were improved when the Institute moved to Bayfordbury in 1946 and, with the invaluable help of the Trustees of the Charity the move to Norwich in 1967 saw the Special Collection housed in a way appropriate to this rare library recording much of the history of botanical science.

## Institutes Founded Between 1912 and 1930

The founding of the John Innes Institute in 1910 marked the start of a period of great activity during the years immediately before and after the 1914–1918 war in which no less than eleven other Institutes were established, the last of which in this series was the Macaulay Institute for Soil Research in 1930 thus bringing this history up to the creation of the Agricultural Research Council in 1931. Brief descriptions of the Institutes in question now follow.

### The National Institute for Research in Dairying

The National Institute for Research in Dairying was established in 1912 at University College, Reading, by the Development Commission in collaboration with the Board of Agriculture. The Shinfield Manor Estate was purchased in 1921 and it provided the present site of the Institute; at the same time, the present name was adopted in place of the original "Research Institute in Dairying". The University College obtained its University Charter in 1926 with the Institute remaining a part. Since the execution of a new trust deed in 1963, a University Delegacy has served as the Governing Body of the Institute. The history of this Institute provides another example of the assistance of a dedicated benefactor in that in the 1920s grants from the Development Fund were made on a pound for pound basis to match the gifts to the Institute from the then Viscount Elveden, the late second Earl of Iveagh.

### The Plant Breeding Institute

In 1912, a grant of £18 000 was made from the Development Fund to the School of Agriculture of the University of Cambridge for the establishment of an Institute which would provide additional facilities for plant breeding, thus was created the Plant Breeding Institute. The relationship between the Institute, the University of Cambridge, and the Agricultural Research Council after the Council's establishment, will be discussed later.

### The Rowett Research Institute

The date 1912 is claimed for the creation of the Rowett Research Institute in that in that year the Development Commission in collaboration with the Scottish Education Department set up an institute for research in animal nutrition in temporary accommodation in Marischal College, Aberdeen. Work was suspended during the war and it was not until 1922 that the institute was opened on its present site. This Institute has a considerable list of benefactors, for example, J. Q. Rowett, J. Duthie Webster, W. A. Reid, Lord Strathcona and C. Alexander. It is no belittling of their generosity to suggest that persuasion and persistence are valuable attributes for a Director to possess. The first Director of "The Rowett", Dr. J. B. Orr (later Lord Boyd Orr), had these characteristics in full measure.

## The East Malling Research Station

The initiative and drive of local fruit growers, this time in Kent, led to the Horticultural Research Station being established in 1913 at East Malling in connection with the South-Eastern Agricultural College at Wye. The Station became independent of the College in 1920 under the governance of the Kent Incorporated Society for Promoting Experiments in Horticulture then becoming known as the East Malling Research Station. One significant feature of the Station's relationship with the local horticultural industry is its vigorous Association comprising well over a thousand subscribing members.

## Three non-survivors in their original status

During this same period of one to two years prior to the 1914–1918 war, three other Institutes were created by the Development Commission. These have not survived in, so to speak, direct lineage to the present establishments conducting research on their subjects. In 1911, the Research Institute in Plant Physiology was founded at the Imperial College of Science and Technology by a grant from the Development Fund. Reference is made to the continuing programme on plant physiology at Imperial College in the chapter on the Units of the Agricultural Research Council. Another Institute created in 1911 by the Development Commission was the Cambridge Institute for Animal Nutrition. This was attached to the School of Agriculture. The Institute consisted of several sections and further attention will be given to that of the physiology of growth and reproduction which existed as an ARC Unit, firstly under the direction of Sir John Hammond, and secondly under Professor T. R. R. Mann, until being incorporated into the Institute of Animal Physiology as recently as 1976 (pp. 53–54). The third institute was for experimental and advisory work on glasshouse crops which was started by the growers in the Lea valley. In 1913 they formed the Nursery and Market Garden Industries Development Society and in 1914 with a pound for pound grant from the Development Fund, the Cheshunt Station was founded in Hertfordshire. The Station became the principal component of the present Glasshouse Crops Research Institute when this was established at Littlehampton, Sussex in 1953.

## The Institute for Research in Agricultural Economics

1913 is a year of note in the history of agricultural economics as the Ministry of Agriculture and Fisheries then established an Institute for Research in Agricultural Economics at Oxford, the need for which had been identified by the Development Commission which assisted with financial support from the Development Fund. The subsequent decisions of the Agricultural Research Council with regard to their involvement with this subject are described later (p. 31).

## The Welsh Plant Breeding Station

The first institute to be founded after the First World War was the Welsh Plant Breeding Station at Aberystwyth. Its creation provides yet another example of a private sponsor of agricultural research. In 1919, Sir Laurence Philipps, later Lord Milford, provided a capital sum of £10 000. The Development Commission provided £11 400 and a further £10 200 was raised by public subscription. The Station is a research department of the University College of Wales, Aberystwyth, which provides the Governing Body. It is the only Institute in Wales of the Agricultural Research Service, but the Agricultural Research Council has for many years provided research grants to various departments of the University College of North Wales, Bangor, besides supporting there the ARC Unit of Embryology from 1953 to 1968.

## The Animal Diseases Research Association

Although programmes of control and eradication of diseases of animals had been an active and successful part of the work of the Agricultural Departments, from the latter part of the nineteenth century onwards, comparatively little research work on animal disease had been conducted in this country during that same period. The most active centre was at the Royal Veterinary College, London, under the leadership of Sir John M'Fadyean. Sir Stewart Stockman was appointed Chief Veterinary Officer in the Board of Agriculture and Fisheries in 1905 and M'Fadyean and he contributed much to the development of veterinary medicine in the earlier part of this century. Although major ills such as rinderpest and bovine pleuropneumonia had been eradicated, tuberculosis, brucellosis, mastitis and the anaerobic bacterial infections were rife. The first attempt by the private sector to take some positive action was that of a group of Scottish farmers who, in 1921, formed the Animal Diseases Research Association and sponsored veterinary research at the Royal (Dick) Veterinary College, Edinburgh, and at the Glasgow Veterinary College. This initiative attracted support both from other private sectors and from the Development Fund through the Department of Agriculture for Scotland. This enabled the Association to become established permanently at its Moredun Institute, Gilmerton, Edinburgh, in 1926.

## The Scottish Plant Breeding Institute

A similar initiative took place at the same time in Scotland on the part of the arable farmers who wished to sponsor breeding of new varieties of crop plants suited to Scottish conditions. The Scottish Society for Research in Plant Breeding was formed in 1920. Over £20 000 was raised by the Society from private sources which was matched pound for pound by the Department of Agriculture for Scotland. The Scottish Plant Breeding Station was thus founded in 1921 at Craigs House, Corstorphine, Edinburgh, where it remained for 23 years before it was transferred in 1954 to the site of the Edinburgh University Centre of Rural Economy.

## The Pirbright Experimental Station, now the Animal Virus Research Institute

A very serious sequence of outbreaks of foot-and-mouth disease began in England in 1922 which continued for more than two years with payments for compensation for slaughter of affected herds amounting to approximately £4 million. In response to the public anxiety which resulted, the Minister of Agriculture in 1924 appointed the Foot-and-Mouth Disease Research Committee "to initiate, direct and conduct investigations into foot-and-mouth disease either in this country or elsewhere with a view to discovering means whereby the invasion of the disease may be rendered less harmful to agriculture". This Committee was the third of its kind to be appointed. The first had been appointed in 1912 to investigate the disease in India so as to avoid experimentation in this country. This project was abandoned after six months as being impracticable. The second Committee was appointed in 1920 and, in deference to agricultural opinion with regard to the risk of working with the virus, the research programme was carried out on an obsolete warship and an attendant lighter moored in the estuary of the River Stour near Harwich. Once again the project was abandoned, this time after eight months for what were described as almost insuperable difficulties in carrying out investigations afloat. This second Committee in presenting its report recommended that any future research on foot-and-mouth disease should be carried out on land.

When the third Committee was appointed in 1924 there was, apparently, no suitable experimental station for the necessary research programme which required accommodation for considerable numbers of farm livestock under reasonable conditions of disease security. It was quite by chance that changes in the method of testing cattle for tuberculosis, specifically the testing of cattle for export, made unnecessary the special isolation accommodation used for this purpose at the Ministry's Cattle Testing Station at Pirbright. This site with its extensive range of loose-boxes and a small laboratory building sited on the periphery of War Department land with a minimum density of susceptible farm livestock nearby was ideal for the Committee's purpose. Thus was established in 1924 the Pirbright Experimental Station. It later became known as the Foot-and-Mouth Disease Research Institute, then as the Research Institute (Animal Virus Diseases). In 1963 the name was formally changed to the Animal Virus Research Institute.

In view of the deference to the feelings of the animal production sector of the agricultural industry about foot-and-mouth disease research being conducted on the mainland of Great Britain, it is interesting to refer to the First Progress Report of the Foot-and-Mouth Disease Research Committee (HMSO, 1925). It is noted that althought the Committee had acquired the Cattle Testing Station at Pirbright, the greater part of the work had to be carried out elsewhere. This was taking place at the Central Veterinary Laboratory at New Haw, Weybridge and at the Lister Institute of Preventive Medicine; some research was later carried out at the University of Manchester; work was also in progress at the University of Liverpool. Investigations were, in fact, begun at the then Institute of Animal Pathology at Cambridge, but it had not been possible for work to be undertaken, as had been intended either at the Royal Veterinary College in London, nor under the auspices of the Animal Diseases Research Association in Scotland. In these two cases the obstacles were apparently administrative, for example, in the case of the Animal Diseases Research Association it was in the process of removal from Glasgow to Edinburgh. The Committee had also obtained the promise of facilities at the Medical Research Council's National Institute for Medical Research which were used from 1927 until 1939. So much for disease security, but it must be accepted that the consequences of any breach of that security would be difficult to identify during that period when there were rarely less than two outbreaks per week. It must be added that there is no evidence of any escape of virus having occurred from these "open" laboratories where work was limited to the bench and to small numbers of laboratory animals. In 1939, the Pirbright Institute became the sole location in the United Kingdom in which the virus of foot-and-mouth disease was examined for diagnostic purposes or used for research.

## The National Institute of Agricultural Engineering

The National Institute of Agricultural Engineering dates its foundation from 1924 when a research organisation was set up by the Ministry of Agriculture at Oxford.

Much discussion subsequently took place about the future rôle and policy of the State for sponsoring agricultural engineering. This subject deserves separate consideration which is given later (pp. 32–33), including reference to the Scottish Institute of Agricultural Engineering which was established in 1946.

## The Hannah Dairy Research Institute, now the Hannah Research Institute

The action of the Development Commission in 1912 to create the National Institute for Research in Dairying at Reading indicated their preoccupation with the problems of milk production and the need for research. It became evident that the field for investigation was larger than could be encompassed by the National Institute, especially because of the different needs of the dairy farmers in the wetter region of the West of Scotland where grassland farming is predominant. This necessity was recognised by the Development Commissioners and thus the Secretary of State for Scotland appointed a Committee of Management to implement a proposal that a dairy research institute might well be established in Scotland. Again the benefactor was at hand. Mr John M. Hannah of Girvan Mains, Ayrshire, offered the estate of Auchincruive to the nation for the purpose of agricultural education and research. This was implemented by the founding of the Hannah Dairy Research Institute in 1928 at the Kirkhill Farm of the Auchincruive Estate. The Institute's principal buildings were opened in 1931 with the great potential advantage that the site adjoined that of the West of Scotland Agricultural College, the properties of which comprise the greater part of the Auchincruive Estate.

## The Macaulay Institute for Soil Research

In 1928, Thomas Bassett Macaulay, President of the Sun Life Insurance Company of Canada, invited the co-operation of the Department of Agriculture for Scotland in furthering his wish to improve the agriculture of the Isle of Lewis. His father as a young man, had emigrated from there to Canada. Macaulay's original intention had been to set up an experimental farm on Lewis but he was persuaded to widen his scheme to include the establishment of an experimental station on the mainland for the study of soils and soil-plant relationships. At that time the significant work on soil chemistry was being done at the Rothamsted Experimental Station, the University College of North Wales, Bangor, and at the Universities of Edinburgh and Aberdeen. The Department of Agriculture sought the advice of Dr. W. G. Ogg (later Sir William Ogg) in Edinburgh and Professor Hendrick in Aberdeen. Thus Ogg was asked to find a suitable location for the investment of the Macaulay benefaction of £27 000; he chose Craigiebuckler House on the outskirts of Aberdeen and in 1930 became the first Director of the Macaulay Institute for Soil Research.

## Institutes in Less Direct Association with the Agricultural Research Service

Reference is made on p. 11 to institutes which were established prior to the first World War which were not fully in the main stream of the development and growth of the current Agricultural Research Service. During the post-war period there was also much activity being initiated in the public and the private sectors that is relevant but which was largely independent. These activities can conveniently be described in the categories of "Plants and Soils" and "Animals".

## Plants and soils

During the 1914–1918 war, the importance of food preservation, as well as food production, had become self-evident. Grants had, therefore, been made by the Ministry of Agriculture from the Development Fund for work on this subject. In 1918 it was decided to concentrate the work on fruit and vegetables in one location by the establishment of the Chipping Campden Station for Fruit and Vegetable Preservation. In 1921, the Station was transferred to the University of Bristol and some ten years later the domestic side of fruit and vegetable preservation was incorporated into the programme of the Long Ashton Research Station with financial support continuing to come from the Ministry of Agriculture. Chipping Campden remained the centre for industrial canning research and is to-day one of the Research Associations supported jointly by both industry and public funds.

A very important component in the development and launching of new varieties of crop plants is testing for suitability for British conditions, including the acquiring of information on disease resistance and susceptibility. For these tests the National Institute of Agricultural Botany was founded at Cambridge in 1919. The funds for its establishment were obtained by donations from agricultural merchants, millers, other agricultural trades and private benefactors which were slightly more than matched from the Development Fund through the Ministry of Agriculture.

In 1923 a modest grant was made from the Development Fund for the establishment of a Horticultural Research Station at Cambridge, the University providing land on one of the farms of the School of Agriculture. For a number of years there was considerable difficulty in identifying an appropriate research programme in view of the work in progress at other Institutes, especially at Long Ashton and East Malling. Eventually this station became incorporated in the National Vegetable Research Station when it was founded at Wellesbourne, Warwickshire, in 1949.

The recognised necessity for a more intensified research programme on the viruses known to affect potatoes led to the establishment in 1926 of the Potato Virus Research Station at Cambridge which was attached administratively to the Plant Breeding Institute, then of the University. A powerful team of Dr. R. N. Salaman, Mr. F. C. (later Sir Frederick) Bawden and Dr. Kenneth M. Smith worked at the Station and maintained close collaboration with the Plant Pathology Department at Rothamsted where Bawden continued his research on joining the Rothamsted staff in 1936, see also p. 49.

## Animals

Work on the genetics of poultry and rabbits at Cambridge University had been funded from the Development Fund since 1911. The programme was enlarged in 1919 by the establishment of the Small Animal Breeding Institute. In 1923 problems associated with the commercial breeding of poultry were given attention by the creation of the National Poultry Institute scheme. The Cambridge Institute was included in the scheme and received an increased Development Fund grant. The specific interests of the poultry breeders in Lancashire and Cheshire were catered for by the establishment at Reaseheath, near Crewe, of the Northern Poultry Breeding Station.

A need had already been identified before the war by the Development Commissioners for research on the genetics of farm livestock, but no action was taken until 1920 when the Institute of Animal Genetics was created as a Department of the University of Edinburgh, under the direction of Dr. F. A. E. Crew. Further development of this subject is described later (pp. 42–44).

All systems of animal production are at risk not only to the prejudicial effects of infectious diseases but also to parasitism, both external and internal. Parasitological research was going on in many Universities and in industrial companies in the private sector, but specific mention in this historical review must be given to the Molteno Institute of Parasitology at Cambridge, founded in 1921 through the generosity of Mr. and Mrs. Molteno, and to the Institute of Agricultural Parasitology at the London School of Hygiene and Tropical Medicine with its Field Station near St. Albans, established in 1924.

Two important Institutes were established in the 1920s in the field of veterinary research. The first, the Research Institute in Animal Pathology at the Royal Veterinary College in Camden Town, London, had been operating in very inadequate accommodation within the College since 1912, but in 1923 new laboratories were constructed adjacent to the College with the assistance of a grant of £31 500 from the Development Fund. The other establishment was founded, also in 1923, namely, the Cambridge Institute of Animal Pathology, the Director of which had the title of Professor of Animal Pathology of the University.

## Early Research in the Private Sector

All the institutes so far listed have been in the public sector, but mention must be made of the research contributions from the private sector. In this history of the antecedents to the founding of the Agricultural Research Council it would be possible to name many industrial companies, especially in the field of pharmaceuticals and biological products but these are specific to veterinary research which is a relatively small section of the whole of the soils, plants, animals, agricultural engineering and food technology remit of agricultural research. During this period of organised agricultural research prior to the creation of the Agricultural Research Council, namely, from 1843 to 1931 there are at least three industrial concerns which must be mentioned. These are, in order of becoming established: (1) William Cooper arrived in Berkamsted in 1843 when he developed his first effective sheep dip. This enterprise, through a complicated history, became Cooper, McDougall and Robertson, Ltd. in 1927. In 1937 the crop protection sector was merged with Plant Protection Ltd which in 1958 became a wholly-owned subsidiary of Imperial Chemical Industries Ltd. The animal products sector was merged in 1959 with the Wellcome Foundation Ltd. (2) Burroughs Wellcome and Co. was established in 1880 and renamed the Wellcome Foundation Ltd. in 1924. (3) Imperial Chemical Industries Ltd. which was formed in 1926. Of these commercial operations the entity most relevant prior to 1931 to the broad field of agricultural research was the ICI Agricultural Research Station, Jealott's Hill, Berkshire, which was established in 1928. The Wellcome Foundation since the 1920s has provided the essential developing and marketing of many veterinary products resulting from research in institutes of the Agricultural Research Service, especially anaerobic bacterial vaccines and sera and, of much more recent date, foot-and-mouth disease vaccines, a product initially manufactured by Cooper, McDougall and Robertson prior to the merger with the Wellcome Foundation.

The principal contribution to agricultural research by ICI and its predecessors has been the production of fertilizers, but its operations in the area of plant protection have been significant. Later, many other commercial firms contributed to agricultural development through their involvement in the pharmaceutical and agrochemical businesses.

## The Scene in 1931

Such then was the scene by 1931: Fourteen institutes of agricultural research which to-day are part of the Agricultural Research Service under the aegis of the Agricultural Research Council, (Table 1).

Table 1

The Agricultural Research Scene in 1931

Research Institutes later brought under the aegis of the Agricultural Research Council but continuing their original identity.

| Year of Founding | Institute |
| --- | --- |
| 1843 | Rothamsted Experimental Station. |
| 1903 | Long Ashton Research Station. |
| 1910 | John Innes Horticultural Institute, now the John Innes Institute. |
| 1912 | National Institute for Research in Dairying. |
| 1912 | Plant Breeding Institute. |
| 1912 | Rowett Research Institute. |
| 1913 | East Malling Research Station. |
| 1919 | Welsh Plant Breeding Station. |
| 1921 | Animal Diseases Research Association. |
| 1921 | Scottish Plant Breeding Station. |
| 1924 | Pirbright Experimental Station (Foot-and-Mouth Disease Research Committee), now the Animal Virus Research Institute. |
| 1924 | National Institute of Agricultural Engineering. |
| 1928 | Hannah Dairy Research Institute, now the Hannah Research Institute. |
| 1930 | Macaulay Institute for Soil Research. |

Eighteen institutes also receiving a large measure of financial support from public funds, only about one third of which have retained their original identity, (Table 2).

Table 2

The Agricultural Research Scene in 1931

Research Institutes which became incorporated into an Institute of the Agricultural Research Service, or which retained their identity out of that service, or which were discontinued.

| Year | Institute |
| --- | --- |
| 1894 | Veterinary Laboratory of the Ministry of Agriculture – now, the Central Veterinary Laboratory, New Haw, Weybridge. |
| 1911 | Research Institute in Plant Physiology, Imperial College of Science and Technology, London. |
| 1911 | Cambridge Institute for Animal Nutrition. |
| 1913 | Institute for Research in Agricultural Economics, Oxford. |
| 1914 | Cheshunt Station, Nursery and Market Garden Industries Development Society. |
| 1918 | Chipping Campden Station for Fruit and Vegetable Preservation. |
| 1919 | National Institute of Agricultural Botany, Cambridge. |
| 1919 | Small Animal Breeding Institute, Cambridge. |
| 1920 | Institute of Animal Genetics, Edinburgh. |
| 1921 | Molteno Institute of Parasitology, Cambridge. |
| 1922 | The Low Temperature Research Station, Cambridge. |
| 1923 | Northern Poultry Breeding Station, Reaseheath. |
| 1923 | Horticultural Research Station, Cambridge. |
| 1923 | Research Institute in Animal Pathology, Royal Veterinary College, London. |
| 1923 | Cambridge Institute of Animal Pathology. |
| 1924 | Institute of Agricultural Parasitology, London School of Hygiene and Tropical Medicine. |
| 1926 | Potato Virus Research Station, Cambridge. |
| 1928 | The Ditton Laboratory, Larkfield, Maidstone. |

The Universities, the Colleges of Agriculture, and other establishments with their research or development capabilities. The invidious choice of citing which were the most important or the most persuasive has been avoided by listing those which appear to have attracted the most support, (Table 3).

Table 3

The Agricultural Research Scene in 1931

The Universities, Colleges of Agriculture and other establishments which were listed in 1931 as receiving financial support from public funds for agricultural research.

(i)   Universities
        Aberdeen
        Bristol
        Cambridge
        Edinburgh
        Leeds
        London
        Manchester
        Newcastle-upon-Tyne — then Armstrong College
        Oxford
        Reading
        University College of North Wales, Bangor
        University College of Wales, Aberystwyth

(ii)  Colleges of Agriculture
        East of Scotland, Edinburgh
        Harper Adams, Newport, Salop.
        Midland, Sutton Bonington
        North of Scotland, Aberdeen
        Seale Hayne, Newton Abbott
        South Eastern, Wye
        West of Scotland, Auchincruive

(iii) Agricultural or Farm Institutes
        East Anglian Institute of Agriculture, Chelmsford
        Lord Wandsworth Agricultural College, Long Sutton
        Norfolk Agricultural Station, Sprowston
        Somerset Farm Institute, Cannington

(iv)  Veterinary Colleges
        Glasgow Veterinary College
        Royal (Dick) Veterinary College, Edinburgh
        Royal Veterinary College, London
        University of Liverpool, Liverpool Veterinary School

## Financial support for research and its organisation up to 1931

In summarising the history of these institutes reference has frequently been made to financial support having been provided from the Development Fund by the Development Commission. For a few years some additional support for agricultural research had been provided by the Empire Marketing Board established in 1926. This Board had been set up following a recommendation of the Imperial Economic Committee. Its purpose was to further the marketing in the United Kingdom of products from the British Empire and one means available to it was the promotion of research. It was relatively short-lived and was abolished in 1933.

The Development Commission worked in close collaboration with the two Agriculture Departments. These departments, the Ministry of Agriculture and Fisheries in England and Wales, and the Department of Agriculture for Scotland, administered the grants provided by the Commissioners. There was, however, no formally constituted body with an overall responsibility for the promotion of agricultural research.

The organisation of the promotion of medical and industrial research was different for the most part of two decades prior to the creation of the Agricultural Research

Council. Medical research became a responsibility of the State as a result of the National Insurance Act (1911) following which the Medical Research Committee was appointed in 1913, becoming the Medical Research Council in 1920, acting under the direction of the Committee of the Privy Council for Medical Research that was also appointed in 1920.

Two years after the appointment of the Medical Research Committee, a Committee of Privy Council for Scientific and Industrial Research had been established. This action was followed in 1916 by a separate Department of Scientific and Industrial Research being created. The Geological Survey, founded in 1835, and the National Physical Laboratory, founded in 1899, were transferred to it.

Although the creation of the Medical Research Council and the Department of Scientific and Industrial Research established the original concept for the organisation of civil scientific research, it was not until 1930 that agriculture was included. By an Order in Council dated the 28th day of July 1930, the Committee of the Privy Council for the Organisation and Development of Agricultural Research was appointed, followed by the signing by His Majesty on the 23rd of July 1931 of the Charter creating a Body Corporate under the style and title of "The Agricultural Research Council".

# Chapter 2

# 1931-1947

## The Establishment of the Council and of its Rôle

### The Agricultural Research Council

The Agricultural Research Council was designed to complete the scientific organisation for the supervision of civil research. That the Council's creation should "complete" this organisation is shown by the statement that is included in the first Report (1934) of the Committee of the Privy Council for the Organisation and Development of Agricultural Research. There were many other research activities in the civil as distinct from the defence field that were not included in the areas of responsibility of the triumvirate of the MRC, DSIR and ARC. For example, research in astronomy, fisheries, forestry, hydrology, meteorology, oceanography, preservation of the environment, also its pollution, and the social sciences. Research in all these fields was being pursued but mostly within the responsibility of the Government Department which was most relevant. The specific responsibility of the Agricultural Research Council as defined by the Lord President of the Council, the Lord Parmoor, was to give advice on agricultural research to the Agricultural Departments and to the Development Commission. A considerable constraint to the Council's operation was that the control of the research institutes then existing remained with the Agricultural Departments, the annual expenditure on which, excluding capital sums, was approximately £390 000. A sum of £5 000 was, however, given to the Council to be used on its own authority for the encouragement of agricultural research. It was made quite clear in the terms of a Provisional Note on Administration issued by the Lord President that the general relationship of the Agricultural Departments with Agricultural Research Institutes, University Departments of Agriculture and Agricultural Colleges was to remain unchanged, that the Agricultural Research Council's duty was to provide criticism and advice on research grants and programmes, that the expenditure for research borne on the Votes of the Agricultural Departments was to so remain and that the Parliamentary responsibility for agricultural research was to stay with the Ministers responsible for agriculture. The rôle of the new Council was, therefore, almost solely advisory. In spite of this very considerable constraint, its influence quickly became obvious and it began to operate effectively within its separate, although minor, remit to encourage research with its, initially, very meagre resources. This situation was to continue for no less than 25 years until a legislative background to the Council's activities was provided in 1956 by the Agricultural Research Act. This provided the Council with the financial control of the research institutes in England and Wales, but with the Department of Agriculture for Scotland still retaining the authority for its institutes in Scotland.

The Royal Charter by which the Council was created is reproduced in Appendix 1. The constitution of the Council was closely modelled on that of the Medical Research Council. This constitution and certain aspects of the Council's responsibilities in relation to Government Departments were, therefore, a consequence of earlier events in the history of the Medical Research Committee and the Medical Research Council. These are related by Sir Landsborough Thomson in his history of the Medical Research Council*. An important event was the appointment by Prime Minister Lloyd George in 1917 of the Machinery of Government Committee under the chairmanship of Viscount Haldane. The Committee reported in 1918 and included recommendations on "Research and Information". The specific requirements by Government Departments for information and research were contrasted with those for the national need. The constitution of the recently established (1916) Department of Scientific and Industrial Research, by which it was directed by its own Committee of the Privy Council, received special commendation. A similar position was thought to be appropriate for medical research. The text of the Report of the Committee referring to this point justifies quotation in view of its importance with regard to a Research Council securing and maintaining scientific independence.

"It is important, also, to observe that, although the Minister in charge of an administrative Department is answerable to Parliament for the work of the Committee [the then Medical Research Committee], we have of set purpose, and for two clear reasons, classified the Committee as a service of a general character, and not as a body engaged upon research for the immediate purposes of a single administrative Department."

As far as the Medical Research Committee was concerned, unless special consideration had been given to its position, it would then have been automatically transferred to the proposed Ministry of Health which was to take over the responsibilities consequent upon the National Insurance Act. The Haldane Committee recommended:

". . . we recommend that, on the establishment of the Ministry of Health, the Medical Research Committee should be reconstituted so as to enable it to act under the direction of a Committee of the Privy Council on the lines already followed in the case of the Committee of Council for Scientific and Industrial Research."

The Committee in its Report anticipated that a number of organisations might be required similar to the Department of Scientific and Industrial Research and the Medical Research Committee. By the following text it forecast the relationship between the Department of Education and Science and the Research Councils that has existed since the passing of the Science and Technology Act 1965, viz:

"It may, therefore, not be premature to anticipate that the distinctive character of the organisation of Intelligence and Research for general use; the proper scope of such an organisation; and its potential relations with analogous organisations throughout the Empire, could thenceforth all be maintained by a Minister specifically appointed on his ground of suitability to preside over a separate Department of Intelligence and Research, which would no longer act under a Committee of the Privy Council, and would take its place among the most important Departments of Government."

Sir Landsborough Thomson describes that before these recommendations had been implemented, other threats to the independence of medical research had had to be neutralised. Apparently the existence of the Department of Science and Industrial Research stimulated ideas of empire-building within which medical research would have been a minor component. Another notion was that the two research organisations,

*Thomson, A. Landsborough (1973) Half a century of medical research. H.M. Stationery Office, London

and probably others, could retain their separate identities but under a single Committee of the Privy Council which could have grown into a "Department or Ministry for Research" as was indeed visualised by the Haldane Committee. The strongest opposition to these proposals came from the Ministry of Agriculture and Fisheries which could not accept yielding its control of agricultural research nor fisheries research. It was thus that medical research, at least, further secured its independence.

The Agricultural Research Council was formally constituted by Lord Parmoor, Lord President of the Council, at its first meeting held on Thursday, the 9th of July 1931 in the Privy Council Office.

Those invited to attend and who became the original members were:

Dr. J. A. (later Sir Joseph) Arkwright.
Sir Merrik Burrell.
Dr. E. J. (later Sir Edwin) Butler.
Professor E. P. Cathcart.
The Rt. Hon. Lord Richard Cavendish
Mr. Joseph F. Duncan.
Sir John Farmer.
Sir Daniel Hall.
Professor Sir Frederick Gowland Hopkins.
Professor T. J. Mackie.
Sir Thomas Middleton.
Mr. Spencer W. Mount.
Professor D. M. S. Watson.

Lord Parmoor, who was in the Chair, invited the Council to suggest their nominee for Chairman, an appointment to be made by the Committee of the Privy Council after consultation with the Agricultural Research Council and the President of the Royal Society. The Council nominated Lord Richard Cavendish (Plate 4) who was subsequently appointed.

*Plate 4* The Rt. Hon. Lord Richard Cavendish, CB, CMG; the first Chairman of the Agricultural Research Council who served from 1931 to 1938.

The Secretary to the Council was an appointment to be made by the Council with the approval of the Lord President of the Council and the President of The Royal Society. The choice of Secretary was discussed by Council. Various criteria were proposed such as being in touch with agricultural research, able to speak on equal terms with scientists, being accustomed to presenting and circulating information, being a man of vision and wide views, able to give his full time and be always accessible, and, reaffirmed, most desirable to have a man of science. At the first meeting it was agreed Mr. E. H. E. Havelock, the Assistant Secretary to the Development Commission, should act as Interim Secretary. At the second meeting of Council on the 30th of July 1931, Sir William Dampier, Secretary to the Development Commission, was invited to act for one year as Honorary Secretary. Dampier (Plate 5) was also appointed by the Committee of the Privy Council for Agricultural Research to be Secretary to that Committee. Havelock was appointed Assistant Secretary to the Council. This second meeting was held in the offices of the Development Commission in 6A Dean's Yard, Westminster, and in these premises the Headquarters of the Council was housed until 1950. Dampier's early career was as a physicist and his work in this science led to his election to the Fellowship of the Royal Society at the age of 34. Subsequently he turned his attention to heredity and genetics in the context of sociology and, later, to agricultural economics. It was this later interest that led to him being selected for various offices in the public service connected with agriculture. He was knighted in 1931.

*Plate 5* Sir William Dampier, FRS; the first Secretary to the Agricultural Research Council who served from 1931 to 1935.

It will be seen from the list of the original members of Council that thirteen had been appointed. The Royal Charter stipulated that on the occurrence of a vacancy the number would be reduced to twelve of whom eight would be appointed after consultation with the President of the Royal Society, on account of their qualification in one or other of the basic sciences underlying agriculture. Four members would be appointed on account of their general experience of and interest in agriculture. A qualification of appointment was the desirability of securing at all times, so far as possible, one member who was also a member of the Medical Research Council and one member of the Advisory Council for Scientific and Industrial Research. The term of office was not mentioned in the Charter except that the members would retire in rotation. This order of retirement was subsequently decided by lot drawn by the Chairman. This subject was discussed at the third meeting of Council when it was agreed that retiring members would not be eligible for re-election until after the lapse of one year. This stipulation was later rejected by the Privy Council Committee for Agricultural Research, which ruled that re-appointment could be immediate.

Following a recommendation from Council an amendment to the Charter was made by the granting of a Supplemental Charter in 1933 by which the membership was increased to not exceeding fifteen nor less than twelve, of whom not less than four nor more than five would be appointed on account of their interest in or experience of agriculture, the remainder to be appointed on account of their scientific qualifications. At that time the Council agreed that the term of office would be five years.

## Relationships with other organisations

The third meeting of Council was attended by invitation of representatives of the Treasury, the Medical Research Council, the Department of Scientific and Industrial Research, the Ministry of Agriculture and Fisheries, the Department of Agriculture for Scotland and the Empire Marketing Board. The establishment and maintenance of close relations was agreed, and the Secretary was authorised to consult and arrange about the exchange of papers, of minutes, and the appointment of Assessors. One action in this connection was the establishment of regular quarterly meetings of the Secretaries to the three "Research Councils". i.e. MRC, ARC and DSIR.

## The review of research in progress

In view of its responsibility to advise the Agricultural Departments and the Development Commission on agricultural research, the first task of the Council was to review the work in progress at the various Institutes. A complete survey of the Research Institutes was planned and at its third meeting in October 1931, six Standing Committees were set up for this purpose with power to appoint Sub-Committees. The Standing Committees and their Chairmen were as follows:-

| | |
|---|---|
| Animal Diseases | Sir Merrik Burrell |
| Animal Nutrition and Breeding | Sir Frederick Gowland Hopkins |
| Dairying and Animal Products | Professor E. C. Cathcart |
| Plants | Sir Daniel Hall |
| Soils | Sir Thomas Middleton |
| Agricultural Economics | Mr. Joseph Duncan |

It was soon found convenient, because of the allied nature of the subjects, for the Animal Diseases Committee to meet together with the Animal Nutrition and Breeding Committee, and for the Plants Committee to meet together with the Soils Committee.

## The animal disease priority

It is recorded in the first Report of the Council (for the period 1931 to 1933) that at an early stage in its general survey, the conclusion was reached that the most urgent subject for enquiry for the economic well-being of the British farmer was that of animal disease. Seven special Committees were immediately formed, most of them consisting of experts from outside the Council, to enquire into the present state of knowledge and the work in progress on the most important diseases of farm livestock, and to co-ordinate further research. These Special Committees were:

Braxy-like diseases in sheep
Contagious abortion (*Brucella abortus* infection in man and animals)
Fowl paralysis and similar diseases and coccidiosis
Helminths of immediate importance in animal health
Johne's disease in cattle and sheep
Swine fever and similar diseases including enteritis in young pigs.
Tuberculosis

The Council had already conducted, by means of an expert committee, an enquiry on the past history and future prospects of research on foot-and-mouth disease. A special report had also been prepared on mastitis by Professor F. C. Minett, the Director of the Research Institute in Animal Pathology, Royal Veterinary College, London.

This early identification of the high priority for research on animal disease raises a number of questions, the most important and relevant of which must be to do with the then status of veterinary science, veterinary education and veterinary practice. This, apparently, was appreciated by the Council as the Veterinary Schools were inspected during their survey. At the Royal Veterinary College, London, it was found in 1931 that owing to the teaching responsibilities of the small staff in cramped accommodation, research was confined almost entirely to the separate staff of the Research Institute in Animal Pathology which, at that time, had no teaching responsibilities. At the Royal (Dick) Veterinary College, Edinburgh, although the buildings were adequate, the small staff were so fully occupied with teaching that they had little time for research. The Glasgow Veterinary College was in a precarious state as the Department of Agriculture for Scotland had decided that it could subsidise only one Veterinary College and it had chosen that in Edinburgh. Only two of the staff at Glasgow were full-time and they and their part-time colleagues, mostly from local veterinary practices, were hard pressed in their dilapidated buildings to comply with the syllabus demanded by the Royal College of Veterinary Surgeons. These adversities stimulated endeavour and the educational attainment was high. There was, however, no opportunity for research. The Liverpool Veterinary School was, at that time, the only one integrated with a University. The Council's Sub-Committee which visited the School at the beginning of 1932 found the teaching to be well organised and all the scientific staff to be engaged in research although their programmes were no doubt relatively limited.

Entry into the veterinary profession up to the passing of the Veterinary Surgeons Act 1948, which permitted the recognition of University degrees, was by the so-called one portal system with all examinations being conducted by the Royal College of Veterinary Surgeons for the award of the College's diploma permitting the practice of the art and science of veterinary medicine. Until the teaching of veterinary science attained University status in 1948, the College courses tended to be conducted in scientific isolation and they were of a vocational rather than an academic nature. The staffs of the Colleges were very small by any standard, it being not uncommon for the Professor and Head of a Department to have no assistant. There was, virtually, no research capability in the veterinary schools at the time the Council was identifying veterinary research as the highest priority. Furthermore, as will be seen from Tables 1 and 2 there were only five veterinary research institutes out of the total of the thirty establishments then existing, namely, the Veterinary Laboratory of the Ministry of Agriculture and Fisheries, the Animal Diseases Research Association, the Animal Virus Research Institute, the Research Institute in Animal Pathology, London, and the Cambridge Institute of Animal Pathology. Also the staffs of these Institues were very small with few subjects or departments having more than one or occasionally two scientists.

Then, as now, the very great majority of veterinary graduates were intent upon entering practice as veterinary surgeons. It was exceptional to find more than two or three a year with an interest in a research career. Also, in the 1920s and 1930s, veterinary research in the United Kingdom had not yet acquired any general prestige sufficient to attract the science graduate nor were those engaged in veterinary research yet planning projects which provided many opportunities for science graduates. At that time it was also unusual to find many veterinarians in non-veterinary establishments. There were, of course, exceptions which provided growing points for future collaboration and there can be no doubt that the establishment of the Agricultural Research Council with its questing for information through its Standing Committees, Special Committees, and expert committees, provided opportunities for improved contacts between veterinary surgeons and scientists working in other disciplines.

## Research training

The Development Commission had appointed an Advisory Committee on Agricultural Science under the Chairmanship of Sir Daniel Hall. In addition to having a budget for research grants it also dealt with Research Scholarships, Fellowships, and the representation of the agricultural sciences at Conferences. Scholarships had been awarded since 1911 with some eight being allocated annually. The Council took over these functions and it decided to offer three scholarships in agricultural sciences and two in veterinary science. The special case of the veterinary graduates was noted, a case which has had to be recognised throughout the years, namely, the greater vocational and financial attraction of practice. For example, in 1932, Council awarded £200 per annum and up to £50 for fees and expenses to the science graduate and £300 per annum inclusive of fees and expenses to the veterinary graduate. During the next year or two the experience was that although the entry for the agricultural scholarships was satisfactory, the number and quality of the candidates for the Studentships in Animal Health were not as high as could be wished. An additional scheme was introduced, therefore, whereby Honours graduates in Natural Science could be awarded a scholarship to enable them to study for a veterinary qualification. This, on a basis of one per year, was introduced in 1937 and was very similar to the successful scheme introduced some years earlier by the Colonial Office which gave science graduates the opportunity of obtaining a veterinary qualification.

## A Growing Concept for an ARC Institute

What may seem undue attention has been given to the veterinary scene. This is deliberate as it obviously had considerable bearing on the future policy of the Council with regard to the choice between sponsoring research in Universities and other establishments of higher education or creating new institutes for research in specific fields. It is also clear from the records of that period that the Council was, in its first years, predominantly concerned with the then very serious handicap to animal production caused by animal disease. It was against this background that, in 1935, the Council had to take account of the findings and recommendations of its Contagious Abortion Committee under the Chairmanship of Dr. J. A. Arkwright (later Sir Joseph Arkwright).

The research work in progress when the Contagious Abortion Committee investigated the matter was at the Ministry of Agriculture's Veterinary Laboratory at Weybridge, the Research Institute in Animal Pathology of the Royal Veterinary College, The Wye College of Agriculture, and at the Moredun Institute of the Animal Diseases Research Association in Edinburgh. The principal effort was directed towards the preparation of a suitable vaccine for cattle with the assessment of effectiveness being tested largely in guinea-pigs. The Committee were unanimous in deciding that more extended work was necessary, especially on large animals. A dispute arose about the means to be adopted.

## Differences of opinion with the Ministry of Agriculture and Fisheries and their resolution

Somewhat unusually the submission made by the Committee to Council consisted of a Majority and a Minority Report. The majority firmly believed that the only satisfactory approach was to establish a "farm centre" under the direct control of the Council and for the bulk of the work to be concentrated there. They were convinced that it could be only in this way that the work could be arranged on a sufficiently large scale. The minority believed that work could be done adequately and more cheaply at existing Institutes. It became obvious in the discussion of this item that there was more to it than that. In view of the involvement and interest of the Ministry of Agriculture and Fisheries, three representatives had been invited to attend. The strongest opposition to the majority view came from the Ministry representatives on the matter of principle that the proposed new centre to be directed by the Council would be a Research Institute, and Research Institutes were the responsibility of the Agricultural Departments. Finally, Lord Richard Cavendish from the Chair asked whether the Ministry would disagree to the Council undertaking the control of any work independently of the Agricultural Departments. The spokesman for the Ministry is minuted as having replied that it could, stating that such a question raised difficult issues beyond the immediate matter of research into contagious abortion. The representatives of the Ministry withdrew and Council adopted unanimously the Majority Report recommending it to the Privy Council Committee and directing that financial provision for the "farm centre" of £40 000 be included in the estimates for 1935–36.

The constitutional issue that had been raised in discussing future work on contagious abortion must have caused some concern and it obviously could not be left unresolved. The Provisional Note on Administrative Arrangements that had been issued by Lord Parmoor, the Lord President, when the Council was appointed, was insufficient for guidance in this case.

## Greater authority for the ARC

The result was a Second Provisional Note on Administrative Arrangements which was adopted on the 26th August 1935, by the Committee of the Privy Council for the Organisation and Development of Agricultural Research with the concurrence of the Treasury.

In this new Note on Administrative Arrangements, it was accepted that the Council could carry on agricultural research themselves and employ staff for the purpose. A qualification was that if the work was to be done at an Institute aided by grants from an Agricultural Department, the agreement of that Department must first be obtained.

It was, however, noted that Parliamentary responsibility for agricultural research would remain with the Ministers responsible for agriculture, save as regards expenditure by the Agricultural Research Council borne on the Vote for Scientific Investigation for which the Lord President would answer.

The consequences of this Second Note were very satisfactory to the Council as they had now been given much wider powers and the relationship with the Agricultural Departments and the Development Commission were more clearly defined. This point in the progress of agricultural research could well be cited as a milestone.

## The first ARC Institute

This constitutional issue having now been adequately resolved from the Council's point of view, it became a matter of high priority to establish the new farm research centre. It was not long before this centre began to be referred to as the "Field Station" as so it was to remain until the name was changed in 1963 to the present "Institute for Research on Animal Diseases". The original concept as outlined in the Majority Report of the Contagious Abortion Committee was for accommodation for at least 200 cows and heifers in rigid isolation on a farm of some 600 acres. Various properties were considered and the purchase was recommended of the Hamels Park estate, some 25 miles south-west of Cambridge. Although authority was obtained to purchase this property, the inevitable delays occurred and the option lapsed. A further two farms near Cambridge were considered but rejected as being unsuitable and too costly. Two of the members of the Contagious Abortion Committee, Professor Minett of the Pathology Institute of the Royal Veterinary College and Dr. McEwan of Wye, drew the Council's attention to the Compton Manor Estate in Berkshire. This consisted of 1 500 acres with suitable buildings and, of great importance, a herd of 400 dairy cattle the health history of which was good and was known to Minett and McEwan. Immediate possession could be obtained and there were no tenants to compensate. The purchase was approved and it was completed in the autumn of 1937. The conditions of sale merit recording, namely, the land and buildings for £37 000 corresponding to £25 per acre, £24 000 for the stock and £23 000 for specified new buildings and cottages, total £84 000. In the meantime, Council had already decided that the Directorship of the new Field Station should be offered to Major G. W. Dunkin, the veterinary superintendent of the farm laboratories of the Medical Research Council at Mill Hill. Dunkin had been Laidlaw's collaborator in the confirmation of the viral aetiology of canine distemper and in the subsequent development of successful vaccination of dogs. This work had involved the use of ferrets and Dunkin in collaboration with Laidlaw, Andrewes and Wilson Smith demonstrated the susceptibility of the first small animal, namely, the ferret, to the very recently isolated virus of human influenza. Dunkin assumed the Directorship of the ARC Field Station, Compton, near Newbury, Berkshire on the 1st of November 1937.

The immediate objective for which the Field Station was established was to provide healthy farm livestock in conditions of isolation for the more adequate testing of vaccines against *Brucella abortus* infection. It was also envisaged that the facilities could, in time, be used for other research involving the use of large animals especially by providing these in larger numbers than could be accommodated by any University, and housed in buildings providing some degree of isolation. The building programme at Compton required for laboratories, cattle isolation, houses for staff, etc., proceeded slowly. Dr. S. J. Edwards was appointed First Scientific Assistant and took up his duties in January 1940. Mr D. L. Hughes became Second Scientific Assistant and Mr. K. C. Sellers was seconded from the Institute of Animal Pathology, Cambridge. The outbreak of war led to some consideration being given to the best use, under the circumstances, of the 1 500 acres of farm land, a matter which sufficiently attracted the attention of the Lord President to request a report. Work had been started on the investigation of the characteristics of an attenuated strain of *Br. abortus* (Strain 45/20) which McEwan at Wye College had advocated for use as a vaccine and in 1941 Dr. Eichhorn, the Director of the then Bureau of Animal Industry of the United States Department of Agriculture visited Compton to provide information about an attenuated strain (Strain 19) which seemed to have great promise as a vaccine. A considerable setback then occurred by Dunkin's sudden death in 1942 at the age of 55. The Directorship then went to Dr. W. S. Gordon who had been Head of the Bacteriology Department of the Moredun Institute of the Animal Diseases Research Association. Under Gordon's direction there was a very definite change from the original concept of a Field Station providing animals and accommodation for the extension of others' work to that of developing a Research Institute in its own right and a centre of excellence in its own subject. Gordon was Director for twenty-five years. He was succeeded in 1967 by the author of this chronicle. From December 1972 Mr. I. H. Pattison, the Deputy Director, was in charge until Dr. J. M. Payne, Head of the Institute's Department of Functional Pathology, was appointed Director in May 1973. The Institute had been delighted to receive a visit from Her Majesty the Queen in May 1972 on the occasion of a State Visit to the Royal County of Berkshire (Plate 6).

*Plate 6* Her Majesty the Queen paid a visit to the Institute for Research on Animal Diseases. The Deputy Director, Mr. I H. Pattison, is pointing out certain features of scrapie research from a demonstration board. Dr. Henderson, the Director, and the then Chairman of the ARC, the Hon. J.J. Astor, can also be seen, together with the Lord Lieutenant of the County.

## Veterinary representation on Council

This attention to problems of animal disease can, appropriately, be left for the moment so as to refer to veterinary representation on Council. The first veterinary member was Mr. John Smith, appointed in 1936. Smith had recently retired at the age of fifty after a distinguished career in Northern Rhodesia in the Colonial Veterinary Service. He served on Council until 1945. He was succeeded by Mr. T. (later Sir Thomas) Dalling who had been Director of the Ministry of Agriculture and Fisheries' Central Veterinary Laboratory, Weybridge, since 1942, and who was appointed the Ministry's Chief Veterinary Officer in 1948 (continuing to hold both appointments until 1950). Mr. J. N. (later Sir John) Ritchie succeeded Dalling as Chief Veterinary Officer in 1952 but he did not become a member of Council until 1954. In the meantime Professor Leslie P. Pugh, of Veterinary Clinical Studies, Cambridge University, was appointed in 1952 to succeed Smith. From the appointment to Council in 1954 of Ritchie when he was Chief Veterinary Officer, the holder of this office became a member of Council, *ex officio*, until the reconstitution by the amended Royal Charter in 1973. This amendment gave the Ministry of Agriculture, Fisheries and Food the right to nominate four members, the pattern of representation currently being the Deputy Secretary (Research and Development), the Chief Scientist, the Director General of the Agricultural Development and Advisory Service, and the Chief Veterinary Officer. Since 1954, when Pugh and Ritchie were both on Council, there have always been two veterinary members.

## Agricultural economics

Another subject which received special attention during the first years of the Council's existence was agricultural economics. The Ministry of Agriculture and Fisheries had established an Economics Division in 1929. Note has already been made (p. 11) of the creation in 1913 of the Institute for Research in Agricultural Economics at Oxford. During the 1920s a number of advisory economists were appointed who were attached to University Departments of Agriculture and to Agricultural Colleges on the basis of eleven regions. A similar arrangement was subsequently established by the Department of Agriculture for Scotland based on its three Colleges of Agriculture. One of the Council's six Standing Committees was "Agricultural Economics" which held initial discussions with a number of these economists as a result of which it was decided that a survey by the Council of the work of the Oxford Institute and the various Economic Centres should be deferred in the face of higher priorities. From 1933 to 1935, however, a preliminary survey was completed. In most of the Centres the main theme of the earlier work had been cost accounting with later modification and expansion of programmes based to a greater extent on survey methods in particular areas or of individual crops. The Oxford Institute was concerned with research into agricultural policy on such issues as land tenure; smallholdings; farm management practices; and marketing. The regional Centres tended to concentrate on problems more specific to the areas. A far-reaching conclusion from the result of this survey was that the independence of the agricultural economics research service must be preserved. Although reference was made to the Agricultural Research Council being consulted about proposed research programmes, it was stressed that the economists must be free to pursue their investigations as independent scientific researchers with the publication of results being on the authority of the economists themselves with the Oxford Institute being identified as their principal point of reference. The effect of these decisions has been very long standing in that from that time onwards Council and the institutes of the Agricultural Research Service have consistently eschewed all topics of economics research.

## Agricultural engineering

The Institute for Research in Agricultural Engineering had been established at Oxford in 1924, after what was described at the time as "much consideration". The financial support was provided from the Development Fund. The Ministry of Agriculture and Fisheries as a result of recommendations of three Departmental Committees had set up a Machinery Testing Committee in 1925. The Agricultural Research Council in its survey of current research at the time it commenced its work referred the subject of agricultural engineering to its Standing Committee on Soils and Plant Nutrition which by then was meeting jointly with the Plant Physiology, Breeding and Disease Committee. It soon became evident that the subject still required "much consideration". The first outcome of the Council's attempt to advise was the production by the Standing Committees of a Majority and a Minority Report. The majority view supported the continued existence of the Institute on the grounds that an organisation which established good relations with both farmers and implement makers could do much to improve both theory and practice and that it was necessary to provide facilities for the testing of machinery when that testing, because of financial or equipment requirements, was beyond the means of implement makers. The performance of the Oxford Institute was judged to be good although its location did not necessarily need to continue to be in Oxford and a ceiling of £10 000 was recommended for annual expenditure. The minority view was that all that was necessary could be provided by a small department of the National Physical Laboratory for an annual cost of £2 000.

The Council obviously found great difficulty in resolving this situation in that at their first discussion of these reports in July 1932, six members were in favour of one and six were in favour of the other. It was not until the next meeting that the Chairman opted for the Majority Report. A divergence of opinion within a newly-appointed body such as the Council on a subject of wide national interest must have caused considerable anxiety. Such an assessment is surely reasonable and it is endorsed by the fact that Council agreed unanimously that when there was a divergence of view, each member or group of members should be free to request that the particular views held by him or them should be communicated to the Committee of the Privy Council for Agricultural Research and to the Department which had sought the advice of Council.

The Majority Report was finally adopted after it and the Minority Report had been submitted, with a record of the Council's voting, to the Committee of the Privy Council, the Treasury, the Ministry of Agriculture and Fisheries and the Development Commission. This, however, was not the end of the matter. Quite apart from the history of what is now the National Institute of Agricultural Engineering at Wrest Park, Silsoe, and the Scottish Institute of Agricultural Engineering (founded in 1946) at the Edinburgh University Centre of Rural Economy, both governed by the British Society for Research in Agricultural Engineering, it has never been easy clearly to identify the purpose of research in agricultural engineering. This is ignoring what grew into an emotive subject, namely, the testing of agricultural machinery or, more simply, "tractor testing". The problem has been, and is, that the research workers at the two Institutes have produced many innovative ideas and have shown how improvements in design could be applied to the manufacture of machinery which would contribute towards more efficient agricultural practice. It has proved to be extremely difficult, however, to have these innovations adopted commercially. The large multi-national manufacturers have their own research capability and their range of models for the international market cannot easily accommodate modifications which may have a relatively restricted application. The alternative outlet is the small manufacturer but to whom sufficient risk capital may not be available. This dilemma is discussed in greater detail in the essay on agricultural engineering (p. 217).

Following the decision in 1932 that the Institute at Oxford should continue to receive substantial financial support from public funds it was kept at that site until 1942 when the Institute was transferred to larger premises at Askham Bryan, near York. During these war years the emphasis of the work was on the testing of machinery and on solving *ad hoc* problems that arose through the need for greater food production. After the war a new site was sought and the Institute moved to its present premises at Wrest Park, Silsoe, in 1947.

## War-time Arrangements and Progress

The last meeting of Council before the outbreak of war in 1939 was held on the 19th of July. For the next eighteen months the business was largely conducted by an Executive Committee, Council meeting only in July 1940, and in March 1941. From May 1941, onwards, the meetings were resumed with their former frequency of approximately one a month, excepting August and, occasionally, December.

## New status for the ARC

During the early part of the war, attention was again given at Privy Council level to the status of the Council and to its relations with other bodies. The Committee of the Privy Council for the Organisation and Development of Agricultural Research adopted in 1941, the recommendations of a committee under the chairmanship of Lord Hankey. This resulted in the cancellation of the First and the Second Provisional Notes on Administrative Arrangements, the granting of complete freedom of the Council to undertake with the funds placed at its disposal such researches as the Council may think fit and the conferring of a status equal to that of the Medical Research Council and the Department of Scientific and Industrial Research. Lord Hankey's Committee also recommended that an effort should be made to attract more workers of outstanding ability into agricultural science. The Council made a significant decision in seeking to implement this recommendation that had a profound effect on the structure of the agricultural research service which was to last for at least the next 40 years. This was to seek to match a problem and a research leader of exceptional ability, to provide financial support for staff, equipment and facilities and to grant a free hand for the pursuit of the relevant research. This was, in fact, the concept of the ARC Unit and the first two were founded forthwith in that same year 1941.

## The first ARC Unit: The Unit of Soil Enzyme Chemistry

Sir John Russell, Director of the Rothamsted Experimental Station who had joined the staff as a soil chemist in 1907, and who had succeeded as Director in 1912 gave strong support to an idea that enzymes from dead bacterial cells might have a profound influence on the fertility of the soil. A very suitable candidate for the initiation of research in this completely new field was Dr. J. H. Quastel, a biochemist who was then Director of Research at the Cardiff City Mental Hospital, and whose scientific specialities were the chemical reactions of bacteria and the chemistry of enzymes. Dr. Quastel had two colleagues, Dr. P. J. G. Mann and Dr. D. M. Webley whom he wished to have in his team if the proposed Unit was established. It was agreed that the Unit should be attached to the Rothamsted Experimental Station and it was founded there towards the end of 1941 under Dr. Quastel's direction. The name was later changed to "Unit of Soil Metabolism". The Unit was moved to South Wales in 1945 and was disbanded when in 1947 Quastel accepted the appointment to the Chair of Biochemistry, McGill University, Canada, with which was coupled the Directorship of the McGill-Montreal General Hospital Research Institute.

## The Unit of Animal Physiology

Sir Joseph Barcroft had succeeded J. N. Langley in the Chair of Physiology in Cambridge in 1925 and had conducted an active research programme which he continued after his retirement from the Chair in 1937. On the outbreak of war he undertook further work at Porton but returned to Cambridge in 1941 as head of the new ARC Unit of Animal Physiology. This Unit was located in the Physiology Department, the accommodation having been provided by his successor in the Chair, Professor E. D. Adrian (later Baron Adrian of Cambridge). Barcroft initiated and directed research on ruminant digestion and metabolism assisted by Dr. A. T. Philipson, seconded from the Institute of Animal Pathology and Miss R. A. McAnally on a temporary appointment.

It would be appropriate while referring to Sir Joseph Barcroft's contribution to research on the physiology of farm livestock to record the Council's response in 1945 to a suggestion that an Institute for Research in Animal Physiology might be established. At that time this subject was included in the programmes of the National Institute for Research in Dairying, the Rowett Research Institute, the Hannah Research Institute and in the ARC Unit directed by Barcroft. Accordingly, Professor H. D. Kay, Institute for Research in Dairying, Dr. D. P. (later Sir David) Cuthbertson, Rowett Research Institute, Dr. N. C. (later Sir Norman) Wright, Hannah Research Institute, and Barcroft were consulted by the Council. Their assessments were correctly objective with only a hint of a partisan response. Kay was concerned that nothing should be done to hinder existing Institutes conducting physiological research in their particular fields. As an example, it would be unfortunate if the new Institute set up a department for the study of the physiology of lactation. Cuthbertson thought that new work was essential and that there was merit in having more than one Institute dealing with a particular subject. He questioned, however, whether a new Institute was required for animal nutrition. He was in favour, nevertheless, of whatever means would yield more efficiently the maximum amount of knowledge. Wright was the least encouraging, being apprehensive about the effect on the work at his Institute. He had already, apparently, expressed anxiety about this when Barcroft's Unit had been established. Barcroft, as might be expected from his greater experience and from the more liberal background of science in the Universities, recommended that fundamental research at the National and the Hannah Dairy Research Institutes should not be discouraged, but with the creation of a new Institute there would be an increase in the number of scientists so engaged. He saw no danger in this. The outcome of the discussion of this agenda item was that familiar to all Secretaries to the Council: "The Secretary to prepare a report for the next meeting." One of the members of Council at that time was Professor I. de Burg Daly (appointed 1943) to whom it was agreed in 1947 that the Directorship of the new Institute should be offered.

## The Unit Principle

The establishment of the Unit of Soil Enzyme Chemistry and the Unit of Animal Physiology provide examples of the two different approaches that have been used by the Council. The Unit of Soil Enzyme Chemistry represented the identification of a problem, the appointment of an expert with supporting staff competent in the relevant science and the finding of a suitable environment for their work. The Unit of Animal Physiology exemplified the more frequently used procedure. This was the identification in a University of the successful scientist working in a field relevant to the Council's interests, providing him with staff and equipment and, in some cases with laboratories, animal accommodation or glasshouses. In the first example, the Director of the Unit and the staff were employees of the Council. If the Unit was set up in a University, the academic recognition of the Director would be likely. In the second example, the Director would remain on the staff of the University, being known as the Honorary Director, but the scientific staff of the Unit would be the Council's employees. The general principle was evolved that on the retirement, resignation or death of the Director the Unit would be disbanded. Exceptions to this practice were made related to the importance of the research programme being continued, usually under the direction of a member of the Unit staff. Note is made of these.

## The Unit of Insect Physiology

This Unit was established in 1943 in support of the work of Dr. V. B. (later Sir Vincent) Wigglesworth, then a Reader in Entomology in the University of London. The terms of reference were intentionally broad and included the entitlement to work on all aspects of insect physiology, and not only on insecticides. Studies of the waterproof waxing of the insect cuticle were pertinent to the penetration of insecticides. Research on the histology and physiology of the insect nervous system provided information about insect resistance to insecticides. This, and other work, including studies on insect behaviour, added greatly to the knowledge required for the development of more rational methods of control of insect pests. The Unit was moved to the University of Cambridge in 1945 when Wigglesworth accepted appointment to a Readership in the Department of Zoology. Following Wigglesworth's retirement from the Quick Chair of Biology in 1966, the Unit was continued under his direction until September 1967, when it was disbanded. Opportunities were found for the staff to continue their research. For example, Dr. J. E. Treherne obtained an appointment in the Department of Zoology, becoming in 1969, the Honorary Associate Director of the Cambridge section of the new Unit of Invertebrate Chemistry and Physiology. An Insect Physiology Group was set up at Silwood Park, the Field Station of the Imperial College of Science and Technology, where Dr. J. S. Kennedy and Dr. A. D. Lees continued their work.

## Chairmen and Secretaries, 1931 to 1948

Throughout this personal account of the history of the Agricultural Research Council an interruption in its continuity has to be made from time to time so as to identify those most immediately concerned with the initiation and implementation of the action. This refers especially to the Chairman of the Council, and to the Secretary to the Council and his supporting staff. The Chairmen, members of Council, the Secretaries and the senior staff of the Secretariat are listed in Appendices but the importance of the influence of the key figures justifies them receiving more than solely that mention.

When the Agricultural Research Council was created in 1931 for the co-ordination of agricultural research then being conducted in what had become a disparate collection of some 30 Institutes, the principal funding agency was the Development Commission. Continuity of research policy was obviously desirable and it was appropriate, therefore, that the first Chairman of the Council should be the Chairman of the Development Commission, namely, the Right Honourable Lord Richard Cavendish. Sir Thomas Middleton, also a member of the Commission, was appointed a member of Council. Furthermore, Sir William Dampier, Secretary to the Development Commission, was appointed part-time Secretary to the Council, and the Committee of the Privy Council for Agricultural Research appointed Dampier to be Secretary to that Committee. Mr. E. H. E. Havelock, Assistant Secretary to the Development Commission, was appointed Assistant Secretary to the Council and in 1934 became Administrative Secretary. This small initial Secretariat of the Council shared the offices and the service of many of the staff of the Development Commission. Dampier was appointed a Development Commissioner in 1933 while continuing as Secretary to the Council. His contribution to the Council was not only the smooth and apparently effortless way in which he brought it into rapid and most effective action, but also his handling of the situation which was resolved by the issuing by the Privy Council Committee of the Second Provisional Note on Administration (pp. 28–29). This note laid the seal on the Council's freedom of action and it enabled him to be succeeded on his retirement from the Secretaryship in 1935 by a full-time Secretary, Dr. E. J. (later Sir Edwin) Butler. At an earlier meeting, the Council had recommended that Dampier should be one of its new members from the date of his retirement from the Secretaryship. He was so appointed and he served for 10 years until 1945. He died in 1952 at the age of 85.

Butler graduated in medicine at Queen's College, Cork, in 1898 but he never practised. He was interested in botanical research and succeeded in gaining a two years' travelling scholarship from the Commissioners of the 1851 Exhibition. The purpose of the scholarship, or the use to which Butler put it, were described as to seek the fungus *Pythium* wherever it might be found. This was the prelude to his career in India for the next twenty years, fifteen of which were holding the office of Imperial Mycologist to the Government. He was appointed the first Director of the Imperial Bureau of Mycology in 1920 and was responsible for starting the "Review of Applied Mycology". Election to the Fellowship of the Royal Society was in 1926 and he was appointed an original member of the Agricultural Research Council in 1931.

Butler succeeded to the Secretaryship at a time when the Council's relations with the Agricultural Departments had been more clearly defined than hitherto and when a decision had been made to establish the Council's own "farm centre". Butler was very much involved with all the various developments, the search for a suitable site, the eventual purchase of the Compton Manor Estate, the appointment of the Director and the first beginnings of the Field Station's programme. In all of this he took a keen personal interest. A new Chairman of the Council was appointed during his term of office. Lord Richard Cavendish retired in 1938 and was succeeded by Sir Thomas Middleton who, as mentioned earlier in connection with the Development Commission, was also an original Council member. Butler had to undertake the strain of the emergency arrangements put into effect prior to the outbreak of war as a result of which the Council's business was predominantly in the hands of the Secretary with the aid only of a small Executive Committee. He was obliged to resign in January 1941, for reaons of ill health and he died in April 1943, at the age of 69. He had received his Knighthood in 1939.

The new Secretary to the Council was Professor William Whiteman Carlton Topley, of the Chair of Bacteriology and Immunology of the London School of Hygiene and Tropical Medicine. Although Topley had not become a member of Council until 1940, during which year the Council met once only, he had had considerable experience of the Council's work on the animals side. His service had included membership of the Standing Committee on Animal Diseases and Animal Nutrition and Breeding, the Special Committee on Helminths of Immediate Importance in Animal Health, and the Scholarship Committee. He had been a member of the Medical Research Council since 1938 and, thus, was well versed in the organisation and management of civil science. That this was so became immediately obvious and the lasting impression of those on the staff of the agricultural research service at that time is of unquestioned leadership in a context of urgency and dedication. Regrettably a further confirmation of this is that he achieved so much in the short period of his office which was terminated by his sudden death in January 1944.

Topley graduated in 1911 from St. Thomas's Hospital Medical School having been at St. John's, Cambridge. His first appointment was Assistant Director of Pathology at his teaching hospital, and he subsequently spent 11 years as Director of the Pathology Department of Charing Cross Hospital. In 1922 he accepted appointment to the Chair of Bacteriology in Manchester and was there for 5 years before becoming the first

Professor of Bacteriology and Immunology at the London School of Hygiene and Tropical Medicine. His great contribution to microbiological research was his quantitative experimental studies of epidemiology. He was elected to the Fellowship of the Royal Society in 1930. Another contribution in the national interest was the very valuable part that he played in the organisation of the emergency laboratory services that had to be undertaken to cope with the consequences of the imminence and the outbreak of war. Little over a year after Topley became Secretary to the Council, Middleton, the Chairman, began to suffer from ill health which prevented him attending the meetings of Council during some months in 1942 and again in 1943. He died while still in office in the spring of 1943. During his absences the chair had been taken by Dampier, Barcroft or Sir Robert Greig. The Earl De La Warr was appointed Chairman and attended his first meeting in September 1943.

The vacancy caused by Topley's death was filled by the appointment of Mr. J. C. F. (later Sir John) Fryer who attended his first meeting as Secretary to the Council in June 1944. John Claude Fortescue Fryer was an entomologist whose first appointment was on the staff of the then Board of Agriculture in 1913. He later became the first Director of the Harpenden Plant Pathology Laboratory of the Ministry of Agriculture and Fisheries to which duty he added, in 1941, that of the Technical Secretary of the Agricultural Improvement Council for England and Wales and, representing it, as Assessor on the Agricultural Research Council from 1942. Topley had welcomed the creation of this body as he saw it providing an improved opportunity of ensuring that the results of research would be wisely applied in agricultural practice. The offer to Fryer of the appointment of the Secretaryship to the Agricultural Research Council forced upon him the making of a very difficult decision. He had been about to be appointed the head of the new National Agricultural Advisory Service of the Ministry of Agriculture and Fisheries for which he felt a strong responsibility as he had had so much to do with its creation. He decided wisely, as far as the agricultural research service was concerned, as he proved to be ideally suited to implementing and furthering the developments initiated by Topley and then adding his own contributions, one of which was the greater participation in the Council's Committee work of the Directors of the Institutes. All these and many other aspects of the Council's work were tirelessly undertaken to an extent which began to tell and he fell ill in the autumn of 1948 and died in November of that year. He had been appointed Knight Commander of the Order of the British Empire in 1948 and elected to the Fellowship of the Royal Society in 1948. One of Fryer's last problems shortly before he became ill was that of securing a new Chairman. De La Warr's term of appointment for 5 years terminated on the 1st of July 1948. His re-appointment had been recommended by Fryer, acting without doubt with the guidance of Council. The Lord President of the Council, apparently, objected to the Chairman serving for as long as 10 years, which could have resulted had he been re-appointed. A special meeting of Council was held to consider the difficult situation thus created at which Professor T. J. Mackie took the Chair. The Council's view favoured the selection of Lord Rothschild who, following the due procedure, was appointed. Rothschild was welcomed to his first meeting in September 1948, but unfortunately, Fryer's illness prevented him from attending.

This record of the changes in the leadership of the Council can best be terminated at this point so that the many events during the Secretaryships of Topley and Fryer can now be described; the next interlude of this type will begin with the era of Lord Rothschild and Sir William Slater.

## The Agricultural Research Council/Agricultural Improvement Councils Relationship

The Agricultural Improvement Council for England and Wales had been established in 1941 with Fryer as the Secretary. The Agricultural Improvement Council for

Scotland had been established in 1941 and in this context they need not be considered separately. Both were concerned with the application of the results of research of benefit to the agricultural industry. In 1943, the Agricultural Research Council reviewed the experience of the first two years of their co-existence. Papers on the subject were prepared by Professor F. L. (later Sir Frank) Engledow (member of Council 1942 to 1947) and by Topley whose Secretaryship had begun at the beginning of this period. As a result of this review a number of procedural principles were agreed for the future management of agricultural research including the relationship between the Council and the Universities, Colleges of Agriculture and Veterinary Schools.

The functions of the Agricultural Improvement Councils were defined as:—

1. Keeping in close touch with the progress of scientific research and also experiments in new farming methods and advising in consultation with the Agricultural Research Council what steps should be taken to test promising results with a view to their introduction into general farming practice.
2. Expediting the incorporation into ordinary farming practice of new knowledge proved to be generally applicable.
3. Reviewing the problems of farmers in order to advise, in the light of current agricultural policy, on problems needing scientific investigation or increased scientific attention.

At the time the Agricultural Improvement Council for England and Wales was created, the Chairman, Sir Donald Fergusson, in a letter to the then Chairman of the Agricultural Research Council, Sir Thomas Middleton, had attempted to define the respective functions of the two Councils as follows:—

"The work of the Agricultural Improvement Council should be supplementary to the work of the Agricultural Research Council as defined in its Charter. The Agricultural Research Council will concentrate their energies on strengthening the efficiency of the research organisation, but will not be concerned to get the results applied in practice. This will be the job of the Agricultural Improvement Council."

Topley, in his memorandum to Council, listed in greater detail its general function with reference to Fergusson's definition.

1. To ensure the recruitment of able scientists for agricultural research.
2. To encourage research in the Science Departments of the Universities on those aspects of biology, chemistry or physics which have a bearing, immediate or remote, on agricultural problems.
3. To encourage research on more specifically agricultural problems in University Schools of Agriculture or of Veterinary Medicine.
4. To supervise and co-ordinate the work of the existing Agricultural Research Institutes, and to promote the establishment of new Institutues, or the modification of old ones as the need arises.
5. To develop systematically, in Universities, Research Institutes or elsewhere, research in particular fields of agricultural science, which, in view of their potential importance, merit increased attention apart from any immediate application.
6. To initiate and supervise *ad hoc* inquiries into practical agricultural problems, either referred to the Agricultural Research Council by the Agricultural Improvements Councils, or arising during the Agricultural Research Council's own activities.
7. To bring to the notice of the Agricultural Improvement Councils any development which has reached a stage at which it can be generally applied in agricultural practice or at which further trials are required under practical farming conditions.

8. To co-operate with the Agricultural Improvement Councils, with the Ministry of Agriculture and Fisheries, or with the Department of Agriculture for Scotland, in applying the results of research in agricultural practice.
9. To do all in its power to ensure that state-aided agricultural research in Great Britain functions as an integrated whole, not as a series of unrelated units each pursuing its own ends without a common purpose.

## The Objectives for the Agricultural Research Institutes (1943)

The assessment of the objectives with regard to Research Institutes had a very important bearing upon subsequent developments. The objectives, in Topley's opinion, were listed as:

1. To cover the field, so that each important activity is represented at one or more Research Institutes, as may prove most convenient. "Subject" and "Crop" activities may well be pursued at different Institutes in different proportions.
2. Subject to (1) to plan Research Institutes so that they are neither too small for adequate staffing and equipment, nor so unwieldy and diffuse that unity of purpose and direction becomes impossible.
3. To place Research Institutes where they have ready access to the soils, crops or livestock that form their essential material for study, or, if this cannot be secured in a single area, to establish sub-stations, or facilities at Advisory Centres, Farm Institutes or elsewhere, that will supply the research staffs with ample opportunities for pursuing their investigations anywhere in Great Britain. It is useless to inform the Research Institutes that their functions are national, if they are given only local opportunities.
4. With regard to (3), to place the Research Institute where the staff will have the maximum opportunities for contacts with their scientific colleagues.

Topley further noted that it might be found, in some cases, that research of the kind required was already in progress in the Science Departments of several Universities, or in other existing Institutes. In such cases it might be more effective, and far more economical, to farm out fundamental problems to those best able to solve them rather than to establish a separate Institute.

In view of the way in which the structure of the Agricultural Research Service eventually developed with the programme of the Agricultural Research Council being conducted almost exclusively in its own Institutes and Units, it is important to study the attitude towards the sponsoring of research in Universities as it was seen by the Secretary to the Council in 1943.

## The Agricultural Research Council/Universities, Colleges of Agriculture and Veterinary Schools Relationship

There appeared to be no constraint on encouraging research in the Science Departments of the Universities. The provision of grants for this purpose was accepted to be a continuous part of the Agricultural Research Council's general policy. The precept was propounded that the whole-hearted co-operation of the Heads of University Departments, and of senior members of their staff, would be secured only by leaving them free to attack those problems that were of most interest to them.

The attitude towards the Colleges of Agriculture and the Veterinary Schools with regard to the sponsoring of research was not quite so liberal. Topley noted, however, that it would be disastrous if the establishment of Agricultural Research Institutes were to reduce research in University Schools of Agriculture or of Veterinary Medicine to a negligible level, so separating research from teaching. An Agricultural Research Institute was thought to have to dedicate its programme to problems of immediate practical importance covering all the more important aspects of the particular field with which it was concerned, and also with the encouragement of fundamental scientific work. The primary purpose of the Schools of Agriculture and of Veterinary Medicine was regarded to be education. Research was an essential part of their activities but had to be adjusted to the primary function. The research programmes would be determined by the interests and capabilities of the members of the teaching staff for the time being and not by the general needs of practical agriculture.

A most interesting distinction was then made by Topley between what can best be described as the research potential of University Departments and of the Schools of Agriculture and Veterinary Medicine. Although some of these Schools were integral parts of their Universities, in many cases the connection with the University was only one of affiliation. The assessment was that research in Schools of Agriculture or of Veterinary Medicine would only be placed on a satisfactory footing when it was regarded as a normal and essential activity of the teaching staffs and their post-graduate students, related to but administratively independent of the work of the Agricultural Research Institutes.

The important observation was then made which implied that the Schools' contribution to the so-called dual support system was quite inadequate in that their research facilities would have to be greatly extended. This, it was pointed out, was primarily the concern of the Ministry of Agriculture and Fisheries or of the Department of Agriculture and Fisheries for Scotland, but the Agricultural Research Council should, however, assist by providing special research grants from time to time.

A rather significant comment is made, considering subsequent developments, namely, that in principle small independent Research Institutes are uneconomic and that it would be as well, as opportunity offers, to dissolve certain of the Institutes situated in Universities and to take the existing staff and equipment into the Schools of Agriculture, or of Veterinary Medicine. As it turned out, the converse appeared to be the rule which increased the concentration of agricultural research within the Institute structure and not within the Universities.

These issues were the subject of much discussion by Council during the course of two meetings, namely, those of November and December 1943. The next meeting was not held until March 1944, when quite the most significant and greatly regretted event that was recorded was Topley's death.

## Principles for research management (1943)

During the Council's discussions a number of points were emphasised that had not been singled out by Topley in his memorandum. The most important of these were:-

1. Great care must be exercised in the appointment of Directors who must be given a large measure of freedom as regards their scientific responsibility.
2. It was essential to provide conditions that would attract and retain able men who must be made to feel that they were part of a co-ordinated Agricultural Research Service.
3. Directors must be freed of having to attend to administration detail by ensuring that competent Secretaries to Institutes were appointed.

4. It would be more advantageous if the Research Institutes could be linked to independent Governing Bodies rather than to a University or a University Department. The advantage of the wider representation of agricultural interests that would be provided by a Governing Body was emphasised but in the context of a bias against the Universities. This bias can be seen to have been developing by the assessment that was made in reference to the Council/University relationship by which it was clearly implied that the academic staff could be trusted to conduct research only when the problems were of interest to them.

Final conclusions were that it was not the main function of the Agricultural Research Council to dictate research programmes but it was to see that good work was being done, that the required range was being covered and, when appropriate, to encourage programmes of co-ordinated research between Institutes; that it was of the highest importance to encourage fundamental research in University Departments and that it must be ensured that the Departments of Agriculture set aside adequate funds for research and its facilities in its grants to the Schools of Agriculture and Veterinary Medicine.

## The management of Institutes associated with Universities

The Council, having discussed its relationships with the Agricultural Improvement Councils, the Agricultural Departments and the Universities, and having debated the principles of research management, turned its attention to determining the most appropriate administrative arrangements for a number of Institutes already having some association with a University. For this task it had available the reports of certain of the various Survey Groups which had been reviewing specific areas of agricultural research. In many cases final decisions were deferred until all the Survey Group reports or the reports of other bodies such as the Loveday Committee on the future of the veterinary profession were available. As of 1943, however, the following guiding principles were agreed which were forwarded to the Agricultural Departments for consideration in consultation with the officers of the Council and subsequently with the Committee of Vice-Chancellors and Principals.

1. Plant Breeding Institute, Cambridge.
   Survey report on plant genetics and breeding awaited but, meantime, it was agreed that an Institute would be required on a larger scale than at present and which would be more appropriately managed by a Governing Body than by remaining within the University.
2. Plant Virus Research Station, Cambridge.
   To be absorbed into the appropriate University Department.
3. Horticultural Research Station, Cambridge.
   Survey report on horticulture awaited, but it was anticipated that the Station might be absorbed into a new Vegetable Research Institute.
4. Institute of Animal Pathology, Cambridge.
   Further consideration to await the publication of the Loveday Report.
5. Institute of Animal Nutrition, Cambridge.
   The joint Committee of the two Agricultural Improvement Councils and the Agricultural Research Council had first to complete its review of animal nutrition.
6. Welsh Plant Breeding Station, Aberystwyth.
   As with the Cambridge Institute, the survey report on plant genetics and breeding was awaited, but it was judged that a Governing Body would be preferable for its management than remaining in the University College.

7. Long Ashton Research Station.

The survey report on horticultural research was awaited. No indication was recorded about its future.

8. Research Institute in Plant Physiology, Imperial College of Science and Technology.

Its future, which it was agreed should not be indefinite, had to be discussed between the Ministry of Agriculture and Imperial College.

9. Research Institute in Animal Pathology, Royal Veterinary College.

It was recommended that adequate financial provision for it should be included by the Ministry of Agriculture in its education grant to the College.

10. Institute of Agricultural Parasitology, London School of Hygiene and Tropical Medicine.

This to be closed on the retirement of the Director with dispersal of the staff to other Institutes.

11. Institute of Animal Genetics, Edinburgh.

The survey report on animal genetics and breeding was awaited.

12. National Institute for Research in Dairying, Reading.

The management of the Institute had, since 1921, been delegated by the University to a Board of Management which arrangement was accepted as being satisfactory.

Five of these establishments were connected with the Faculty of Agriculture of the University of Cambridge. They were controlled by a Central Committee of the University of which the Drapers Professor of Agriculture was *ex officio* Chairman. The future of these institutions at Cambridge, Bristol and Aberystwyth was complicated by the fact that their Departments of Agriculture were advisory centres for the then Agricultural Advisory Service based on the County Councils. The National Agricultural Advisory Service was constituted in 1946 by the Minister of Agriculture and Fisheries under the Agriculture (Miscellaneous Provisions) Act 1944. The result of the Council's review in 1943 and the proposals for a fundamental change in the local advisory services led to considerable discussion by the Central Committee and the General Board of the University of Cambridge. A meeting took place in October 1946 between representatives of the Agricultural Research Council and the General Board when it was agreed that the Central Committee would relinquish control of the Institutes on the 1st of October 1947. It was accepted that there had to be an interim period following that date during which final arrangements would be completed. It was agreed that, in due course, the Plant Breeding Institute would pass from the control of the University and that the Plant Virus Research Station would become a Unit under the direct control of the Council. In most cases, therefore, subsequent developments came about as had been proposed in 1943. Perhaps the most complete exception was the future management of the Plant Virus Research Station (p. 49).

## Animal Genetics and Breeding

Throughout the life of the Agricultural Research Council, animal genetics and breeding have, from time to time, demanded a considerable amount of attention. Intrinsic features of the subject have contributed to this. For example, the ease with which animal breeding research could be expanded into the limitless fields of endocrinology and the physiology of reproduction periodically led to the criticism that the coverage of the programme was too wide. The long-term nature of animal breeding research regularly tried the patience of those who were accustomed to time the duration of a project within, say, three years and the cost of setting up and maintaining an experiment using farm livestock was a heavy and seemingly perpetual financial burden. Another feature of these particular aspects of the activities supported by the Council was the zeal and the single-minded way with which the principal personalities pursued their wide-ranging interests.

As far back as 1911, the Development Commissioners had identified the need for an Animal Genetics Research Institute. No action was taken until after the 1914–18 war when a scheme submitted by the University of Edinburgh was approved with the appointment in 1921 of Dr. F. A. E. Crew as Director of the Institute of Animal Genetics. During the next ten years generous financial support was provided by the Rockefeller Foundation, the Empire Marketing Board, the Development Fund, Lord Woolvington, T. B. Macaulay and the University. Crew held this appointment until 1944, apart from absence on war service. In 1928 he was appointed to the Buchanan Chair of Animal Genetics. The Agricultural Research Council, soon after its establishment, sent an *ad hoc* Sub-Committee to the Institute in 1932 to examine its work. Dr. A. W. Greenwood's research on the sex endocrinology of the fowl attracted favourable attention. Many years later, Greenwood was invited to submit a proposal for a comprehensive programme of poultry research. This the Council approved in 1947 with the result that the ARC Poultry Research Centre was established in Edinburgh with Greenwood as the first Director.

Another member of the staff of the Institute of Animal Genetics when it was inspected in 1932 was Dr. A. D. Buchanan Smith (later Lord Balerno). His subject was livestock breeding and, in particular, the investigation of milk yields by analysis of herd books by statistical methods. The report of the Council's Sub-Committee records that much attention was given to this work. It was agreed that further progress could be made only by planned experimentation on a large scale. It was, however, decided that this was not urgent. Although Lord Balerno was by that time no longer involved, provision was made in 1948 by the purchase of Cold Norton Farm in Staffordshire for large-scale experiments using dairy cattle.

The Council and the Agricultural Improvement Councils had set up a Survey Group on Animal Breeding and Genetics. The report of this Group was received in 1944. It is important to note that the Group concluded that a National Institute must be established and that it must be concerned initially with fundamental genetic principles based on the results of a series of long-term observations. This conclusion recognised that scientific methods for the breeding of livestock were not translatable by the Agricultural Improvement Councils into advice to the farmer for the breeding of his livestock. Thus, it became clearly established at an early date that the Agricultural Research Council's responsibility was not to produce improved breeds of animals. The responsibility was to determine the genetic basis of biological characteristics. These contributions to knowledge might then be applied by the breeder to introduce desirable features into his farm livestock.

In November 1944, it was decided that the new National Institute should be established with the recommendation that Professor R. G. White of the University College of North Wales, Bangor, be appointed Director and, as Deputy Director and Chief Geneticist, Dr C. H. Waddington who at that time was on war service with the Operational Research Section of Coastal Command, RAF. Both accepted the Council's provisional invitation but by the time Treasury approval had been obtained in 1945, Waddington had been offered the Buchanan Chair of Animal Genetics at the University of Edinburgh in succession to Crew who had moved to the Chair of Public Health and Social Medicine. Waddington, however, decided to stand by his acceptance of the Council's offer. No consideration had yet been given to locating the new Institute in Edinburgh but subsequently this possibility was recognised and successfully pursued by White. Waddington and his genetics section were accommodated with the University Department of Genetics in the University building known as the Institute of Animal Genetics. White, whose work was largely on the various farms which he had been selecting for the Council to purchase, was accommodated in a converted house in a select residential area of the south side of Edinburgh. At that time, the appointment of other staff was recommended including that of Dr. H. P. Donald of the Institute of Animal Genetics. In 1947 Waddington was appointed to the University Chair while remaining on the staff of what was then known as the Animal Breeding and Genetics Research Organisation. Following White's retirement, a Visiting Group was appointed which in 1950, made the curiously impractical recommendation, no doubt based on the two locations, that Professor Waddington and Dr. Donald be appointed as co-equal heads with a Committee of Council to co-ordinate their activities. It took more than a year to begin to resolve this difficult situation by appointing Donald, in 1951, Director of the renamed Animal Breeding Research Organisation with Waddington responsible for the University Department but with his research programme supported by a block grant from the Council. A further step in the attempted rationalisation of this complex situation was taken in 1957 when the Council established its Unit of Animal Genetics under Waddington's direction within the University's Institute of Animal Genetics. An unusual feature of the Council's decision in setting up the Unit was that this Unit would not be disbanded if Waddington were to leave. And so it was, that when Waddington relinquished the Directorship of the Unit, but not his Professorship, in 1968, the Deputy Director was given a personal chair by the University and he, now Professor D. S. Falconer, was appointed Director of the Unit. The following year, 1969, Falconer became head of the University's Department of Genetics. The Council, on considering the future of the Unit prior to the time for Falconer's retirement, decided that it should not be continued after that date and it was disbanded in September 1980.

Donald retired from the Animal Breeding Research Organisation in 1973 and was succeeded by Dr. J. W. B. King, who had been responsible for the pig breeding programme of the Organisation. One feature of the Organisation is the number of farms which the Council has made available for its research programme. The research has been carried out in a wide range of properties from Mountmarle and Skedsbush in the Lothian Region; Blythbank, Broughton Knowe and Stanhope in the Border Region; Cold Norton, in Staffordshire: and to Rhydglafes in Clwyd.

## A Changed Committee Structure

In 1931, the newly appointed Council having received the very wide spectrum of its responsibility, decided to set up six Standing Committees each empowered to form Sub-Committees. It was soon found convenient for two of the three Committees dealing with animals to meet together and for the two Committees dealing with plants and soils to meet together. Nevertheless, this structure survived for some fourteen years. It was not until 1945 that the research interests were formally divided into two areas with the establishment of two Standing Committees, namely, the Standing Committee on Research affecting Animals and the Standing Committee on Research affecting Plants and Soils. These two Committees were retained at the summit of the Council's Committee structure for twenty-seven years until they were replaced by the Boards of the Joint Consultative Organisation early in 1973. Two more specialised Committees were also formed in 1945, the Finance and Staff Committee and the Estate Committee. Subservient to the two Standing Committees was a relatively large system of Technical Committees, Technical Conferences and *ad hoc* Groups. The differences between these various grades of Committees is best reflected in their composition. The Standing Committees consisted of ". . . — those members of Council whose main interests lie in the appropriate field, together with other scientists of repute, whose specialised knowledge on the many different scientific interests involved is necessary." The original wording of this precept contained the phrase ". . . and scientific representatives not themselves members of the Council and whose Institutes were not in receipt of general grant-aid from the Government." This exclusion of Directors of the grant-aided

Institutes was based on an earlier ruling of the Privy Council Committee which had excluded the Directors from membership of the Agricultural Research Council.

The composition of the membership of the Standing Committees was again discussed a year later (1946) when Council decided that the contribution of Directors was too valuable to be so lost and that there was no justification in applying a rule about membership of Council to the Council's Committees. This decision was immediately implemented by inviting Dr. W. G. (later Sir William) Ogg (the Rothamsted Experimental Station), Dr. J. Russell Greig (the Moredun Institute), and Professor Kay (the National Institute for Research in Dairying), to be Standing Committee members. Subsequently, it was not unusual to find Directors of ARC Units on the Standing Committees, but Directors of Institutes were more likely to be found on the Technical Committees with members of their staffs on the Technical Conferences and Groups. In course of time other Committees were formed some with the status of a Standing Committee, for example, the Standing Committee on Agricultural Engineering Research and the Standing Committee on Research affecting Farm Buildings. Nevertheless, the major themes of "Animals" and "Plants and Soils" became and has continued to be the main beams of the structure of the Council's activities, of the organisation of the Secretariat and of the Institute and Unit framework. Difficulties of classification have been few and have been solved in a convenient if not necessarily a logical manner. For example, food research is an "Animals" subject, whereas agricultural engineering and insects are "Plants and Soils" subjects.

## The Soil Surveys of Great Britain

Although differences in types and qualities of soil must have been recognised since earliest times it was not until about the beginning of this century that systematic studies of the soil were commenced in this country. At that time the Agricultural Education Association stimulated and sought to co-ordinate and standardise methods of soil analysis. The subjects of soil physics, soil chemistry and soil biology were being developed and expanded at Rothamsted but soil surveying became more an activity of the agricultural advisers although the earliest surveys were based on geology with the attempted translation of the surface geology map into a soil map. The inadequacies of this practice gradually became apparent and from 1930 soil survey work in England and Wales was co-ordinated under a Soil Survey Executive Committee which included representatives from Scotland. In 1939, the Ministry of Agriculture and Fisheries appointed Professor G. W. Robinson of the University College of North Wales, Bangor, Director of Soil Surveys for England and Wales. In Scotland, the Macaulay Institute for Soil Research had been engaged on surveying under Ogg's direction since 1930. In 1946 it was mooted that it would be more advantageous for the soil survey to be associated more with research than with advisory activities. The Agricultural Research Council accepted the responsibility for the supervision of this work and set up the Soil Survey Research Board as an advisory body. It was then decided that the Soil Survey of England and Wales should be conducted from the Rothamsted Experimental Station and that for Scotland should continue to be conducted from the Macaulay Institute for Soil Research. This arrangement has continued to the present day with the two Agricultural Departments being responsible for the costs in spite of the various changes in financial responsibility that have taken place since the Agricultural Research Council assumed the supervisory responsibility in 1946.

## Hop research

In view of the restricted areas in which it is profitable to grow hops, the principal one of which is in the south-east of England, it is not surprising that Wye Agricultural College has been involved in hop research for many years. Various aspects of breeding, nutrition, culture and harvesting had been the subject of research at Wye since the beginning of the century, but in 1947 the importance of the crop was recognised by the establishment of a separate Department of Hop Research. These principal research activities continued with the East Malling Research Station being responsible for research on the disease of hops. The Agricultural Research Council assumed the responsibility for the supervision and financing of the Department jointly with the Brewers' Society and the Hops Marketing Board; the Department has continued very successfully in its untidy status of being neither an Institute nor a Unit.

## The Experimental Husbandry Farms and Horticulture Stations

It having been recognised that the Agricultural Research Institutes had no facilities to carry the results of their research to the larger field scale and that it was a responsbility of the Agricultural Improvement Councils to ensure that the results of research reached the farmer, the Agricultural Improvement Council for England and Wales established a Joint Committee with the Agricultural Research Council. The first interim report of this Committee was discussed by the Agricultural Research Council in the autumn of 1945. The opinion was that the new National Agricultural Advisory Service should provide the facilities for the intermediate stage between Research Institute and the integration of new systems into the practical working of the farming industry. The Agricultural Research Council gave this attitude its full support, but did not appear to have been involved in the immediate developments of the acquisition of suitable experimental farms or stations. Within the next three years three farms had been acquired and negotiations were in hand for two more. These farms were to operate under a controlling Committee and the Council was invited to nominate three representatives. A very close relationship continued to exist between the staffs of the Research Institutes and the staff of the Advisory Service and that of its farms.

## Nature Conservancy

In 1948, the Council was asked, by the Committee of the Privy Council for Agricultural Research to assume, for an experimental period, responsibility for nature conservation which meant in the terms of the invitation ". . . providing advice through Nature Conservation Boards and Committees on the conservation and control of the natural flora and fauna of Great Britain, for establishing nature reserves in Great Britain and for the organisation and development of research and scientific service related thereto." This invitation would have led to much work outside the range of the Council's activities and there must have been considerable relief when, for legislative reasons, it was found necessary that the Nature Conservancy must be a legal entity established under its own Charter.

## The Plant Breeding Institute, Cambridge

Mention has already been made of the establishment in 1912 of the Cambridge University Plant Breeding Institute at the School of Agriculture under the direction of R. H. (later Sir Rowland) Biffen. Biffen retired in 1936 and was succeeded by Mr. H.

Hunter who remained in office until resigning in 1946. From 1939 to 1945 he had acted as Director of the National Institute of Agricultural Botany. The results of the survey of the various Institutes associated with Universities made by the Agricultural Research Council in 1943 led the Council to decide that the importance of plant breeding justified a greater effort than was being accommodated within the limitations of the School of Agriculture and the University Farm. The Council also expressed its opinion that the greater scale required would be better suited to an Institute with an independent Governing Body rather than seeking to expand within the University. The future of the other institutes at Cambridge had also to be considered, namely, the Horticultural Research Station, the Plant Virus Research Station, the Institute of Animal Nutrition and the Institute of Animal Pathology (p. 41). At the time of Hunter's retirement from the Directorship of the Plant Breeding Institute much discussion was under way between the Council and the General Board of the University. It is relevant to note that during this period Cambridge University was well represented on the Council, namely, by Sir Frank Engledow, Drapers Professor of Agriculture (member of Council 1942–1947), Professor J. Gray, Professor of Zoology (member of Council 1942–1947 and 1949–50), and by Professor A. C. Chibnall, firstly, as the Sir William Dunn Professor of Biochemistry and subsequently as Fellow of Clare College (member of Council 1947-1957). A year after Hunter's resignation the Council agreed (1947) that the Directorship of the Institute should be offered to Dr. G. D. H. Bell, Acting Director of the Institute and also a University teacher in the Lecturer grade. It is debatable whether the Council, at that time, had any authority to pronounce upon the appointments of staff at the University's Institute and it must have been reassuring to Bell that two months later the Ministry of Agriculture and Fisheries wrote to Sir Frank Engledow recommending, on behalf of the Ministry and the Agricultural Research Council, that the post of Director of the Institute should be offered by the University to Bell. This post became Bell's in 1948 when he was charged with the responsibility to find a suitable site, to develop the facilities required for the agreed expansion and to recruit the necessary staff. The Maris Lane site at Trumpington was acquired in 1950, the Institute was re-established in 1952 with its own independent Governing Body with Engledow as the first Chairman, the staff were transferred from their University accommodation as soon as the premises were ready. All those except the cereal group had been transferred by 1953 and the move was completed in 1955.

This history of the Plant Breeding Institute is of considerable significance as regards the development of the policy of the Agricultural Research Council which has made it to-day so different from the other Research Councils. The point to be made is the very high proportion of the Council's funds that are in support of research in its own establishments. The other Research Councils, with the partial exception of the Natural Environment Research Council, depend to a very much greater extent upon the Universities by means of research grant support, or by the creation of Units. In 1946 there was a concensus that research on plant breeding was a high priority and that much larger facilities were required than were at present available within the University of Cambridge. In that the first official plant breeding centre had been established some thirty years before at the School of Agriculture of the University of Cambridge, in that its staff had been especially successful in their work, in that those entrusted with the furtherance of agricultural research had identified plant breeding as being a high priority, one must assume that the University of Cambridge was thus presented with an opportunity to expand in a science that had a high potential for success, for easy application in industry and, consequently, for greatly increasing the productivity of British agriculture. This opportunity was not taken and it is, perhaps, hardly surprising that the Agricultural Research Council developed a policy by which it could have more faith in the outcome if it directly sponsored research in its own Institutes or in Institutes to which it supplied the grant-in-aid. It would be wrong to infer that the Plant Breeding Institute provided the one example which so influenced the Council's policy. When, for example, a great expansion was required in the 1930s in veterinary research there was no research competence in the Veterinary Schools; at which time only one was wholly within a University (Liverpool). The Plant Breeding Institute's situation was specific to the University of Cambridge and, subsequently, further decisions were made with regard to the future of some of its other Institutes which led to their activities being continued as ARC Units, or within Institutes under the aegis of the Agricultural Research Council. It is necessary to note that the already established Agricultural Research Service which the Council inherited, and its expansion by which new Institutes were created, was by no means the whole of the Council's activities. It was still to depend to a very considerable extent upon the research competence in the relevant sciences within the Universities. This was especially so in the late 1940s and in the 1950s.

# Chapter 3

# 1947-1960

## The Post-War Expansion

### An Emphasis on Units

The Agricultural Research Council, in its discussion of its future procedures which it debated at length in 1943 when Topley was Secretary, strongly emphasised that the highest importance should be given to encourage fundamental research in University Departments as well as in the Research Institutes. This policy, as far as the Universities were concerned, was strongly implemented in the post-war years. Implementation was of two types, namely, the award of research grants or the establishment of Units. In the early years of the Council's existence the sole and rather meagre funds in its gift were ". . . for the initiation or encouragement of special researches". These it disbursed by means of research grants to University Departments, Agricultural and Veterinary Colleges, and the Research Institutes. Grant applications were considered by the appropriate Standing Committee. It was not until 1973 that the present Research Grants Board system was instituted. The Council's policy with regard to the creation of Units is described on pages 34-35.

Three Units had been established during the war, namely, Quastel's Unit of Soil Enzyme Chemistry, Barcroft's Unit of Animal Physiology, and Wigglesworth's Unit of Insect Physiology.

The following Units were established during the post-war period now being described.

### Unit of Virus Research, University of Cambridge, 1947.

In the review of the Institutes associated with Universities, attention had been given to the Plant Virus Research Station in the University of Cambridge. This Station had existed as the Potato Virus Research Station from 1926 until 1939 when the name was changed and Dr. Kenneth M. Smith became Director. The decision about its future in the mid 1940s was that it should be absorbed into an appropriate Department of the University. It managed to retain its separate identity, however, and, in 1947, the Agricultural Research Council undertook to provide its financial support, designating it the Unit of Virus Research and, later, building laboratories on a site off Huntingdon Road. Smith retired in 1960 and was succeeded by Dr. Roy Markham. In 1967 the Unit was absorbed into the John Innes Institute at Norwich when Markham was then appointed the Institute Director.

### Unit of Plant Biochemistry, University of Cambridge, 1947.

The Director was Dr. C. S. Hanes, Reader in Plant Biochemistry. Hanes resigned in 1951 on being appointed to the Chair of Biochemistry, Toronto University.

## Unit of Animal Reproduction, University of Cambridge, 1949.

The future of the University's Institute of Animal Nutrition had been under discussion for some time and in 1948 it was decided that the staff should be dispersed. Consideration was given to salvaging an animal physiology group under Dr. J. (later Sir John) Hammond, within the Department of Agriculture and financed by a grant-in-aid from the Ministry of Agriculture or the Agricultural Research Council. This idea was abandoned in favour of the Council establishing a Unit. Hammond was particularly interested in the different phases of the growth of farm livestock and the relative development of bone, muscle and fat. He recognised that in this relationship lay the basis for the study of meat production. The work of his Unit contributed to such studies but he always believed that something much larger was required on the lines of a Meat Research Institute. He retired from his Readership in Agricultural Physiology in 1954 and died in 1964 by which time it had at last been decided that a Meat Research Institute should be established but such were the delays in the negotiations about funding that he failed to see the final realisation. The future of the Unit is related with reference to the Unit of Reproductive Physiology and Biochemistry.

## Unit of Experimental Agronomy, University of Oxford, 1950.

For some years prior to 1950 the Council had financed work in the Department of Agriculture on the chemical control of weeds. This programme was expanded and given the promise of long-term support by the creation of a Unit under the direction of Professor G. E. Blackman, Sibthorpian Professor of Rural Economy. The Colonial Office contributed part of the cost because of its interest in the relevance of much of the work to tropical agriculture. The Unit's work extended from fundamental research in plant physiology to field experiments in many parts of the country to evaluate new herbicides and in the development of practical weed control procedures. Another aspect of the Unit's programme reflected by the title "Experimental Agronomy" was the investigation of new crops of potential use in British agriculture. Those selected included oilseed crops and hybrid maize. In course of time, however, the increasing demand for the services of the Unit's staff in the evaluation and application of herbicides made some reorganisation essential. The resources of the more applied part of the programme had become severely strained and in 1960 a group of eight of the Unit staff headed by the Assistant Director, Dr. E. K. Woodford, were transferred to Begbroke Hill Farm, near Kidlington, to form the Weed Research Organization. The remainder of the Unit continued under Blackman's direction until his retirement in 1970. A number of the staff were transferred to the then recently established Unit of Developmental Botany, Cambridge.

## Unit of Biometrical Genetics, University of Birmingham, 1950.

This Unit was directed by Professor K. (now Sir Kenneth) Mather. The subject was the investigation of the cause and the control of continuous variation using biometrical techniques. Continuous variation is characteristic of so much of animal and plant production that this fundamental research approach of a long-term nature exemplifies the type of work for which the establishment of a Unit is so appropriate. Mather was appointed Vice-Chancellor of the University of Southampton in 1965 and the Council took the unusual step of continuing to finance the work of Mather's group at Birmingham for a further two years until the start of the new quinquennium. Professor J. L. Jinks, a member of the Unit staff and appointed to the Chair of Genetics in succession to Mather, supervised the work during that period.

## Unit of Soil Physics, University of Cambridge, 1951.

In 1934 Dr. E. C. Childs was appointed to the staff of the School of Agriculture to study problems of soil structure relevant to land drainage. In 1951 the continuity of this work was assured by the establishment of a Unit with Childs as Director. Childs died in 1973 and the senior member of the staff, Dr. E. G. Youngs, was appointed Acting Director until a decision was made about the future of the Unit. A proposal to incorporate the work with that of the nearby Land Drainage Unit of the Agricultural Development and Advisory Service did not materialise and in 1978 the Unit was disbanded and the staff transferred to the Rothamsted Experimental Station.

## Unit of Microbiology, University of Sheffield, 1952.

Dr. S. R. Elsden, Senior Lecturer in Bacteriology, had been receiving grant support for his microbiological research on bacteria of relevance to agriculture. To provide greater continuity, the Council established a Unit under his direction in 1952. The programme consisted of three principal lines of work, namely, the metabolism of rumen micro-organisms, the physiology of microbial growth and the metabolism of photosynthetic bacteria. Dr. Elsden was appointed Director of the Council's new Food Research Institute in 1965. His Unit was then terminated and he and other members of the staff transferred to temporary accommodation in Norwich until the Institute's buildings were ready for occupation.

## Unit of Plant Nutrition (Micro-nutrients), Long Ashton Research Station, University of Bristol, 1952.

Professor T. Wallace became Director of the Long Ashton Research Station in 1943. During and after the war he led a small group investigating practical field problems of crop production associated with deficiencies or excesses of plant nutrients other than nitrogen, phosphorus and potassium. This work was extended with additional facilities being provided by the establishment of the Unit. Particular use was made on a large-scale of highly purified sand for culture of the test plants thus permitting studies to be made of the effect of nutrients at minimal levels. Wallace retired in 1959 at which time the Unit was disbanded with a number of the staff transferring to the Research Station.

## Unit of Plant Cell Physiology, University of Oxford, 1953.

The Council was desirous of creating a Unit for Dr. R. Brown who had been a Reader in Plant Physiology at the University of Leeds from 1946 until 1952 when he became Professor of Botany at Cornell University (1952-1953). As he was not then in a University in this country, accommodation had to be found and this was provided by the Department of Agriculture, Oxford. The programme of the Unit was concerned with the fundamentally important phenomena of cell growth and differentiation. The record states (ARC Report for 1956–57) that the Unit was started with Brown as the sole member of the staff. A small group began to be formed but in 1958 Brown was appointed to the Chair of Botany in the University of Edinburgh, the Unit was disbanded, and his staff were found posts at the John Innes Institute.

## Unit of Plant Growth Substances and Systemic Fungicides, Wye College, University of London, 1953.

Professor R. L. Wain, Head of the Department of Physical Sciences and Professor of Agricultural Chemistry at Wye College had been leading a programme of fundamental research on plant growth-regulating substances with special reference to the relationships between structure and biological activity. A similar approach led to the study of fungicidal chemicals which might, on structural grounds, be expected to have little effect on plant growth but which would still move systematically in the plant. The importance and potential value of this work for the development of selective herbicides and of effective fungicides led the Council to establish a Unit under Wain's direction. A very active multi-disciplinary group was created including organic, physical and natural products chemists, biochemists, plant physiologists and plant pathologists. The programme embraced the action of synthetic and natural plant products as growth regulators, herbicides, fungicides and molluscicides. The results of this research added very considerably to the knowledge about such products and their application in agriculture and horticulture. The Unit was continued for twenty-five years under Wain's direction until his retirement from Wye College in 1978 when the staff were dispersed, the majority to the Long Ashton Research Station.

*The Wain Fund.* This is an appropriate place to refer to the very generous benefaction of Professor Wain who, in 1958, offered to the Council an income from the patents on his discoveries in the field of selective herbicides. The Wain Trust Fund was thus established which, since 1960, has been known as the Wain Fund. Professor Wain's wish was that this fund should be used to provide grants for members of the staff of universities in the United Kingdom who wished to spend a period abroad either to work in a laboratory, or to consult with scientists working in their field but not, normally, solely to attend conferences. The size of this income grew to an extent which was more than sufficient for these purposes and in 1977, with Professor Wain's agreement, the Wain Fellowships were established. Six of these are currently being offered each year to enable younger research scientists to work or study abroad at an academic, industrial or agricultural institution of their choice for a period of up to three months. These Fellowships may be awarded in any science relevant to agriculture, including animal and veterinary sciences. The point about Wain's generosity is made by noting that the income from the Fund during the year ended the 31st of March, 1980, was £13 538.

## Unit of Embryology, University College of North Wales, Bangor, 1953.

The establishment of this Unit was a consequence of some years of support by grants for research on reproduction and prenatal mortality in rabbits. The key point became the study of the transfer of immunity from mother to young. Professor F. W. Rogers Brambell had played a leading part in this work and, in order to extend it, the Council granted him "Unit" support. The subject of this research was of great fundamental and practical interest. The young animal derives its immunity to disease, and its ability to survive in a usually hostile environment, from its mother. Antibodies produced by the mother are transmitted to the offspring either before or after birth or both. A characteristic of these phenomena of importance to livestock production is the difference that occurs between species. In monkeys, rabbits, guinea-pigs and man, the antibodies are transferred before birth by their transport across the foetal membranes. Calves, lambs, kids, piglets and foals are born without having received any maternal antibodies but they obtain them from the mother's first milk or "colostrum". These antibodies can be absorbed from their gut during only a short period of hours after birth. Young rats, mice and puppies are intermediate between these two groups as they obtain their maternal immunity before and, also, after birth. An understanding of this acquisition of immunity by the new born is of fundamental importance for the successful management and rearing of young farm livestock. Brambell retired in 1968 and the Unit was then disbanded.

## Unit of Statistics, University of Aberdeen, 1954–1966; University of Edinburgh, 1966–.

This Unit was established by the Council for the specific purpose of providing for agricultural research in Scotland the kind of service available in England and Wales from the Statistics Department of Rothamsted Experimental Station. Dr. D. J. Finney was appointed in 1954 to a Readership in the University of Aberdeen on the understanding he would also head this new Unit. He succeeded to the Chair of Statistics in Aberdeen in 1964 and on accepting appointment to the Chair of Statistics in Edinburgh in 1966, the location of the Unit was thereby changed. The Unit was established with a predominantly service rôle for the benefit of the agricultural research institutes in Scotland, the three Scottish agricultural colleges, and the Agricultural Scientific Services of the Department of Agriculture and Fisheries for Scotland. The Unit has always had a strong research programme in collaboration with the staff of the Department of Statistics, firstly in Aberdeen University and latterly in Edinburgh. In many cases the projects have arisen from problems encountered in its consultative and service activities. The work of the Unit has contributed greatly to the development of farming practices in Scotland, for example, by the surveys it has conducted such as that on fertilizer use. It has made a national contribution by the development of a computing system for cereal experiments, the co-ordinated variety trial system. An adaptation of this is used for the statistical and computing procedures required for the present National Variety Testing Scheme run by the three Agricultural Departments of England and Wales, Scotland, and Northern Ireland, respectively. The essay by Professor Finney and Dr. Yates on "Statistics and Computing in Agricultural Research" (pp. 219–236) provides more examples of the Unit's programme.

## Unit of Reproductive Physiology and Biochemistry, University of Cambridge, 1955.

Sir John Hammond retired in 1954 and the future of his Unit of Animal Reproduction became a matter of discussion and negotiation between the Council and the University of Cambridge, a Sub-Committee appointed to consider its future having endorsed the importance of the research programme and recommended its continuation. It would seem that the University were disinclined to assume the responsibility of taking over the Unit. In view of the fact that a topic for serious consideration had by then been identified, namely, the financing of research in the Universities, it can be concluded that the constraint on the University's part was financial. It is convenient at this point to note that in 1957 the Advisory Council on Research Policy requested the Research Councils, the Royal Society, and the University Grants Committee, to discuss the financing of University research. The reluctance on the part of the Research Councils to give support for research for a period longer than the normal three years of a research grant was to avoid becoming permanently committed to considerable expenditure within a restricted budget, and thus being unable fully to respond to new and promising developments. This particular section of the history of the Agricultural Research Council devoted to the establishment of its Units indicates the importance attached to the University of Cambridge, (Table 4, p.78). It must have been clear for objective as well as subjective reasons that Hammond's Unit of Animal Reproduction had to be continued as indeed it was by the Council establishing the Unit of Reproductive

Physiology and Biochemistry under the direction of Dr. T. R. R. Mann. Mann was then a Reader in Physiology of Animal Reproduction in the Department of Veterinary Clinical Medicine of the University of Cambridge. In 1967 he was appointed Professor of Physiology of Reproduction. Dr. L. E. A. Rowson, who had been a senior member of the staff of Hammond's Unit while also being Director of the Cambridge and District Cattle Breeders' Artificial Insemination Centre, was appointed Mann's Deputy Director in 1955. When Mann retired in 1976, Rowson took charge at Huntingdon Road of what became a Department of the ARC Institute of Animal Physiology. During the life of the Unit its main research themes have been fundamental studies in the physiology and biochemistry of reproduction and the application of scientific knowledge to problems of animal breeding such as male and female infertility, artificial insemination, ovum transplantation and the synchronisation of oestrus. The success of the Unit's research programme has contributed immeasurably to the knowledge of the physiology and biochemistry of reproduction and the usefulness of this research has been proved by the many practical procedures which have been developed by its staff for the greatly expanded application of genetic material both from the male and from the female in animal breeding. What is now taken as being commonplace with regard to the storage of semen, techniques of superovulation, the synchronisation of oestrus, the storage of embryos and the transplantation of fertilized ova and of embryos is no more than the application of the results of the Unit's research. Mann reached the age of retirement in 1976 and the Council decided that although the entity under his direction as a Unit would disappear, the research programme must be continued with full utilisation of the laboratories and animal houses that it had built on the University's land at Huntingdon Road. This was achieved by retaining the Unit staff in that accommodation but by transferring the administrative responsibility to the Director of the Institute of Animal Physiology, Babraham. One of the appointments held by Sir John Hammond some 45 years before this final disbandment of what had originally been his Unit was that of Superintendent, Animal Research Station, Cambridge. In perpetuation of this, the present address of the Department of the Institute of Animal Physiology at Huntingdon Road is "The Animal Research Station". Rowson, who took charge in 1976 retired in 1979, and he was succeeded by another former member of the Unit of many years' service, Dr. E. J. C. Polge.

## Statistics Group, Cambridge, 1956.

Hammond's Unit of Animal Reproduction had contained a statistics group which continued initially as part of the new Unit of Reproductive Physiology and Biochemistry. The Council decided that it could serve a more useful purpose as a separate entity, providing a statistics service to the then many Institutes and Units in the Cambridge area. The senior member of the Group was Dr. R. C. Campbell and he was appointed Officer-in-Charge. Dr. Campbell retained this appointment while also a Lecturer in the Department of Applied Biology. In 1976, to enable Campbell to devote more time to his University responsibilities, Mr. J. G. Rowell was appointed Officer-in-Charge with Campbell's services being available as a consultant.

## Unit of Animal Genetics, University of Edinburgh, 1957.

Reference has been made to the establishment of this Unit under the direction of Professor C. H. Waddington, (p. 44). The separation between the programme of the Animal Breeding Research Organisation and that of the University's Institute of Animal Genetics dated from 1951. This action by Council to create a unit within the Institute was little more than giving a formal constitution to Waddington's group without any accompanying change of programme or, for the moment, any increase in staff or facilities. A very obvious difference between the work of ABRO and the work of the Unit was the extensive use by the former of farm livestock and the use by the latter of the laboratory species such as the fruit fly and the mouse. The Unit was particularly interested in the understanding of fundamental genetic principles especially with regard to the genetics of quantitative characters in animals such as the variations in size, growth rate, yield, etc.; the genetics of evolutionary processes; and the genetic control of production factors such as protein synthesis. Another of the Unit's activities was operational research with regard to the evaluation of animal breeding programmes, especially the results of the Milk Marketing Board's extensive programme of artificial insemination. On Waddington's retirement from the Honorary Directorship of the Unit in 1968, its direction passed to Professor D. S. Falconer who also succeeded to the Chair of Genetics in 1969. Since 1975 a gradual run down in staff numbers was begun by the Council in anticipation of the disbandment of the Unit on Professor Falconer's retirement in September 1980.

## Farm Buildings Unit, National Institute of Agricultural Engineering, Silsoe, Bedfordshire, 1957.

In 1956 the Council accepted the responsibility for farm building research and undertook, as first tasks, a study of what was already known and an attempt to determine the most pressing needs. The Special Survey Department of the National Institute of Agricultural Engineering was asked to begin this work and a small number of additional staff were appointed to form this Farm Buildings Unit under the direction of the Director of the Institute, Mr. W. H. Cashmore. A Farms Buildings Research Committee was also set up, initially under the Chairmanship of Lord Rothschild, Chairman of the Council. The compilation of the bibliography of research on farm buildings was continued for a number of years with the publication of various sections as they were completed. In 1960 an experimental scheme was introduced for the development and testing of new types of buildings. Under this scheme selected applicants qualified for a grant of up to half the cost of a building incorporating new features or ideas when their proposals were suitable for inclusion in a planned experiment under the supervision of the Unit. The scale of this enterprise can be gauged from the fact that at 1961–62 prices about £30 000 was paid during that financial year in first instalments of grants in respect of building work totalling nearly £100 000. The need for retaining a separate Unit at Silsoe became less obvious in a few more years and it ceased on the 1st of January 1966, by being integrated within the Institute as a new Farm Buildings Department.

## Units of Plant Physiology, Imperial College of Science and Technology

At the end of December 1958, Professor F. G. Gregory retired as Director of the Research Institute of Plant Physiology, Imperial College of Science and Technology. The Institute as such was dissolved and the Agricultural Research Council set up two Units formed from members of the staff of the Institute.

## 1. Unit of Plant Physiology, Imperial College of Science and Technology, University of London, 1959.

This Unit was established under the direction of Professor Helen K. Porter. It had two principal lines of research, namely, the metabolic processes associated with starch and sucrose synthesis in higher plants and the study of the physiology of vernalisation (exposure of seeds or plants to low temperatures which advances the flowering date), and the annulment of the effect of vernalisation by exposure to high temperatures. Professor Porter retired in 1964, but the Unit was continued under the direction of Professor C. P. Whittingham who had been Professor of Botany, Queen Mary College, and who had succeeded Porter in the Chair of Plant Physiology at Imperial College. The Unit was disbanded in 1971 when Whittingham was appointed Head of the Botany Department at Rothamsted Experimental Station.

## 2. Unit of Plant Morphogenesis and Nutrition, 1959, at Rothamsted Experimental Station and from 1960 at Wye College, University of London.

This Unit was under the direction of Dr. F. J. Richards and it comprised a section of the Research Institute of Plant Physiology which had been stationed at Rothamsted. After a year, however, the Unit was transferred to Wye College. The programme of the Unit was broadly physiological and included studies of metabolic deficiencies, flowering and photoperiod behaviour and interrelationships between growth and form at the stem apex. Richards died in 1964 and the Unit was disbanded. Dr. W. W. Schwabe of the Unit's staff was by that time Professor-designate of Horticulture at Wye College and the work of the Unit was absorbed into Professor Schwabe's Department with the aid of a bridging grant from the Council.

During this period of twelve years from 1947 to the beginning of 1959 no less than sixteen Units and one Group were established. During the next ten years, that is up to 1969, six more Units were created. These six are dealt with in a later section.

## Research Institutes — 1947 to 1960

In various places throughout this historical account mention has already been made of proposals for an increased research effort in one subject or another and also of the degree of development of research in a particular subject that indicated the desirability of expansion. Although the subjects in question cover a wide range and do not form a coherent whole, it is convenient to describe the Institutes concerned together, in the order of their founding, within the period covered, namely, 1947 to 1960.

### The Poultry Research Centre

This has been mentioned in the section on animal genetics and breeding in that the original research programme and the first Director, Dr. A. W. Greenwood, had been part of the Institute of Animal Genetics of the University of Edinburgh under the direction of Professor F. A. E. Crew. Poultry research was the subject of study of a Joint Committee of the Agricultural Research Council, the Agricultural Improvement Council for England and Wales and of the Scottish Agricultural Advisory Council, which reported in 1947. It was agreed that the possibility should be explored of establishing a poultry research institute in the north of Great Britain and another in the south. There had been considerable interest in poultry research during the previous thirty to forty years especially in genetics and commercial breeding, firstly at the University of Cambridge and, secondly, at the Northern Poultry Breeding Station, Reaseheath, (p. 15). Furthermore, work on poultry was included in the programmes of many of the Colleges of Agriculture, and in some of the Veterinary Schools. The proposal in 1947, however, was for the development of a comprehensive programme of poultry research and for the co-ordination of which a Technical Committee was formed. It was the Institute for the north of the country that got off the ground by the establishment in 1947 of the Agricultural Research Council's Poultry Research Centre and its later occupation of a new laboratory building on the King's Buildings site of the University of Edinburgh. The programme of the Centre is essentially one of poultry production and includes the subjects of anatomy, physiology, nutrition and behaviour. The Centre's work on nutrition has been of inestimable value to the poultry industry not only by defining nutritional requirements but also by determining how these may be supplied from alternative sources, thus providing options in times of fluctuating supplies and costs. Greenwood retired in 1962 and was succeeded by Dr. T. C. Carter. One of Carter's tasks was to solve the problem of accommodating the physical expansion of the Centre, especially the increasing demand for space for birds for experimental work, within the limitations of the strictly confined University site. An extensive range of poultry houses and ancillary service buildings were constructed on an out-station at Roslin, some 6 miles from the Centre. In 1975, the Council approved Carter's proposal that the University site should be vacated and new laboratories provided on the Roslin site. Construction was commenced in 1977. Carter retired in 1978 and the move from Edinburgh to Roslin thus became the responsibility of the new Director, Dr. D. W. F. Shannon.

## The Houghton Poultry Research Station

This research station was founded in 1948 by the Animal Health Trust, a charitable institution dependent for its funding upon voluntary subscriptions and dedicated to veterinary research in species not included to any significant extent in the work supported by the public sector, for example, its Equine Research Station and its Canine Research Station. The Station was established specifically to investigate the causes and the control of diseases of poultry, especially those causing serious economic loss to the industry. Early in the history of the Station the Agricultural Research Council provided a grant-in-aid for work on Newcastle Disease. The high costs of running an Institute required to maintain some degree of disease security began to put an increasing burden on the resources of the Animal Health Trust. Recognition of the value of the work of the Station and of the competence of its staff led the Council to discuss the future of the Station with the Trust. The first proposal was for the Council to purchase the Station but this was unacceptable to the Trust whose preference was for an Institute receiving a grant-in-aid with a Governing Body with the Trust represented, and with the Trust continuing to make some financial contribution. Agreement was reached on this basis in 1956. In subsequent years the contribution from the Animal Health Trust gradually diminished and the Agricultural Research Council assumed full responsibility in 1970. The first Director of the Station was Dr. R. F. Gordon. Following his retirement he was succeeded in January 1974 by Dr. P. M. Biggs. The Station has a high record of success in its research on virus-induced tumour conditions of the fowl especially Marek's disease and lymphoid leukosis; on other microbiological infections, including salmonellosis, with particular reference to the transmission by plasmids of specific biological characteristics of bacteria such as antibiotic resistance and lethal factors; and on poultry parasitology.

## The Institute of Animal Physiology

In describing the Agricultural Research Council's Unit of Animal Physiology directed by Sir Joseph Barcroft, reference was made to the Council's discussions in 1945 about establishing an Institute for Research in Animal Physiology. These discussions continued for some time. Largely on the grounds that facilities for research on farm animals on the required scale would be inappropriate for direct University management, it was decided by the Council to establish an Institute, preferably near Cambridge. The next step was to appoint a Director so that a site could be chosen and the plans for the Institute prepared. The choice was made of Professor Ivan de Burgh Daly, Professor of Physiology in the University of Edinburgh and a member of Council. The Director took office and the Institute was formally established in 1948 on the Babraham estate some six miles south-east of Cambridge. For the next seven or eight years the Institute of Animal Physiology occupied a great deal of the Council's attention. There was a lack of concurrence between the Director and the Council on the objectives of the Institute and on how they should be achieved. There can be no question about Daly's scientific status, nor about the eminence of those whom he attracted to work at Babraham including, for example, Sir Rudolph Peters, as Head of the Department of Biochemistry, and Sir Alan Drury, Head of the Department of Experimental Pathology. There can be no question about the past and present prestige of the Institute and the fact that it has always been a place which other scientists wished to visit. The project got off to a bad start in that the Council had made financial provision of £150 000 in 1948 for the development of the Institute. The plans presented by Daly had a cost estimate of over £500 000. This considerable discrepancy produced the delays that must be expected under these circumstances. By 1952 the Council was pressing for the erection of certain prefabricated laboratories so as to increase the speed of the implementation of the research programme. This, Daly, with a longer term view, objected to most vigorously. Nevertheless, the prefabricated laboratories were erected and now, thirty years later, they are still in use.

The next point of disagreement was about recruitment of staff. The Council sent a Visiting Group to the Institute in 1954. Its finding reaffirmed that the purpose for which the Institute was founded was to conduct research on the physiology of farm animals. The Visiting Group apparently found some difficulty in identifying the implementation of this objective. The Director, therefore, was counselled to bear in mind, in making appointments, the availability of veterinary graduates. It was agreed that he should be encouraged to recruit these in preference to members of the medical profession. The following year, 1955, the Council again felt bound to draw the attention of the Director to the terms of reference for the Institute, namely, research on the physiology of farm animals. It is understandable that this he greatly resented and he threatened to resign. It was concluded that there must have been some misunderstanding. It was agreed by Council, however, that a Scientific Advisory Group should be set up. The Council, at its meeting in November 1955, did so by nominating Professor R. E. Glover (Principal and Dean of the Royal Veterinary College, London), Professor A. L. (later Sir Alan) Hodgkin, (Foulerton Research Professor, Royal Society), Dr. David Keilin, (formerly Quick Professor of Biology, Cambridge University), and Professor Solly Zuckerman (later Lord Zuckerman) (Professor of Anatomy, University of Birmingham). Daly retired in 1958 and Professor John Henry (later Sir John) Gaddum, Professor of Materia Medica in the University of Edinburgh was appointed to succeed him. Under Gaddum's direction the programme of the Institute came closer to the Council's original intention to increase knowledge of the physiology of farm livestock as a means towards improving animal health and production. Gaddum retired in 1965 and was succeeded by Dr. Richard Darwin Keynes, who had been Head of the Physiology Department in the Institute since 1960. Keynes continued to maintain the very high standard of scientific achievement for which the Institute was now so well known while, at the same time, keeping in the forefront the remit for concentrating the bulk of the programme on the physiology of cattle, sheep, and pigs with the use of goats as more appropriate experimental animals for a number of tasks. Keynes, in 1973, accepted the invitation to the Chair of Physiology in the University of Cambridge. The Council's reminder to Daly in 1954 about recruiting veterinary graduates became especially appropriate in 1973 when the successful candidate for the Directorship was Professor Barry Albert Cross, a member of the Royal College of Veterinary Surgeons, who was then Professor and Head of the Department of Anatomy of the University of Bristol.

The Institute's research programme covers a wide range but with a concentration of effort on reproduction, the initiation of parturition, and lactation; metabolism, growth and behaviour with particular regard to the animal's response to its environment; the biosynthesis of immunoglobulins and related cell function; and neuro-hormone synthesis and release. Since 1976, the Unit of Reproductive Physiology and Biochemistry has been continued as a Department of the Institute, (p. 54). The type of work tends to place much of the programme more towards the basic than the applied end of the research spectrum but there have been many examples of a rapid application of knowledge of practical value. The criticism that there was insufficient attention given to the principal objectives for which the Institute was established, is certainly no longer valid.

## The Grassland Research Institute

Although this Institute, now at Hurley, near Maidenhead, Berkshire, was founded in 1949 as a grant-aided Institute with its own Governing Body, the history of research on the improvement of British grassland dates back to when Sir George Stapledon was Director of the Welsh Plant Breeding Station during the 1920s and 1930s. At that time Stapledon's principal interest was in the reclamation of hill land and a demonstration area was established to show what could be done, the Cahn Hill Improvement Scheme. He then turned his attention to the use of ley-farming for the rehabilitation of the then often derelict clay soils of the English lowlands. A Grassland Survey of England and Wales directed by Stapledon and completed shortly before the outbreak of war in 1939, had emphasised the potential that existed for increasing home food production. The Ministry of Agriculture and Fisheries agreed to provide funds for a Grassland Improvement Station with Stapledon as Director and early in 1940 a derelict 500-acre farm was purchased at Drayton, near Stratford-on-Avon. Two other farms were later included, one of 1 300 acres of poor moorland in Staffordshire and 1 000 acres of scrub land in the Cotswolds. Stapledon described these as the epitome of all that was wrong with rural Britain. The reclamation of these farms soon demonstrated the need for a research programme. Stapledon retired in poor health in 1945 and his chief collaborator, Dr. William Davies, succeeded him. The future of the Grassland Improvement Station had then been studied by a group appointed by the Agricultural Research Council and by the Agricultural Improvement Councils of England and Wales and of Scotland. It was recommended that a permanent institute for grassland research should be established but in a more suitable location than Drayton with respect to University and Advisory Service contacts. Suggested areas were in the neighbourhood of Reading/Oxford or Nottingham. Hurley was selected, suitable property having come on the market which would provide for the needs of the new Institute and also for a Berkshire Farm Institute. The purchase was made by the Ministry of Agriculture and Fisheries and the land divided between the two establishments. Field trials were begun at Hurley in 1950 and the staff from Drayton progressively moved as laboratory accommodation became available. Davies retired in 1964 and was succeeded by Dr. E. K. Woodford, the then Director of the Weed Research Organization. Woodford retired in 1977 and was succeeded by Professor A. Lazenby. The Institute plays a key rôle in the improvement of grassland management for the greater efficiency of animal production.The effort in terms of staff numbers is divided approximately 2:1 with regard to "Plants and Soils" and "Animals".

## The National Vegetable Research Station

From the time that the Council reviewed the programmes of the then existing research establishments in 1932, it became concerned from time to time whether adequate attention was being given to the subject of vegetables. The relatively small Horticultural Research Station had been established in Cambridge in 1923 and research on certain vegetable crops was included in the programme of some of the "Plants and Soils" institutes. Some 20 years later the findings of a survey report on horticulture suggested that this Station might be absorbed into a new Vegetable Research Institute and in 1944 this subject was being discussed to the extent of considering suitable sites of which one at Paglesham in Essex, was identified. In 1945, the Standing Committee on Research affecting Plants and Soils recommended that a Governing Body and a Director should be appointed forthwith with the responsibility of finding a suitable site with Paglesham not being ruled out. In 1949 the National Vegetable Research Station was eventually established at Wellesbourne, in Warwickshire, with a Sub-Station at Paglesham. The first Director was Dr. James Philp. The programme covers all aspects of the improvement of vegetable crops; the needs of the amateur, the small-holder, and the market gardener, receive attention as well as those of large acreage growers of field vegetables. Philp retired in 1967 to be succeeded by the Deputy Director, Professor D. W. Wright. Wright retired in 1977 when the then Deputy Director, Professor J. K. A. Bleasdale, was appointed Director.

## The Glasshouse Crops Research Institute

The subject of protected crops provides another example in which research had been in progress for many years before a specific institute was established with a national responsibility. The Glasshouse Crops Research Institute was founded in 1953 at Rustington on the outskirts of Littlehampton, West Sussex. It took over the functions of the Experimental and Research Station which had been established at Cheshunt, Hertfordshire, in 1914 (p. 11) and which was subsequently closed in 1955. The programme of the Mushroom Research Station at Yaxley was similarly absorbed. In both cases these incorporations of work included some transfer of staff, including Dr. W. F. Bewley, who had been Director of the Cheshunt Station since 1921. Bewley became the first Director of the new Institute. He was responsible for the development of the Littlehampton site and for the move there in 1953. In addition to research on protected crops, work is also undertaken on the improvement of bulbs, flowers and shrubs grown in the open. The work of the Institute is especially important for the horticultural industry which must operate with the maximum efficiency in its very vulnerable position of competing with imports of produce from more favoured countries with regard to the need for glasshouse heating. Very significant contributions have been made by the Institute, for example, the production of virus-free bulb and nursery stocks, the control of diseases of mushrooms, the biological control of the red spider mite in glasshouses, the establishment of better control of the glasshouse environment with regard to light, heat and the proportion of carbon dioxide in the atmosphere, also the more recent development of the nutrient film technique of hydroponics for the growing of tomatoes, cucumbers and other glasshouse crops. Mr. F. W. Toovey was Director from 1956 until 1971 when he was succeeded by Dr. D. Rudd-Jones.

## The Scottish Horticultural Research Institute

Horticultural production in Scotland is concentrated in three principal areas, namely, the Clyde valley, the Perth-Angus area and in East Lothian. The Strawberry Disease Investigation Unit was established at Auchincruive in Ayrshire in 1930 to investigate red-core disease of strawberries. The Raspberry Disease Investigation Unit was established in Dundee in 1943. In 1946, the Department of Agriculture for Scotland sought to implement a need, identified for some time, of a central horticultural research centre. It proved to be difficult to find a suitable site and a start was delayed until 1951 when the present location at Mylnefield, Invergowrie, on the western outskirts of Dundee, was purchased and its development begun. This was under the direction of Dr. T. Swarbrick who was appointed Director of Horticultural Research in Scotland. The Institute was legally constituted in 1953 with Swarbrick as the Director. He retired in 1965 when he was succeeded by Dr. C. H. Cadman, Head of the Department of Plant Pathology. Cadman died in office in 1971 at the age of 55 and was succeeded by Dr. C. E. Taylor. The Strawberry and the Raspberry Units were included in the Institute at its establishment with the Auchincruive laboratories being retained as a substation. Work on all aspects of these soft fruits has remained a prominent part of the Institute's programme with considerable success having been obtained in the breeding of new varieties most of which can be recognised either by their names being places in Scotland or with some literary association, for example, Ben Nevis, Glen Clova, Red Gauntlet and Saladin. The primary function of the Institute is to study the problems of Scottish horticulture and to seek varieties, cultural methods and plant protection procedures appropriate to Scottish requirements. In 1980, the Department of Agriculture and Fisheries for Scotland accepted a recommendation of a Working Party that the Scottish Horticultural Research Institute should be amalgamated with the Scottish Plant Breeding Station and the joint Institute be named the Scottish Crops Research Institute.

## The Hill Farming Research Organisation

The Department of Agriculture for Scotland set up a Hill Farming Research Organisation in 1953 based on a small headquarters' staff of five people housed in the business centre of Edinburgh. In 1954 it was formally established as one of the Scottish grant-aided Institutes with its own Governing Body appointed by the Secretary of State for Scotland and including members from England and Wales as well as from Scotland in that the Organisation's responsibility includes the study of relevant problems in Great Britain. Three hill farms were transferred to it by the Department: Glensaugh, Grampian Region; Lephinmore, Strathclyde Region; and Sourhope, Border Region. Later House o'Muir, Lothian Region was acquired and, recently, Hartwood, Strathclyde Region. The original terms of reference of the Organisation were to investigate the problems of the agricultural use of hill land in order to obtain greater knowledge of the factors limiting production, of the ecology of hill grazings, of the nutritional needs of hill sheep and of the methods that could be adopted to secure greater output. Since then the programme has been extended to include cattle and, in collaboration with the Rowett Research Institute, red deer. Long-term studies include the integration of hill land for forestry and for animal production. Although the headquarters staff increased in number and central research facilities were added, the accommodation continued to be provided in a series of converted dwelling houses in Edinburgh until a new Institute building at the Edinburgh University Centre of Rural Economy was occupied in 1973.

The first Director of the Organisation was Mr. A. R. Wannop, that is from 1955 to the end of 1963. He was succeeded in 1964 by Dr. R. L. Reid who, after four years, resigned on being appointed to the Chair of Agriculture at La Trobe University, Melbourne, Australia. Reid was followed by Dr. J. M. M. Cunningham who had the responsibility of specifying the requirements for the new Institute building. This had to include laboratories and appropriate facilities for research embodying those for both "Animals" and "Plants and Soils". The success with which Cunningham implemented this difficult task has had the not unexpected consequence of advancement. In 1980 he was appointed Principal of the West of Scotland College of Agriculture. He was succeeded as Director by Mr. J. E. Eadie, previously Head of the Animal Production and Nutrition Department of the Organisation.

## The Letcombe Laboratory

The Letcombe Laboratory had a precursor named the ARC Radiobiological Laboratory. In the first few years following the 1939-1945 war the need became obvious for information on the consequences of the release of fission products into the global environment as a result of the military or the peaceful uses of atomic energy. This especially occupied the attention of the Atomic Energy Authority, the Medical Research Council and the Ministry of Agriculture, Fisheries and Food. An agricultural research priority became a study of the movement of fission products in soils and plants. A suitable research team would be one studying the movement of plant nutrients and Professor G. E. Blackman's Department of Agriculture in the University of Oxford had the necessary experience and skills. A grant-in-aid was given to the Department for a group headed by Dr. R. Scott Russell. Close collaboration was established with the Radiobiological Research Unit of the Medical Research Council and the Atomic Energy Research Establishment. A Joint Agricultural Research Council/Development Commission Committee on Biological Problems (Non-Medical) of Nuclear Physics was set up in 1950 with Lord Rothschild as Chairman. It soon became apparent that the facilities in Blackman's Department were inadequate for the growth of the work and in 1954 it was decided to construct a suitable laboratory within the grounds of the Council's Field Station at Compton. This was achieved with commendable speed and it was staffed by some of the scientists from Oxford and some from the Field Station. Scott Russell was in charge of the project but in an uneasy relationship with Gordon, the Director of the Field Station. By 1957, accumulated experience had shown that much more was required of the agricultural group. An investigation was necessary of the degree of contamination of food and of agricultural land in addition to the already initiated research on the movement of the fission products.

The consequence of increasing pressures, not only the need to accommodate and provide for the requirements of a larger staff, but also with respect to management, indicated that a new and separate establishment had to be created. The result was the founding in 1957 of the ARC Radiobiological Laboratory under the directorship of Scott Russell. It was decided that a new site was needed but with the qualification that it should be close to the Medical Research Council's Radiobiological Research Unit and the Atomic Energy Research Establishment, both at Harwell. The Letcombe Manor Estate, near Wantage, was purchased where new laboratories could be built. The necessary conversions and new buildings were completed in 1962.

A major responsibility of the Radiobiological Laboratory became the monitoring of the levels of radioactivity in food. Most attention was given to strontium-90 (half-life 28 years) because of its deposition in bone with resulting radiation of that tissue and of bone marrow. Caesium-137 (half-life 30 years) was another long-lived fission product causing contamination of food. Milk was the principal food examined as it was the main source of strontium-90 in the diet. Representative samples of other foods continued to be examined but to a considerably lesser extent than milk. In course of time the necessity for this work declined. This was anticipated by Scott Russell and he brought about a change of emphasis which based a comprehensive research programme on the use of radioactive tracers to determine the passage of plant nutrients from the soil to the plant under a variety of conditions of soil types and physical conditions. When, therefore, the original need for the Radiobiological Laboratory had diminished to a level approaching non-viability, a flourishing research programme had already been substituted on the growth of crops especially with regard to their root/soil relationships. To mark this change the name of the establishment was changed in 1969 from the Radiobiological Laboratory to the Letcombe Laboratory. Scott Russell retired in 1978 and was succeeded by Dr. J. V. Lake, formerly a Scientific Adviser and latterly an Assistant Secretary in ARC Headquarters.

## The Weed Research Organization

In describing the Unit of Experimental Agronomy (p. 50) reference was made to a group headed by Dr. E. K. Woodford being transferred in 1960 to Begbroke Hill Farm so that the study of the more practical aspects of the evaluation and the use of herbicides could be expanded. This move created the Weed Research Organization with Woodford as the first Director. The discovery or the synthesis of new compounds with herbicidal properties has very largely been in the hands of the chemical industry with the Weed Research Organization interested in their evaluation but not as a testing body. In its research programme it studies the interactions between herbicide and weed, crop, method of application, soil and climate. It thereby attempts to improve the efficiency of existing control measures and to devise new ones combining the best of the chemical and the cultural methods. An example of the importance of this approach is its programme in collaboration with the Plant Breeding Institute, Cambridge, on the choice of the most suitable herbicide for use with each new variety of cereals since considerable variation in resistance is found to different chemicals. An important part of the Organization's work is devoted to developing procedures for the control of the most persistent weeds of arable crops and grassland, for example, couch, wild oat and black-grass. The Organization's Tropical Weeds Group, with the same objective, has achieved considerable success in the control of nutsedge, a very persistent weed in tropical and sub-tropical countries. Techniques of herbicide application have received much attention, especially droplet size and volume of application of sprays directed towards greater safety and lower cost. Woodford was appointed Director of the Grassland Research Institute in 1964 and was succeeded at Begbroke Hill by Mr J. D. Fryer, also a former member of the Unit of Experimental Agronomy.

## Chairmen and Secretaries, 1948 to 1960

Lord De La Warr served one term of office of 5 years as Chairman of the Council, which period ended in July 1948. Sir John Fryer was the Secretary at that time but owing to ill health he was unable to attend any meetings of Council between July 1948 and his death in December of that year. The Chairman and the members of Council were appointed by the Committee of the Privy Council for the Organisation and Development of Agricultural Research, a procedure changed in 1965 by the passing of the Science and Technology Act. The Lord Rothschild had been approached and had accepted the appointment as Chairman, attending his first meeting in September 1948. Dr W. L. (later Sir William) Slater had been appointed in 1944 to the Secretaryship of the Agricultural Improvement Council (England and Wales) and since that date had attended the meetings of the Agricultural Research Council as the Improvement Council's Assessor. There could hardly have been a more suitable candidate for appointment of Secretary to the Council in succession to Fryer and so it was that in March 1949, the Council were informed that Slater was willing to accept. The day to day work of the Council's Secretariat in the absence of the Secretary from the summer of 1948 to the spring of 1949 was certainly in good hands as Mr. E. H. E. Havelock of the Development Commission, who had been Interim Secretary to the Council during the first weeks of its existence, was still in office as Administrative Secretary. Also, the Secretariat had recently acquired a new Assistant Secretary, Mr. W. G. Alexander.

At the time of his appointment in 1948 as Chairman of the Agricultural Research Council at the age of 37, Nathaniel Mayer Victor Rothschild, Baron, had already achieved much and had received many cachets. He was a practising and a successful scientist and, as such, he must have presented a challenge to the Secretary. He had not been in office for a year before he raised the subject of research priorities by the presentation of a memorandum to the Council entitled "The importance of agricultural research problems". In the accepted way, the Secretary was asked to prepare a list of all projects, the staff involved in each and the cost. Furthermore, the Chairman proposed that a special Research Unit should be established to collect quantitative data on selected problems. Council's reaction was that consideration of this particular proposal should be deferred. Faced with this stimulation, the Council's Secretariat and the Ministry of Agriculture produced, respectively, an "Office Note" and a "Memorandum". The Council's discussion again followed predictable lines in that a small committee was to be set up by the Secretary in consultation with a designated member of Council. This member was Professor Solly Zuckerman, who had been appointed in 1949. Study of the records provides no easily identifiable consequence of their deliberations. As has so often happened, the Agricultural Research Service no doubt demonstrated its strength by the Directors and the staffs of its Institutes producing their research priorities based on an assessment of the work required in their particular sectors. An assessment of priorities must always be attempted but there are two approaches, namely, the attempt to identify subjects in a socio-political economic context, or the attempt to choose the best growing points of current research.

The Long Ashton Research Station celebrated its Jubilee in 1953 and, to mark the occasion, Rothschild spoke on the theme of "Agricultural Research 1953".* This lecture provides a most interesting assessment of the agricultural research service as made by the Chairman of the Council at the time he was being reappointed for a second term of office of 5 years. He would not have done justice to the occasion had he not praised some scientists in general and some of those at Long Ashton in particular. The greater part of the lecture was, however, devoted to his judgement, with much criticism, of the then current scene. Four subjects were thus identified:

Inadequate contact between the research worker and the farmer;
Inadequate pressure on short-term problems;
Inadequate knowledge of the order in which these short-term problems should be tackled;
Inadequate organisation of agricultural research.

Similar veins that run through the analysis of each of these subjects are the necessity to deal more closely and more quickly with the problems of the farmer, the necessity of identifying the short-term problems and of providing the increased effort required for their speedy solution. Rothschild anticipated that the achievement of what he considered to be a better way of doing things might involve some hardship "... in the sense that people may have to devote some part of their time to tackling problems which, if not strange to them, are at any rate not precisely what they have been working on before." In elaborating on this theme Rothschild discounted the use of any regimentation or pressure but he did equate expenditure with work of direct and immediate importance to the country in increasing the efficiency of national food production. There can be no disagreement with this precept except, perhaps, with regard to the time-scale thought to be appropriate and the degree of urgency demanded for the

* This lecture was published in the Station's Jubilee Volume "Science and Fruit" University of Bristol (1953).

project. It does, however, tend to anticipate a view about the appropriateness to agricultural research of the customer/contractor principle which he was to recommend so strongly some 18 years later when head of the Central Policy Review Staff.

In the Long Ashton Jubilee Lecture, Rothschild deplored the fact that few farmers knew about the Agricultural Research Service as a whole, and even fewer knew what it did. This comment serves to identify a curious state of affairs which was that the Council did not publish any Reports between 1938 (for the years 1935-1937) and 1958 (for the year 1956-57). This lack of formal accountability for almost 20 years was, perhaps, symptomatic of the Council's response to its limited administrative and executive responsibility with its principal rôle being to advise the Agricultural Departments which funded the agricultural research institutes. The move by the Council into establishing its own Institutes and Units had been gaining much ground, as reported in the previous sections, but the extent of its jurisdiction did not compare with that enjoyed by the Medical Research Council on which it had originally been modelled. These limitations were most certainly judged to be unacceptable constraints by Rothschild and by Slater. Both, but especially the Secretary, were engaged for some 5 years on the negotiations which culminated in the passing of the Agricultural Research Act in 1956. Lord Rothschild's term of office ceased on the 30th June, 1958, when he was succeeded by His Grace the Duke of Northumberland (see pp. 81-82). The Council on that occasion recorded its great indebtedness to Lord Rothschild for his guidance of its affairs during 10 years whereby the stature of the Council had been greatly enhanced by his insistence on the highest standards in scientific work and in the administration of its affairs.

William Kershaw Slater graduated with 1st Class Honours in Chemistry in the University of Manchester in July 1914. His defective eyesight which necessitated wearing spectacles excluded him from the armed forces but he obtained an appointment on the staff of the Chief Inspector of Explosives. Slater's father was a Lancashire cotton manufacturer and he wanted to see his son use his scientific training for the benefit of the cotton industry. Slater, in 1921, after a brief spell as Assistant Lecturer in Chemistry at Manchester, was appointed Scientific Adviser to the Belgrave Group of cotton mills in Oldham. The death of his father in 1922 released him from this family obligation and, having become attracted to biochemistry, he approached Professor A. V. Hill who was then about to move from the Chair of Physiology in Manchester to that in University College, London. Hill took him into his Department and put him on an MRC grant. Slater then obtained a Beit Memorial Fellowship which enabled him to follow Hill to London. A division of the large Department of Physiology and Biochemistry at University College resulted in Slater coming under Professor J. C. Drummond in Biochemistry. His research was on lactic acid production in muscle especially in creatures thought to survive in an anaerobic environment. In 1925, Leonard Knight Elmhirst and his wife had purchased Dartington Hall, Devon, for the founding of their experiment in rural industry, research and education. This was intended to be a long-term investigation of land management and the economics of country living. A scientist was required to take an active part in the main project and to establish an estate laboratory. Slater was picked out and he moved to Dartington Hall in 1929 at the age of 35. It was not long before he became Bursar to the experimental co-educational boarding school that had been started by the Elmhirsts and his flair for administration assured his involvement in the management of the later development of Dartington Hall Limited. This rapid adaptation to a new environment with a demonstration of considerable competence did not escape notice and, in 1942, the Ministry of Agriculture sought his services through secondment. This was followed by his appointment as Senior Advisory Officer in the Ministry and Secretary to the Agricultural Improvement Council from 1944 to 1949. During this period he was much involved in the creation of the National Agricultural Advisory Service. His Secretaryship to the Agricultural Research Council started in May 1949.

By far the most important of Slater's contributions to the strength and importance of the Agricultural Research Council and to the furtherance of its work was the part he played in the negotiations with the Treasury and the Agricultural Departments to give effect to the proposal to transfer the full financial and administrative responsibility for the grant-aided Institutes in England and Wales from the Ministry of Agriculture, Fisheries and Food to the Council. These negotiations were started in the early 1950s and the final decisions for the transfer were effected by the passing of the Agricultural Research Act in 1956. Slater had greatly helped in gaining this position of much greater authority for the Council by the sympathy for the proposal shown by the House of Commons Select Committee on Estimates which made the final recommendation to Government. Slater's contribution at the time was described as being one of patient and tenacious endeavour.

The Agricultural Research Act 1956 came into force on the 1st of April of that year. It established an Agricultural Research Fund into which were to be paid such sums as from time to time might be provided by Parliament for agricultural research. Another significant change was that the Council was made directly responsible to Parliament for its expenditure instead of this being borne, as previously, by the Treasury. The same Act made the Council responsible to a new Committee of Privy Council for Agricultural Research. The membership of the Council was enlarged to provide for representation of the two Agricultural Departments. A further provision of the Act was that the Council, each year, present a report of its proceedings to Parliament. Thus was initiated the series of Annual Reports, or occasionally Biennial Reports, which has been unbroken since that for the year 1956-57. The Act did not, however, alter the arrangements in Scotland with the Department of Agriculture and Fisheries for Scotland continuing to provide the grant-in-aid to the Scottish Research Institutes and the Council providing scientific advice.

An indication of the heavy administrative load of the Secretary to the Council during Slater's term of office is that in that period five Institutes, eleven of the Units and the Statistics Group described in the two previous sections of this history were established. This led to the acceptance that the Secretariat was inadequately small. The situation at the beginning of Slater's term of office was that the Secretary had three Assistant Secretaries equally responsible to him but there was no official deputy. When this matter came up for consideration in 1952 the Assistant Secretaries were William Ness, Percy Arthur Charles Thorne and William Gordon Alexander. By agreement between them, Alexander had undertaken the responsibility of deputising for the Secretary when the need had arisen.

Gordon Alexander following a distinguished under-graduate and post-graduate period at Edinburgh and Oxford respectively, was selected for the Indian Civil Service. A very experienced and competent civil servant thus became available in 1947 and, to the benefit of agricultural research, Alexander was first given temporary employment by the Council in its Secretariat. The need to strengthen the Secretariat resulted in the establishment of a new post of Deputy Secretary to the Council to which Alexander was appointed. This post was occupied by Alexander until his untimely death in 1971. Alexander's influence in the affairs of the Agricultural Research Council had two features. One was that of a breakwater and the other was that of a stimulator of new approaches. As a breakwater, he listened to all sorts of proposals and recommendations which he repelled for them to be presented again, if they had any substance. He had a very perceptive eye for future developments and delighted in initiating the required appointments. He had one guiding principle which was never to present a proposal to a higher authority until confident of the success of so doing. A corollary from this was obvious. Any presentation to him of a half-baked case evinced such cutting, but none the less kindly comment that it was again attempted only by the most obtuse.

In 1953 Rothschild had objected to the length of the agenda for a meeting of Council. Slater proposed that if the Council established guide-lines for the implementation of its policy, the Secretariat could take many decisions without the need to put the matters to Council on an *ad hoc* basis. This would, however, require an expansion of the staff. It was agreed, therefore, that a Scientific Assistant to the Secretary should be appointed with the latitude to consider the recruitment of further assistants with supporting staff. This was the beginning of the establishment of the group of Scientific Advisers to the Secretary. Those who have occupied these important appointments are listed in Appendix 5.

Slater would normally have retired in 1958 at about the same time as Rothschild. In anticipation of the advantage of having the Secretary cover the period of the change of Chairman, the Council recommended to the Lord President of the Privy Council that his appointment should be extended for some twelve months. He retired at the end of June 1960, within 3½ months of his 67th birthday. In view of the untimely deaths of the majority of his predecessors, subsequent holders of the office could only be encouraged that he remained very active for a further 10 years. Slater was appointed a Knight Commander of the Order of the British Empire in 1951 and was elected to the Fellowship of the Royal Society in 1957.

## The Council's Headquarters

For some twenty years following the establishment of the Agricultural Research Council in 1931, the Development Commission had housed the Headquarters of the Council and had provided the Secretariat. It will be recalled that Lord Richard Cavendish, the first Chairman of the Council was the Chairman of the Commission and that Sir William Dampier, the Secretary to the Commission was appointed part-time Secretary to the Council. Senior members of the Commission's Secretariat also served as senior members of the Council's Secretariat, for example, Mr. E. H. E. Havelock and Mr. F. R. W. Jameson. The address of the Commission's and the Council's offices was 6A Dean's Yard, Westminster. By the late 1940s, however, the joint staff had to be accommodated in three separate buildings in addition to the offices in Dean's Yard. New accommodation had to be sought and the Council moved out of the Commission's offices in 1950 to occupy its own rented premises in Cunard Building, 15 Regent Street, London S.W.1. From that date the joint staffs separated into two distinct Secretariats with Havelock relinquishing his appointment as Administrative Secretary to the Council so as to give his full time to the work of the Development Commission.

## The Underwood Fund

By the terms of its Charter the Council may accept and administer private funds which have been donated or bequeathed. Reference has been made to the Wain Fund (p. 52) established by the generosity of Professor R. L. Wain. In 1949 the Council received a bequest valued at about £60 000 under the will of the late Miss L. M. Underwood. This bequest was used to establish the Underwood Fund for the provision of grants to enable visits to be made to this country by overseas scientists whose presence here is likely to be of assistance to the Council's work. The Annual Reports of the Council since that for 1956-57 list those who have received such grants. The availability of this fund has been a great asset by enabling Institutes to sponsor visiting workers. In 1956-57, the income from the fund was £2 853. In 1979-80 it was £17 748.

# Chapter 4

# 1961–1972

## Continued Growth

The contribution provided by Sir William Slater as Secretary to the Council from 1949 to 1960 was so very significant that it seems appropriate to start a new chapter dated from his retirement. It is, of course, difficult to divide research into specific periods and it is impossible when the range is as wide as that which pertains to agriculture. It is inevitable that overlaps occur and it must be accepted, therefore, that a division of this history into chapters is somewhat arbitrary and that each is, as such, something superficial to underlying movements. One of these movements was the Council's increasing preoccupation with food research.

### Food Research

The achievement of greater efficiency in the production of food was always a priority for the Council but having, no doubt, dealt with the major problem of establishing a sound and comprehensive programme of agricultural research, a greater responsibility for food research began to become more dominant in the late 1950s. In its Annual Report for 1957–58, the Council referred specifically to the future of food research and it identified meat production as presenting a series of problems urgently in need of more work. At that time the problems related to the breeding, rearing and feeding of animals for meat were clearly seen to be the responsibility of the Council. On the other hand, the slaughter, handling and processing of the carcasses were the responsibility of the Department of Scientific and Industrial Research. It was then concluded that this was an unsatisfactory arrangement in that what was in effect one research problem had to be administered by two different organisations. This dual responsibility also applied to other branches of food production, in particular to the handling, storage, packing and distribution of fruit and vegetables.

The first move in an attempt to improve this situation came in 1956 when the Department of Scientific and Industrial Research proposed that the Agricultural Research Council should take over the responsibility of certain of its establishments dealing with food research. These were, in fact, the Low Temperature Research Station at Cambridge, and the Ditton Laboratory at East Malling. The Council's response was to welcome the proposal but to insist that the present and future needs of the food industry should be defined before accepting two specifically identified laboratories. As a result of further study, the Council proposed that the transfer should also include the Pest Infestation Laboratory at Slough, and the four Food Research Association establishments. In the meantime the Ministry of Agriculture, Fisheries and Food, through its Meat Research Committee, was determining to what extent a meat research institute was justified. By 1958, it was agreed that the Low Temperature Research Station, the Ditton Laboratory, and the Pest Infestation Laboratory, should be transferred to the Agricultural Research Council but that the Research Associations should remain with the Department of Scientific and Industrial Research. Later, the Research Associations became the responsibility of the Ministry of Agriculture, Fisheries and

Food. With regard to the inclusion of the Pest Infestation Laboratory in the transfer, the Council supported this by the expression of its belief that taking over the three research stations as one group would be in the interests of the efficient conduct of food research. The formal transfer took place on the 1st of July 1959. At about this same time, the case for a meat research institute had become generally accepted.

The Low Temperature Research Station was housed in premises on a ten-year lease from the University of Cambridge. When this had been renewed in 1956 only a year-to-year extension was promised from 1966 because of the pressure on space in the centre of Cambridge. New accommodation would have to be found and as the staff of the Station included the largest single group of scientists in the country working on problems related to meat research, their future became an integral part of the discussions about the establishment of a Meat Research Institute. An apparently very short-term move was made by the Council agreeing to providing temporary cold room and laboratory accommodation at an abattoir at Cherry Hinton on the outskirts of Cambridge. The programmes of the three stations were continued under the Council's supervision while it was considering the long-term needs for research on food. Throughout this period leading to the inclusion and development of food research as a responsibility of the Council, Dr. E. C. Bate-Smith, Director of the Low Temperature Research Station (1947–1965) played an influential part, especially in relation to meat research. The Council's deliberations were much helped by Professor A. C. Frazer who had been appointed a member in 1961 especially to provide a new dimension by his knowledge of the subjects of food science and nutrition research.

It is now convenient to deal specifically with what emerged as the Meat Research Institute and the Food Research Institute.

## The Meat Research Institute

Although it had been agreed in principle by the Ministry of Agriculture, Fisheries and Food and by the Council from about 1958 that a Meat Research Institute should be created, prolonged discussions ensued about the extent to which the meat trade should contribute financially. During 1960, 1961 and 1962 it became customary for the Secretary to inform Council that a Ministerial decision was soon to be expected, or that a statement was shortly to be issued. In the meantime, the Council was well able to discuss the location of the new Institute. From an early stage it agreed that there would be advantages for the Institute to have close association with a University and the Secretary was empowered to engage in informal discussions. By the middle of 1961, Council approved that the Meat Research Institute and the proposed Food Research Institute should be located close together and in association with a suitable University. The Secretary was authorised to proceed with discussing the Council's preferences which were 1) Bristol, 2) Norwich and 3) elsewhere. In view of the future developments it is important to note that an early view was to have the two Institutes near each other, but at no time did there appear to be any consideration given to establishing a single Institute. By November 1961, no Ministerial decision had yet been announced about the industry's involvement in financing meat research but the Secretary was able to report that the Vice-Chancellors of the Universities of Bristol and of East Anglia were receptive to his soundings. By January 1962, no Government statement had yet been made but Council was now firmly of the opinion that the Meat Research Institute should be located on the Langford site of the University of Bristol in close proximity to the School of Veterinary Science. A few months later, the Council's proposals for the site were accepted by Ministers and by representatives of the meat industry. The appointment of an Advisory Committee on Meat Research under the Chairmanship of Sir George Wilson was approved although this decision was not implemented until 1964. It was agreed that the post of Director-Designate should be advertised, and subsequently Dr. Maurice Ingram, Deputy Director of the Low Temperature Research Station was appointed. The Institute was opened by Her Majesty the Queen on the 19th of April 1968.

The financial contribution from the meat industry was to be made by the proceeds of a levy on animals sold for slaughter and handled through the Meat and Livestock Commission. The Northern Ireland Livestock Marketing Commission also contributed. It was decided that these contributions would provide half the cost of the Institute's expenditure. It was further agreed that the Institute's principal interest would be confined to carcass meat, namely, meat in which the gross structure is retained and that it would not include manufactured products. In comparison with Institutes of Meat Technology in other countries, this limitation was undoubtedly unduly restrictive but it was made in deference to the well-established responsibilities of the British Food Manufacturing Industries Research Association.

The contribution from the meat industry was initially maintained at about half of the total expenditure through the financial year ending the 31st March 1971. In that particular year the industry contributed £296 250, 57% of the Institute's total budget. This actual figure in pounds sterling was never again exceeded so subsequent contributions obviously became less in real terms. It is more noteworthy, however, that the Institute's expenditure as then published increased by 17% between the financial years 1970–71 and 1971–72, whereas the proportion contributed by the industry sharply decreased from 57% to 35%. From that year on the proportion contributed by industry progressively diminished, until finally in 1978–79 it had dropped to 14%. In March 1980, the Meat and Livestock Commission finally announced its intention to cease its contributions to the Meat Research Institute as from September 1980.

Ingram, whose staff at Langford included former colleagues from the Low Temperature Research Station such as those of the renowned collagen chemistry group under Dr. S. M. Partridge, established the Institute on a very firm basis. On his retirement in 1973 Ingram was succeeded by Professor J. R. Norris, formerly Director of the Borden Microbiological Laboratory, Shell Research Limited, who did much to consolidate and deepen the relationship between the Institute and the meat industry. Professor Norris returned to industrial research in 1979 by joining Cadbury Schweppes Ltd., as Director of Group Research. He was succeeded by Dr. A. J. Bailey, Head of the Meat Structure Division at the Institute.

## The Food Research Institute

It has already been mentioned how the Council in discussing the establishment of the two food research institutes decided that they should be located close together in association with a suitable University with a declared preference for Bristol or East Anglia. Their Vice-Chancellors were both interested in any such developments. The first decision by the Council was to locate the Meat Research Institute at Langford, Bristol. The site for the Food Research Institute had then to be discussed and the choice was steered towards the Council's second preference for the University of East Anglia at Norwich. This was on the grounds that, having decided to build the Meat Research Institute at Langford, further utilization of that site might limit any need for future expansion. Thus it was that two Institutes requiring staffs of very similar disciplines and facilities with much in common became sited some 200 miles apart. The inconvenience of this had become apparent by the mid-1970s when any easing of the then financial restrictions by sharing or amalgamation could be seen to be impracticable.

Following the decision to site the Institute at Norwich, a Director-Designate was appointed, namely, Professor S. R. Elsden, Director of the Council's Unit of Microbiology at the University of Sheffield. In the meantime the future of the Ditton

Laboratory had been decided. It was to be closed in 1969 on the retirement of the Director, Dr. R. G. Tomkins. The work was then to be transferred as follows:—

The storage of apples and pears and the chemical composition of fruit — to the East Malling Research Station.
Prolonging the life of cut flowers — to the Glasshouse Crops Research Institute.
The laboratories, cold stores and other buildings — to the East Malling Research Station.
The advisory function — to the Ministry of Agriculture, Fisheries and Food.

In view of staff already having been identified for work at the new Institute, that is from the Low Temperature Research Station, from the Ditton Laboratory, and from the Unit of Microbiology, temporary accommodation had to be found until the new Institute building had been completed. This was leased from the Norwich City Council and what became known as the Earlham Food Research Laboratory was occupied in November, 1964, by an advance party from the Low Temperature Research Station. The Institute building was completed in 1968 on a site adjacent to that of the John Innes Institute which had been moved to Norwich the previous year, also in association with the University of East Anglia.

The task of the Institute was to continue and extend research on food, other than red meat, but including poultry-meat and eggs, and to incorporate work on the storage of fruit and vegetables previously carried out by the Ditton Laboratory but excluding that on apples and pears in controlled atmospheres. This latter was to remain at East Malling and be continued in the former Ditton Laboratory buildings. The Institute also had to establish contacts with the Food Research Associations and with the food industry in general. This latter responsibility proved to be difficult to fulfil and satisfactory relationships with the industry were not established as quickly as had been hoped. Both sides took some time to learn that the more pragmatic approach of the industrialist, the wholesaler or retailer, and the more rational approach of the scientists had to be adjusted one to the other for a fruitful understanding to be reached. In spite of these difficulties, the Institute as designed by Elsden, its first Director, provides excellent laboratories and other research facilities for the progressive development of its research programme under Dr. R. F. Curtis who succeeded Elsden in 1977.

## Other food research activities

It would be a mistake to conclude that the Meat Research Institute and the Food Research Institute plus the other Institutes that have been cited in reference to research on the storage of fruit and vegetables, completes the catalogue of food research in the Agricultural Research Service. Quite apart from the fact that the very great majority of the Service's research projects are to do with food production, a number are concerned with what can legitimately be classified as food research. For example, it has long been traditional for agricultural research to include consideration of agricultural products up to the farm gate. Thus, the foods that were once processed in the farm house, in the farm dairy, etc., have tended to be included in agricultural research. Examples of these are butter and cheese making, and cider making. Thus the National Institute for Research in Dairying and the Hannah Research Institute have contributed much by their research on improving the quality of milk and dairy products. It has already been recorded how the cider apple growers of the west country set up the Long Ashton Research Station and thus the science of the fermentation of fruit juices and of flavours has become a speciality of that Institute.

The plant breeding institutes have always had as one of their targets the need to meet user requirements. A part of their programmes has always included research on the baking quality of flour prepared from new varieties of wheat, on the malting quality of new varieties of barley, on the chipping quality and other cooking qualities of new varieties of potatoes, and so on. Also the animal production institutes have been at pains to find the fat and lean proportions desired by the consumer and how to provide them. Those engaged on research on animal nutrition are conscious in their recommendation of new sources of animal feed that there must be no possibility of taint. The microbiologists and the veterinarians are aware of the necessity of maintaining the wholesomeness of products of animal origin by seeking to prevent the transmission of disease to the consumer. This approach is also true of the mycologist working with plant products, and of the biochemists concerned with the avoidance of residues of fungicides, herbicides, antibiotics and growth-promoting chemicals. This brief summary of diverse examples of food research must be added to the more detailed description of the food research institutes if the correct perspective of the subject is to be conveyed.

## The Pest Infestation Laboratory

When, in 1959, the Agricultural Research Council assumed responsibility for food research, it took over from the Department of Scientific and Industrial Research the Low Temperature Research Station, the Ditton Laboratory and the Pest Infestation Laboratory. In giving this matter earlier consideration, the Council had agreed that the transfer of these three research stations as one group would be in the interests of the efficient conduct of food research. The section on food research in which the establishment of the Meat Research Institute and the Food Research Institute is recorded also described the integration of the Low Temperature Research Station and the Ditton Laboratory. The future of the Pest Infestation Laboratory at Slough became a subject of prolonged discussion as its place within the Agricultural Research Service was not so clearly apparent. The Laboratory had been set up in 1940 by the Department of Scientific and Industrial Research, at the request of the food handling industry, to undertake research on the insect pests of stored products and on their control. Prior to 1940 the control of insect pests in warehouses had obviously been of some concern and the research contribution to alleviating the problem had been provided by the Imperial College of Science and Technology. The Director appointed in 1940, and in office at the time of the change in management, was Mr. G. V. B. Herford with Dr. E. A. Parkin, Deputy Director. The Council reviewed the Laboratory's programme in 1960 by means of a Visiting Group which reported favourably except for the housing of two of its Departments. These had not yet been provided with modern laboratories as had the remainder of the establishment.

The first years of the Laboratory's existence had been taken up with the solving of many immediate and urgent problems associated with safeguarding the large stocks of grain and other foodstuffs held during the war and the post-war period. These problems stimulated new lines of research and extended existing ones. A major activity became the study of infestations of imported foodstuffs in the countries of their origin. This led to the establishment of a Tropical Liaison Group financed by the then Colonial Office. The growth of the work of this Group warranted expansion firstly to the Tropical Liaison Department in 1962 and then, in 1964, to the Tropical Stored Products Centre for which the Ministry of Overseas Development then took responsibility. The Centre is now known as the Tropical Products Institute. The growth of knowledge about control methods put such demands on the staff for advice to industry that the then Ministry of Food set up the Insect Infestation Division through which advice from the Laboratory's scientists was channelled. This Division subsequently became the Infestation Control Laboratory of the Ministry of Agriculture, Fisheries and Food.

In 1966 the Agricultural Research Council again sent a Visiting Group to the Pest Infestation Laboratory and in view of Herford's retirement from the Directorship becoming due in 1968, the future of the Laboratory and its programme was thoroughly discussed. There was, apparently, complete acceptance of the relevance of the work of the Biochemistry Department to the Council's interests which were identified as being basic studies in chemistry and biochemistry of the relationships between insect pests, host plants, and pesticides. It was felt, however, that the work of the other Departments was much more applied in nature and that there might be difficulties in producing sufficient change to correspond to the recommendations of the Visiting Group. In the meantime, Parkin, the Deputy Director was appointed to the Directorship for a fixed term of three years. As a result of negotiations with the Ministry of Agriculture, Fisheries and Food, the Pest Infestation Laboratory, excluding the Biochemistry Department, was transferred in 1970 to the Ministry. It was amalgamated with the Infestation Control Laboratory with the new entity becoming known as the Pest Infestation Control Laboratory. The Biochemistry Department was largely incorporated into the Council's new Unit of Invertebrate Chemistry and Physiology (p. 76).

## ARC Units — 1962 to 1969

The decade of the 1960s was not marked with the same activity as regards the establishment of Units as was that of the 1950s. Nevertheless, six new Units were created as follows.

### Unit of Flower Crop Physiology, University of Reading, 1962

In 1962 this Unit was set up by the Council in the Department of Horticulture at Reading University and under the direction of Professor O. V. S. Heath, Head of that Department since 1958. One of the objectives of the research programme was to seek to extend the range of glasshouse flowers as alternative crops for the glasshouse industry then mainly dependent upon tomatoes. The principal approach was to study the effects of light intensity and its interaction with day-length and temperature variations in influencing growth and flowering. Much of such work is dependent upon the use of growth cabinets, the design of which was then being developed by the National Institute of Agricultural Engineering. In view of the substantial investment that had been made by the Council in supplying the Unit with these cabinets consideration was given to the possibility of the Unit being continued after Heath's retirement. As it happened, Heath retained his Chair for the first half of the academic year 1968/69 and then stayed with the Unit until the end of the following academic year in 1970. The Unit was then disbanded and the growth cabinets handed over to the University of Reading.

### Unit of Nitrogen Fixation, University of Sussex, 1963

Although the Unit under the direction of Professor Joseph Chatt was founded in 1963, the Council had been supporting research on the biological fixation of nitrogen for a considerable period. For example, various aspects of fixation by the symbiotic organism *Rhizobium* in the root nodules of legumes were being studied at Rothamsted, the Welsh Plant Breeding Station, the Hill Farming Research Organisation and in the Department of Agriculture at the University of Edinburgh. In 1960 a definite move was made towards establishing a Unit in the University of Edinburgh but the Council's interest in its financial support appeared to become secondary to that of the Department of Scientific and Industrial Research. Other research supported by the Council was on the nature of the mechanism by which micro-organisms are able to fix atmospheric nitrogen. This included work by Dr. D. J. D. Nicholas at the Long Ashton Research

Station and by Dr. E. R. Roberts at the Imperial College of Science and Technology. This resulted in the demonstration of nitrogen-fixation activity in cell-free extracts prepared from the bacterium *Azotobacter*. This identification of an enzyme complex had already been made in the USA and all these results provided a great stimulus. The Council's response was a decision made in the autumn of 1962 that a Unit should be established under a chemist of some distinction with Nicholas contributing on the biological side. A possible location was also identified in laboratories to be vacated by the Government Chemist in Clement's Inn, London. Although Council showed a preference for the Unit to be more closely associated with a University, the time that could be saved by moving into an existing building was accepted as being too advantageous to reject. Informal approaches identified Chatt, then Group Manager of the Research Department of the Heavy Organic Chemicals Division of I.C.I. Ltd. as being willing to accept the Directorship with Dr. J. R. Postgate from the Microbiological Establishment, Porton, coming in on the biological side, Nicholas having declined the invitation to move. The possibility of using the Clement's Inn laboratories fell through, but the Unit's programme was started in temporary accommodation at the Royal Veterinary College and at Queen Mary College, London. About a year later the University of Sussex became the favoured location for the Unit's permanent site and the present association was then formed. Again it was necessary initially to occupy temporary accommodation. This was provided in the University's Chemistry Laboratories for some three years until the Unit's permanent building was completed in 1968.

Since its inception, the programme of the Unit has been based on two approaches, namely, biological and chemical. The groups engaged on each have made very considerable advances which have included the extraction, purification and characterisation of the enzyme nitrogenase, a greater understanding of how aerobic bacteria prevent the destruction of the nitrogenase proteins by oxygen, the identification of the nitrogen-fixing genes and their transfer from nitrogen-fixing bacteria to bacteria which do not naturally fix nitrogen and on the chemistry side, the preparation of complexes in which transition metal salts are combined with the nitrogen molecule for further study of their reactions.

When the Council came to review the work of the Unit some two years prior to the date for Chatt's retirement, the high priority that the work merited was immediately recognised and subsequently Postgate was appointed to succeed Chatt, which change-over took place in April 1980.

## Unit of Structural Chemistry, University College, University of London, 1966

This Unit was established in 1966 under the direction of Professor R. S. (later Sir Ronald) Nyholm, Head of the Department of Chemistry at University College, London. The Council had agreed some three years earlier about the relevance of Nyholm's interests to agricultural research but difficulties, principally of finding suitable accommodation delayed the creation of the Unit. Temporary accommodation was found in Inveresk House at the acute angle formed by Catherine Street and Wellington Street at the junction of the Strand and Aldwych. The plan was that in course of time the Unit would be moved into the proposed new Chemistry Building at University College. Most tragically, however, Nyholm was killed in a road accident in December 1971. The work of the Unit was continued under the Deputy Director, Professor Mary R. Truter pending a decision about the Unit's future. The five years of the programme directed by Nyholm which had concentrated on the co-ordination chemistry of the alkaline earth metals had been sufficient to demonstrate its value. It was decided by the Council that the programme must be continued but integrated into the Rothamsted Experimental Station with the Unit staff headed by Truter becoming a new Department of Molecular Structures. The intention to time this move to the completion of the

Daniel Hall Building at Rothamsted was thwarted by some of the structure of Inveresk House, in the rooms occupied by the Unit, beginning to collapse. Temporary accommodation was provided at Rothamsted with a minimum of delay but since 1977, the new Department has been housed in the new laboratories.

Much of the work of the Unit had been based on crystal structure analysis backed by a very comprehensive set of crystallographic programmes on the Unit's computer. An important feature of the Molecular Structures Department at Rothamsted is the extension of such work in relating chemical structure with biological activity in collaboration with other scientists, not only at Rothamsted but also at other Institutes of the Agricultural Research Service.

## Unit of Muscle Mechanisms and Insect Physiology, University of Oxford, 1966

Work on insect physiology began to be supported by the Council in 1963 in Professor J. W. S. Pringle's Department of Zoology in the University of Oxford. In 1965 an *ad hoc* group was set up by Council under the Chairmanship of Professor Rogers Brambell to advise whether support to Pringle should be increased to the dimension of a Unit. There was apparently little doubt that the fundamental research that was proposed by Pringle could, if successful, have a wide application to the Council's interests. It was emphasised, however, that in seeking Treasury approval it would not be possible to hold out any prospect of short-term economic advantage to agriculture or horticulture. This realistic and straightforward approach for the cause for fundamental research succeeded and the Unit was established in 1966. The scope of the programme has included various aspects of insect flight, neurophysiology and the control of metabolism directed largely towards obtaining a better understanding of the fundamental molecular mechanism of muscle contractility. Large tropical insects have been used for much of the work and techniques were established for breeding and rearing a number of species in the laboratory. This practical zoological part of the programme has been balanced by elegant preparations using single muscle fibres linked to the most modern equipment for measurement of rapidly occurring events requiring analysis by computer techniques. The routine evaluation of the Unit with regard to its future led to the decision to begin to reduce the programme from around 1977 as opportunities arose for transfer of the staff with final closure on Pringle's retirement in 1979.

## Unit of Invertebrate Chemistry and Physiology, University of Sussex and University of Cambridge, 1969

When the Council, in 1967, gave consideration to the future of the Pest Infestation Laboratory, it was so impressed with the work of the Laboratory's Biochemistry Department that the possibility was discussed of establishing a new Institute based on it. Further discussion was directed towards establishing a Unit rather than an Institute. This reduction in size might well have been influenced by the fact that the buildings off Huntingdon Road, Cambridge, of the Virus Research Unit had just been vacated by the transfer of the Unit to the John Innes Institute. The proposal in 1967 then became, at least, that a Unit based on the Biochemistry Department of the Pest Infestation Laboratory should be established at that Cambridge site. It was also proposed that Professor A. W. Johnson of the University of Nottingham should be invited to head the Unit. Without going into any detail about the negotiations between the Council and others during the next year, the outcome was the establishment in 1969 of the Unit of Invertebrate Chemistry and Physiology but in two sections, the main group with Johnson as Director, at the University of Sussex, where he now had the Chair of Organic Chemistry, and a Sub-Group in the Department of Zoology in the University of Cambridge with Dr. J. E. Treherne, Reader in Zoology, as Associate Director. Another use found for the vacant laboratories off Huntingdon Road is described below.

Both groups started work in laboratories of the respective Universities but a Unit building was later provided at the University of Sussex. The division between the two groups is that chemists and the biochemists, including those from the Pest Infestation Laboratory, are at Sussex whereas physiologists and biochemists are in Cambridge. The programme of the Unit is essentially the study of various aspects of insect hormones including isolation, identification, metabolism and mode of action; of certain insect pheromones and fungal pathogens, all directed towards the eventual development of improved methods of insect control. The work of the Unit has added greatly to knowledge about the diuretic hormones and the juvenile hormones of insects, both groups of which have characteristics of potential for the development of novel insecticides. The work on insect pheromones has been in connection with studies in collaboration with entomologists of the Forestry Commission on the principal beetle vector of the causal fungus of Dutch elm disease.

## Unit of Developmental Botany, University of Cambridge, 1969

The Unit was established in 1969 shortly after Professor P. W. Brian left the Regius Professorship of Botany in the University of Glasgow for the Chair of Botany in the University of Cambridge. The laboratories previously occupied by the Virus Research Unit were used to house the staff of Brian's Unit. This staff contained two groups of scientists, some who had worked with Brian in Glasgow and some who were transferred to Cambridge following the disbandment in 1970 of Blackman's Unit of Experimental Agronomy in Oxford. The programme of the Unit was concerned with the developmental biology of higher plants and also with the physiology of the host/parasite relationship in certain diseases. This included studies on the rôle of hormones in the control of growth of young shoots and of leaf abcission; cell growth and differentiation; the molecular biology of seed dormancy, senescence and germination; and the host/parasite relationship in various downy mildew diseases, in club-root disease of *Brassica* species and in crown-gall tumours.

The Council decided to close down the Unit on Brian's retirement in 1977. In reaching this decision, one factor that was taken into account was the appropriateness of the contributions that the various members of the staff could make in research areas of high priority in the Council's interests. The majority of the staff were, thus, transferred to the Plant Breeding Institute, and a smaller group were transferred to the Weed Research Organization.

## Units — a Summary and an Assessment

Twenty-seven Units were established by the Council if the count includes those which were, in a sense, a continuation of an existing entity but with a clear difference occurring in management or direction. For example, the Plant Virus Research Unit is thus credited to the Council in 1947 although it was a continuation of the Potato Virus Research Station, similarly the Unit of Reproductive Physiology and Biochemistry (1955) has been counted separately from the Unit of Animal Reproduction of which it was a continuation. On the other hand, the Unit of Animal Genetics has been counted once although it has had two Directors. The Unit of Statistics has been counted once although it has had two locations. The Statistics Group has been included in this count. In Table 4 the Units and the Statistics Group are listed in chronological order of their establishment. In Figure 1 the period of the existence of each is set out to show the

Table 4

Agricultural Research Council Units

| | Unit | Location | Period | Director |
|---|---|---|---|---|
| 1. | Soil Enzyme Chemistry/Soil Metabolism | Rothamsted Experimental Station/Cardiff City Mental Hospital | 1941–1947 | J. H. Quastel, DSc, FRS |
| 2. | Animal Physiology | University of Cambridge | 1941–1947 | Professor Sir Joseph Barcroft, CBE, FRS |
| 3. | Insect Physiology | University of Cambridge | 1943–1967 | Professor Sir Vincent Wigglesworth, CBE, MD, FRS |
| 4. | Plant Biochemistry | University of Cambridge | 1947–1951 | C. S. Hanes, ScD, FRS |
| 5. | Virus Research | University of Cambridge | 1947–1967 | 1. K. M. Smith, CBE, DSc, FRS<br>2. R. Markham, PhD, FRS |
| 6. | Animal Reproduction | University of Cambridge | 1949–1954 | Sir John Hammond, FRS |
| 7. | Experimental Agronomy | University of Oxford | 1950–1970 | Professor G. E. Blackman, FRS |
| 8. | Biometrical Genetics | University of Birmingham | 1950–1965 | Professor Sir Kenneth Mather, CBE, DSc, FRS |
| 9. | Soil Physics | University of Cambridge | 1951–1978 | 1. E. C. Childs, ScD<br>2. Acting Director: E. G. Youngs, ScD |
| 10. | Microbiology | University of Sheffield | 1952–1965 | Professor S. R. Elsden, PhD |
| 11. | Plant Nutrition (Micronutrients) | Long Ashton Research Station | 1952–1959 | Professor T. Wallace, CBE, MC, DSc, FRS |
| 12. | Plant Cell Physiology | University of Oxford | 1953–1958 | R. Brown, DSc, FRS |
| 13. | Plant Growth Substances and Systemic Fungicides | Wye College, University of London | 1953–1978 | Professor R. L. Wain, CBE, DSc, FRS |
| 14. | Embryology | University College of North Wales | 1953–1968 | Professor F. W. Rogers Brambell, CBE, DSc, FRS |
| 15. | Statistics | University of Aberdeen/University of Edinburgh | 1954–present | Professor D. J. Finney, CBE, ScD, FRS |
| 16. | Reproductive Physiology and Biochemistry | University of Cambridge | 1955–1976 | Professor T. R. R. Mann, CBE, MD, ScD, FRS |
| 17. | Statistics Group | University of Cambridge | 1956–present | 1. R. C. Campbell, PhD, Officer in Charge<br>2. J. G. Rowell, Officer in Charge |
| 18. | Animal Genetics | University of Edinburgh | 1957–1980 | 1. Professor C. H. Waddington, CBE, ScD, FRS<br>2. Professor D. S. Falconer, ScD, FRS |
| 19. | Farm Buildings | National Institute of Agricultural Engineering | 1957–1966 | 1. W. H. Cashmore, CBE, BA, MIAgrE<br>2. Professor C. J. Moss, CBE, BSc, CEng, FIMechE, FIAgrE |
| 20. | Plant Physiology | Imperial College of Science and Technology, University of London | 1959–1971 | 1. Professor Helen K. Porter, DSc, FRS<br>2. Professor C. P. Whittingham, DSc |
| 21. | Plant Morphogenesis and Nutrition | Rothamsted Experimental Station/Wye College, University of London | 1959–1964 | F. J. Richards, DSc, FRS |
| 22. | Flower Crop Physiology | University of Reading | 1962–1970 | Professor O. V. S. Heath, DSc, FRS |
| 23. | Nitrogen Fixation | University of Sussex | 1963–present | 1. Professor J. Chatt, CBE, ScD, FRS<br>2. Professor J. R. Postgate, DSc, FRS |
| 24. | Structural Chemistry | University College, University of London | 1966–1974 | 1. Professor Sir Ronald Nyholm, DSc, FRS<br>2. Acting Director: Professor Mary R. Truter, DSc |
| 25. | Muscle Mechanisms and Insect Physiology | University of Oxford | 1966–1978 | Professor J. W. S. Pringle, MBE, ScD, FRS |
| 26. | Invertebrate Chemistry and Physiology | University of Sussex and University of Cambridge | 1969–present | Professor A. W. Johnson, ScD, FRS<br>Associate Director: J. E. Treherne, ScD |
| 27. | Developmental Botany | University of Cambridge | 1969–1977 | Professor P. W. Brian, CBE, ScD, FRS |

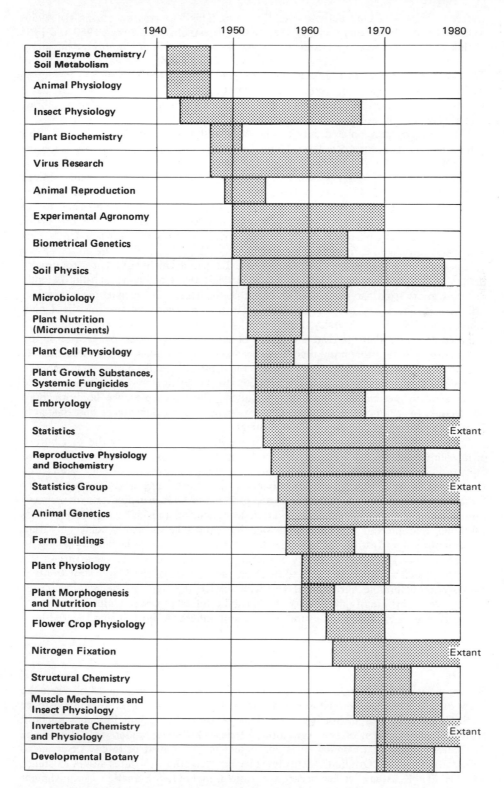

Figure 1.  Agricultural Research Council Units – the Periods of their Existence.

different degrees of Unit activity over the years. This was greatest during the 1950s and the 1960s, there being no fewer than ten Units established between 1950 and 1955 with a peak of seventeen in existence in 1963. The University of Cambridge has never been without an ARC Unit presence since 1939. Since the disbandment of the Unit of Developmental Botany in 1977 and the final winding up of the Unit of Soil Physics in 1978, this presence has not been at its strongest, in a purely nominal sense, in that it has consisted of the Statistics Group and the Sub-Group of the Unit of Invertebrate Chemistry and Physiology.

It has already been pointed out that the Agricultural Research Council is markedly different from the other Research Councils by the high proportion of its resources allocated to its own and its grant-aided Institutes with a relatively small amount in support of research in the Universities through Units and research grants. In the financial years 1963/64 and 1964/65, for example, when the number of Units in existence was at its highest, only some 10% of the Council's funds went to the Universities. By the late 1970s the percentage dropped to around 6%. The proportion spent on Units and on research grants had varied from about 2:1 when Units were numerous to about 1:1 from 1976 onwards.

It is not easy to assess the contribution of a Unit to a University. The structure of the Unit with the majority of the staff having little, if any, teaching responsibility tends to set it apart from the normal functioning of the University Department. Also, in some cases, there has been a physical separation or even isolation of the Unit's laboratories from the University Department of the Director. In such circumstances it is difficult to claim that the Unit is evidence of the Council's support of research in the Universities. On the other hand there have been as many examples where it was difficult to find the lines of demarcation between the Council's staff in the Unit and the University staff in the Director's Department. In the particular circumstances of the larger Unit in the smaller University or College, the Unit's presence becomes more obvious as, for example, that of the Unit of Plant Growth Substances and Systemic Fungicides during its 25 years at Wye College.

The scientific productivity of the Units has been very great and by the very nature of the Unit principle, the work has been relevant to the Council's interests. These two facts fully justify the Council's policy although the above assessment indicates that the Unit tends to be a Council's establishment rather than being a University activity funded by the Council. A pertinent factor is that the Unit principle provides opportunities for the Council to choose research leadership of the highest quality as it is available, relevant and affordable in a way that cannot be so readily achieved within the structure of an Institute. The ability to exercise this choice of leadership is largely dependent upon following the policy of disbandment of a Unit on the departure of the Director. As disbandment is likely to result in the transfer of the Unit's staff to other employment within the Agricultural Research Service, the high cost element of salaries is not saved. This greatly diminishes the feasibility of establishing Units in periods of financial constraint, hence the dwindling in the numbers of Units during the 1970s.

## The "Original" Institutes — A Further Mention

Reference is made on page 17 to the agricultural research scene in 1931 when the Agricultural Research Council was established. Thirty-two Institutes were in existence at that time. Fourteen of these (Table 1) have retained their original identity and still form a strong element of the Agricultural Research Service under the aegis of the Agricultural Research Council. It is convenient in the context of to-day's Service to refer to these as the "Original" Institutes. The eighteen other Institutes also in existence in 1931 (Table 2) have either been discontinued, merged with another establishment or their continuation has not been as part of the Agricultural Research Service. The subsequent history of any of these Institutes that became incorporated into an existing establishment of the Service has been recorded in the appropriate place in this text.

The "Original" Institutes, as now named in December 1980, are as follows:

England:    Rothamsted Experimental Station
Long Ashton Research Station
John Innes Institute
National Institute for Research in Dairying
Plant Breeding Institute
East Malling Research Station
Animal Virus Research Institute
National Institute of Agricultural Engineering

Wales:    Welsh Plant Breeding Station

Scotland:    Rowett Research Institute
Animal Diseases Research Association
Scottish Plant Breeding Station
Hannah Research Institute
Macaulay Institute for Soil Research

Each has already been mentioned in its appropriate place with reference to its creation and to the part which it played in the earlier development of organised agricultural research in this country. In a number of cases there is no subsequent mention of their activities nor mention of those who, by their direction and leadership, ensured that the contribution of each of these Institutes was of significance in the furtherance of British agriculture. It is impossible to extend this history of British Agricultural Research and the Agricultural Research Council to include the history of each of the component Institutes and Units. A list of the Directors of each has, however, been compiled and this is included in Appendix 6.

## Chairmen and Secretaries, 1958 to 1971

Lord Rothschild's term of office as Chairman ceased in June 1958. He was succeeded by Hugh Algernon Percy, Duke of Northumberland, who attended his first meeting of Council in July 1958. The ten years of his chairmanship which followed included a change of fundamental importance in the status and relationship of the Council within the Research Council system. This resulted from the passing of the Science and Technology Act in 1965 which removed the Council, together with the Medical Research Council and Department of Scientific and Industrial Research, from its position under the Privy Council to that of a body grant-aided by the Department of Education and Science, see pages 83 to 85. An important innovation during the Duke of Northumberlands's Chairmanship was the assumption of the formal responsibility for food research in 1959 which is described at the beginning of this chapter.

The Duke, because of his eminence, wide interests and competence, was much in demand in the service of the nation. During his Chairmanship of the Council he was also Lord Lieutenant of Northumberland, Chancellor of the University of Newcastle, and Alderman of the Northumberland County Council, a Chairman of no less than three Departmental Committees, and a member of Advisory Committees on Forestry and Hill Farming, quite apart from taking a very active part in the management of his considerable estate. His Chairmanship was wise and devoted. It firmly established the basis of the working relationship between the Chairman of the Council and the Secretary to the Council that has since persisted. This is the identification of the

"Meetings Chairman" and "Head of the Research Council" respectively. An indication of the success of the Duke's Chairmanship of the Agricultural Research Council was that on his retirement from that office in 1968, he was immediately appointed in 1969 to the Chairmanship of the Medical Research Council. This office he held, also with great distinction, until 1978.

The Hon. J. J. (later Sir John) Astor had accepted the invitation of the Secretary of State for Education and Science to succeed the Duke of Northumberland as Chairman of the Agricultural Research Council and he attended his first meeting in October 1968. An account of his term of office is given later as the bulk of it was concerned with the events described in the next chapter.

Sir William Slater remained in office as Secretary to the Council until June 1960. This was for nearly two years beyond the more usual age of retirement of 65 so as to cover the period of the change in the Chairman of the Council in 1958. In 1957, Professor Ernest Gordon (later Sir Gordon) Cox of the Chair of Inorganic and Structural Chemistry in the University of Leeds had been appointed a member of the Council. On Slater's retirement Cox was appointed to the Secretaryship and took office on the 1st of July 1960. Cox was born in the City of Bath where he was at school before entering the University of Bristol to obtain a 1st Class Honours degree in physics in 1927. He spent two years after graduation as a Research Assistant in the Davy-Faraday Laboratory of the Royal Institution before moving to the Chemistry Department of the University of Birmingham where he remained, apart from absence on war service, until 1945. By that time his scientific reputation in crystallography was firmly established. It will be recalled that Slater was involved with explosives during the 1914–1918 war, a subject with which Cox was concerned during the 1939–45 war, for the last year of which he was attached to the Headquarters of 21 Army Group in France and in Germany. In 1945 he was appointed to his Chair in the University of Leeds where he remained until joining the Council's service. He was elected to the Fellowship of the Royal Society in 1954 and appointed a Knight Commander of the British Empire in 1964.

There were two contrasting aspects of Cox's term of office as Secretary to the Council. One was that related to a very constructive period during which food research was established as a Council activity, with the creation of two new Institutes. There was also the creation during this same period of six new Units. All this required patient negotiation with the Vice-Chancellors of a number of Universities in which activity Cox excelled. The six Units were all of the greatest scientific interest to him but especially the three with the strongest chemistry component, namely, Nitrogen Fixation, Structural Chemistry and Invertebrate Chemistry and Physiology. The other aspect which was in contrast to the creative period was the constant need during the same years to champion the cause of the Council and the Agricultural Research Service. This was throughout the consultations and negotiations associated with the Trend Committee, the Science and Technology Act, and discussions which arose in the Council for Scientific Policy as a consequence of proposals from a Committee of officials which questioned the future responsibilities and autonomy of the Research Council.

Throughout whichever of these two contrasting situations were in play, one criterion to which Cox steadfastly adhered was to preserve the highest standards of scientific excellence. British agricultural research owes much to his refusal to accept anything less. There was a potential hazard, however, in such single-mindedness in that there were those who considered that scientific research was one thing and agricultural research was another. In such circumstances it was sometimes concluded that the Council's research programme was not as relevant to agriculture as those disposed to criticise thought it should be.

Cox retired from the Secretaryship on the 30th of September 1971, some five months after his 65th birthday. From about the beginning of the previous year, the Council had been engaged in the normal procedure of seeking for the Secretary's successor.

There is little doubt that a suitable candidate would have been found had it not been for the unprecedented situation that arose with regard to the Council's future. During this period of uncertainty the Council, for the time being, failed to find a suitable permanent successor who was willing to take on an unknown commitment. The situation was saved temporarily, however, by Sir Ronald Baskett, formerly Director of the National Institute for Research in Dairying, accepting the Council's invitation to return from his retirement to take on the Secretaryship for a year from the 1st of October 1971.

## Second Secretary to the Council

The increasing work load for the Secretary had been a matter of concern for the Council and an additional post of Second Secretary was authorised. Professor Helen K. Porter, was appointed to the post in January 1969 for a period of eighteen months. Professor Porter had previously been a Director of the Council's Unit of Plant Physiology at the Imperial College of Science and Technology. She was elected to the Fellowship of the Royal Society in 1956. Her occupancy of the post of Second Secretary was longer than originally intended but she relinquished it in 1971. It was then agreed that no appointment of a successor would be made, at least, until a new Secretary had been appointed.

## Other senior staff changes in the Secretariat

In January 1971, the death occurred, while still in office, of Mr. W. G. Alexander, who had been Deputy Secretary since 1952. Dr. W. E. Berry, an Assistant Secretary since 1961, was appointed to succeed Alexander as Deputy Secretary until his retirement at the end of June that same year. It was then decided to divide the duties and responsibilities of the post of Deputy Secretary between a Chief Scientific Officer, responsible for the research activities of the Council, and an Under Secretary responsible for administrative and management activities. These posts were filled, respectively, by Dr. C. C. Webster, a Scientific Adviser to the Secretary since 1965, and by Mr. D. J. Parkinson, an Assistant Secretary since 1965. At this same time, Mr. L. S. Porter, a Principal, was given the formal title of Clerk to the Council.

## A Reorganisation of Civil Science

The Agricultural Research Council, since its creation in 1931, had been involved or affected to varying degrees by Government policy with regard to the organisation of civil science. During the war, for example, the Lord President of the Privy Council had available the advice of the Scientific Advisory Committee to the War Cabinet, the membership of which included the Secretaries to the Research Councils. In 1944 a White Paper on Scientific Research and Development was published which was a statement of the existing arrangements. The following year the White Paper on the Scientific Civil Service appeared and the Committee on Future Scientific Policy was appointed. This Committee recommended the creation of the Defence Research Policy Committee and, to deal with civil science, the Advisory Council on Scientific Policy. The function of this Advisory Council was to advise the Lord President in the exercise of his responsibilities for the formulation and execution of Government scientific policy. It replaced the Scientific Advisory Committee to the War Cabinet and again the membership included the Secretaries to the Research Councils. In 1958 the Lord President appointed a Committee on the Management and Control of Research and Development. Its terms of reference included defence research as well as civil research. Its report published in 1961 included the use of a system of classification of research projects into five categories ranging from pure basic research to applied research and development. This was a regrettable taxonomic introduction which became the cause of much difficulty because of the vogue that developed for its use. In 1959 the office of Minister for Science was created with responsibility to Parliament for the Department of Scientific and Industrial Research, the Medical Research Council, the Agricultural Research Council, the Overseas Research Council and the Nature Conservancy.

During this period quite the most important event for the Council was the passing of the Agricultural Research Act in 1956, see page 65. This was essentially a matter for the Agricultural Departments, the Council and the Treasury and was somewhat apart from the considerations of the various Advisory Councils and Committees listed above. Although the next major change in Government policy had little immediate effect on the Agricultural Research Council, the current Research Council scene was thereby created with a marked influence developing on the affairs of the Councils. This reorganisation began with the appointment of the Trend Committee.

In March 1962, the Prime Minister, the Rt. Hon. Harold Macmillan, appointed a Committee of Enquiry into the Organisation of Civil Science under the chairmanship of Sir Burke Trend (later Lord Trend). A factor of some note at that time was the rapid rise that had been taking place in the level of Government expenditure on civil scientific research and that new developments would inevitably cause it to increase still further. The Committee in its report, having reiterated the principles of the Haldane Committee's recommendations (1918), defined the nature of the then current problem as being that the various agencies concerned with the promotion of civil science failed, in general, to provide a coherent organisation and that the arrangements for co-ordinating the Government's scientific effort and for allocating its resources were imprecise and unclear. Nevertheless, it was noted that the Research Councils created to promote research in medicine and agriculture had "stood the test of time". Two items were, however, selected for comment with respect to the Agricultural Research Council. The first was the responsibility for research in relation to food processing. This was considered to be less than satisfactory and it was recommended that the subject should be examined in more detail when the Council had reviewed the then existing facilities for research. The second issue was with regard to the Council's greater responsibility for the agricultural research institutes in England and Wales compared with that for the institutes in Scotland. The Committee found, however, that the arrangement worked satisfactorily and that there was no need to alter it for the sake of what was described as administrative symmetry. The Committee had, in fact, no major change to recommend for either the Medical Research Council or the Agricultural Research Council. On the other hand it recommended the disappearance of the Department of Scientific and Industrial Research, the establishment of a new Science Research Council and of a new Natural Resources Research Council; that the Privy Council Committees, under which the existing Research Councils had hitherto operated, should be dissolved and that a new advisory body to the Minister for Science should be constituted. These principal recommendations provided the basis for the Science and Technology Act. It is of interest to note that the proposal to bring together a variety of agencies concerned with natural resources and the environment into one organisation was the principal recommendation of a Committee appointed in 1961 by the Advisory Council for Scientific Policy under the chairmanship of Sir William Slater who had retired the previous year from the Secretaryship to the Agricultural Research Council.

## The Science and Technology Act, 1965

The purpose of this Act was "to make further provision with respect to the responsibility of powers in relation to scientific research and related matters of the Secretary of State for Education and Science, the Minister of Technology and certain chartered bodies and other organisations, and, for purposes connected therewith". The Trend Committee had recognised that the Research Council system as it existed at the time of its enquiry was based on the Haldane principle that the control of research should be separated from the executive function of Government. Although the Committee's attitude towards this principle went a considerable way towards maintaining such autonomy, it believed that improvements could be made by conferring wider powers on the Minister for Science and by demanding his greater involvement in the allocation of funds among the agencies for which he was responsible. This attitude was implemented by Government through the 1965 Act which finally abolished the direct link of the Research Councils with the Privy Council, bringing them under the responsibility of a Government Department. This was not, however, the Department or Departments immediately relevant to the fields of research of the Councils. By choosing the Department of Education and Science, the Haldane principle was being preserved to a certain extent.

The Science and Technology Act implemented other major recommendations of the Trend Committee such as the establishment of the Council for Scientific Policy to advise the Secretary of State for Education and Science in place of the Advisory Council on Scientific Policy which had advised the Minister for Science; the dissolving of the Department of Scientific and Industrial Research and the creation of the Science Research Council and the Natural Environment Research Council. The Social Science Research Council was also created in 1965 under this Act but on the recommendation of the Heyworth Committee it did not come under the aegis of the Council for Scientific Policy until 1971. Thus was established the present Research Council System which, although still continuing to-day, had yet to be subjected to considerable stresses and strains.

There were a number of issues that caused the Agricultural Research Council some unease during the period of consultation between the publication of the Trend Report in 1963 and the passing of the Science and Technology Act in 1965. The anxiety about some of these issues was also shared by the Medical Research Council. For example, the Trend Committee had recommended that the direction of the work of the research agencies should be vested in the chairmen who would serve on a full-time salaried basis and possess the appropriate professional qualifications. This cut right across the well-tried practice of both these Councils of having an honorary or a "Meetings" Chairman, with the Secretary to the Council the one who was full-time and professionally qualified. The Secretary was regarded as being the Head of the Council and was financially accountable. In the case of both Councils the existing practice was allowed to continue. The Agricultural Research Council felt obliged to question the proposal that the remit of the new Science Research Council should include the biological sciences and that the Natural Environment Research Council should be responsible for the Soil Surveys, although not for soil science research. The multiple responsibility for the biological sciences which resulted has not caused insurmountable problems, and the Soil Surveys were allowed to remain under the aegis of the Agricultural Research Council.

The relationship of the Secretaries of the Research Councils to the new Council for Scientific Policy was initially that they would receive all papers and seek permission to attend when there were matters of interest and importance to their own Councils on the agenda. Later they became assessors, and in 1972 the Heads of the Research Councils became members of the Advisory Board for the Research Councils which then replaced the Council for Scientific Policy.

## A Number of Miscellaneous Subjects

### The Veterinary Therapeutic Testing Board

In 1957, following representations by the British Veterinary Association regarding the need for facilities for the impartial testing of therapeutic substances for veterinary use, the Council, having also consulted the Association of the British Pharmaceutical Industry, set up a Veterinary Therapeutic Testing Board. The intention was that this Board would be similar in function to that of the Medical Research Council for the testing of drugs for use in human medicine. The number of proposals received was very small and the Board encountered difficulties in dealing adequately with some of the products which it felt warranted trial. The Council dissolved the Board in 1962.

## Toxic chemicals

In December 1959, the Minister of Agriculture, Fisheries and Food, together with the Minister for Science, the Secretary of State for Scotland, and the Minister of Health, set up a Research Study Group on Toxic Chemicals under the chairmanship of Sir Harold Sanders, Chief Scientific Adviser to the Ministry, to study the need for future research into the effects of the use of toxic chemicals in agriculture and food storage. The Study Group produced a report in 1961 which did not call for any great change but the need was emphasised for the Research Councils to review what each was doing especially in relation to the interactions between pesticides and wildlife. The Agricultural Research Council was requested by the Minister for Science to take the lead in this matter. An inter-departmental Research Committee on Toxic Chemicals was accordingly appointed under the chairmanship of Professor A. C. Frazer, a member of the Agricultural Research Council. Following the death of Professor Frazer in 1969, Professor A. Neuberger, who had been appointed a member of the Council in place of Professor Frazer, took over the chairmanship. This Committee again expressed concern about the need to devote more attention to ecological studies of wildlife. In general, however, it appeared to be reasonably satisfied with the control of the use of herbicides and pesticides that was then being exercised by official and industrial organisations. The Committee was disbanded in 1972.

## Feeding standards for livestock

One of the very practical and important activities initiated by the Agricultural Research Council has been the studies on the nutrient requirements of farm livestock. This particular interest can be dated back to 1958. It was then recognised that the current basis for the calculation of livestock rations was out of date. Furthermore, there had been very active research on animal nutrition with the publication of a voluminous literature which presented the feed compounder or the farmer with an impossible task of extracting the information which he most needed. The Council, therefore, appointed a Technical Committee on "Nutrient Requirements of Farm Livestock" with Dr. D. P. (later Sir David) Cuthbertson, Director of the Rowett Research Institute, as chairman. This Technical Committee was continued until 1972 under Cuthbertson's chairmanship. It was disbanded as part of the general reorganisation of the committee structure at the time of establishing the Joint Consultative Organisation, but detailed work on the nutrient requirements of the different species of farmstock was continued by separate Working Parties. A series of reports have been published by the Council from time to time under the general title of "Nutrient Requirements of Farm Livestock". The first of these on poultry appeared in 1963 and there have since been others on ruminants and pigs, and also on the composition of British feedingstuffs. A fuller account is given by Sir Kenneth Blaxter (pp. 247–250).

## Research Studentships and Fellowships

Reference has been made (page 27) to the award of scholarships in the agricultural sciences by the Development Commission starting in 1911. The Council, when established in 1931, undertook the duty of advising the Commission and the Agricultural Departments on the award of such studentships. In 1946 the Council took over the responsibility for the scheme and the number of studentships was increased to thirty per year, each tenable for three years. In addition, three Junior Agricultural Research Fellowships were awarded each year tenable for three years, and Veterinary Research Fellowships were also available. The Annual Reports of the Council from 1956–57 to 1965–66 contain lists of the awards made annually. It had, however, become increasingly difficult to find candidates suitable for the awards in the Council's gift and from the beginning of the academic year 1966–67 the scheme was discontinued. The effect of this made no difference to the number of awards then available as the Science Research Council and the Agricultural Departments agreed to assume responsibility for studentships of the kind which had previously been awarded by the Council. The Council retained the small number of grants for certain training courses and the right to award Veterinary Research Fellowships. It soon became apparent that there was then some difficulty in obtaining a studentship for postgraduate work at an Agricultural Research Institute. For an interim period, the institutes were solely dependent upon the availability of studentships not taken up by the Universities. The availability of these did not become known until about August of each year by which date the most promising candidates had committed themselves elsewhere. The problem was solved by the Council receiving a small allocation of studentships from the Department of Education and Science for use at the Institutes within the Agricultural Research Service. This scheme was initiated in 1973 with fifteen studentships being awarded in the first year. These studentships were not tenable at Units. The allocation was given on the advice of the Standing Committee on Postgraduate Education of the Advisory Board for the Research Councils. The number was increased progressively reaching thirty for the academic year 1976–77. This was possibly an indication that strong opinion in some quarters was being overcome that a Research Institute, as distinct from a University department, was an unsuitable place for postgraduate training.

Since 1952 Veterinary Research Fellowships had been offered by the Council. These were tenable for three years to enable veterinary graduates to continue their researches for a further period before seeking a post. Not less than three years postgraduate experience was a requirement for eligibility. No awards had been made since 1954 and the scheme was withdrawn in 1969. In 1970 the Council introduced a scheme for up to six one-year Veterinary Training Grants to enable veterinary graduates to undertake a formal course of instruction in a specific scientific discipline before embarking on a career in research on farm animals. The uptake was small and in recent years the scope of these one-year grants has been extended to enable non-veterinary graduates to take M.Sc. courses in subjects relevant to agricultural research. This inequality between supply and demand for veterinary research workers had been noted by the Committee of Inquiry into the Veterinary Profession under the chairmanship of Sir Michael Swann (1975). One of its recommendations referred to the need to provide a realistic opportunity to the veterinary graduate to train for research by taking into account the earnings to be expected in general practice. The Committee sought to equate the postgraduate training stipend with the bottom of the University Lecturer scale. The Council, encouraged by this recognition of the need to attract veterinary graduates into a research career whether within its service or in the Universities, successfully presented its case to the Standing Committee on Postgraduate Education of the Advisory Board for the Research Councils. In 1977 one ARC Veterinary Schools Fellowship was offered to each of the six Veterinary Schools with a stipend related to the University Lecturer scale. It was hoped that this scheme would help to meet the need for further expansion of research in the Veterinary Schools and by affording financial support at a higher level than that offered by normal postgraduate studentships would interest either the best of the recent veterinary graduates, or young veterinarians who, having gone into practice, had decided that their interests were more with research.

## Change of Headquarters address

The address of the Council's Headquarters had been the Cunard Building, 15 Regent Street, London S.W.1., since 1950. In 1967 the owners of the building were planning its refurbishment and this provided an opportunity to consider whether other premises of more convenient accommodation might be sought. Suitable vacant accommodation was found at 160 Great Portland Street, London W1N 6DT, to which the Headquarters were moved on the 29th January 1968.

## Financial assistance from outside bodies

Each year since the beginning of the current series of Annual Reports in 1956–57 the Council has gratefully recorded the receipt of financial assistance from many diverse organisations. At one time or another the well-known grant-awarding bodies such as the Kellogg Foundation, the Rockefeller Foundation, the Ford Foundation, the Nuffield Foundation and the Wellcome Trust have all donated substantial sums. So also have national or international agencies such as the US National Institutes of Health, the US Department of Agriculture, the North Atlantic Treaty Organisation, the International Atomic Energy Authority, the World Health Organisation, the Food and Agriculture Organisation and the European Economic Community. Very many British organisations and industrial companies have supported research over many years and the following examples give an indication of the wide range of interests: the Milk Marketing Board, the British Egg Marketing Board, the Potato Marketing Board, the Hops Marketing Board, the Home-Grown Cereals Authority, the Home-Grown Sugar Beet (Research and Education) Fund, the Meat and Livestock Commission, the National Research Development Corporation, the Overseas Development Administration, the Commonwealth Agricultural Bureaux, the Forestry Commission, the Brewers' Society, the Wine Consortium, and the Horserace Betting Levy Board.

To be more specific, the Council's Annual Report for 1978–79 lists ninety-four outside bodies which donated funds to research at one or other of the Institutes and Units of the Agricultural Research Service. The total of these donations was £1 752 572. This sum does not include the funds received for the commissioning of research by the Ministry of Agriculture, Fisheries and Food, nor by the Meat and Livestock Commission but it does include £556 736 from the Home-Grown Sugar Beet (Research and Education) Fund; £372 986 from the then Ministry of Overseas Development; £76 000 in support of hop research from the Brewers' Society and Hops Marketing Board, and some £65 000 for research at Long Ashton Research Station on various aspects of fermented fruit juices from cider and wine producers.

## Research in overseas territories

During the era of the British Empire the agricultural research and advisory services of many countries were dependent upon a cadre of British graduates in science, agriculture and veterinary medicine employed by various services of the then Colonial Office. With the burgeoning of independence and the growth of the Commonwealth there was, inevitably, a marked restriction in the number of territories in which British graduates could continue to be employed. Nevertheless, there was still a demand for their services. Some administrative arrangements had to be devised to provide sufficient incentive and sufficient financial stability to make it possible for Britain to continue to provide the technical services for which it had such competence. There was no question about the desirability of finding some way in which British graduates could work in Commonwealth Territories. The scientists from the United Kingdom had something to offer and a spell overseas was a most formative element in the post-graduate education of the research worker in any UK service. The principal concern was security of tenure. Following a visit in 1961 by the Secretary to the Council to East African Territories a procedure was adopted by which "dormant contracts" could be offered to scientists already overseas. Through these they might be encouraged to remain, in the knowledge of a guarantee that an appointment would be provided for them in the United Kingdom if they had to return home through no fault of their own. This arrangement proved to be satisfactory but it took no account of recruitment for service overseas. The number involved in the "dormant contract" scheme was about 50.

So that a similar opportunity could be offered to graduates without overseas experience, another scheme was launched in 1963 by which the Ministry of Overseas Development established a number of supernumerary posts to be administered by the Agricultural Research Council within the Agricultural Research Service. The principle of this scheme was that an Institute of the Agricultural Research Service would receive an allocation of one or more supernumerary posts. The first option open to the Institute was to recruit a scientist to the Institute staff for service overseas with the obligation to employ him or her within the UK if circumstances demanded return to this country. The second option was to identify an existing member of the staff for overseas service and to recruit a scientist to replace him or her at the home Institute. A total of 25 such supernumerary posts were made available. This scheme ran well during the late 1960s, and even into the early 1970s. By that time, however, the original recruits for overseas were interested in returning to the UK for the education of their children and the financial constraints on recruitment in the UK made it almost impossible to maintain a younger intake.

## International contacts, collaboration and liaison

Throughout the history of scientific research one of the most pressing demands has been the need for communication between scientists. When such communication has been made easier by congregation, scientific research has prospered. It may still prosper if the opportunity is provided for contact and communication between dispersed groups. For this reason the Agricultural Research Council has encouraged contact with the progress being made in agricultural research in other countries. Funds have been provided for the staffs of the Institutes and Units to attend international scientific conferences and to visit research laboratories. Many of Britain's agricultural research workers have frequently received invitations to visit this or that country. The Council has always sought to make possible the acceptance of such invitations. An equally important feature of scientific communication is the readiness to receive visiting scientists. Again the policy indicated by the Council has been a responsive one. In these respects the Underwood Fund and the Wain Fund have been of great value. Every Institute or Unit Director is aware of the administrative difficulties and of the time/benefit ratio of a visitor to judge whether the hospitality demands three or more weeks or three or less hours.

The Council has treated this question of scientific exchange at two levels. The most beneficial is without question the scientist to scientist communication and this has been given every encouragement, within the limitations of the funds available. The other level is formal, based on formal agreement between countries, groups of countries or with international organisations such as the United Nations' Agencies. The administrative arrangements to permit the Service's scientists to accept assignment with, for example, the Food and Agriculture Organisation or the World Health Organisation, have been reasonably lenient. All parties have benefited. The special situation of research in overseas territories which, in so many cases, were once British Colonies or Protectorates has already been dealt with. There are, however, a number of specific relationships which merit individual attention.

*Anglo-Soviet Agreement for Co-operation in Agricultural Research.* This agreement was the outcome of a visit to Moscow in 1964 of a British delegation led by Sir William Ogg, former Director of the Rothamsted Experimental Station. Visits between scientists had previously been made by negotiation between the Soviet Relations Committee of the British Council and the USSR State Committee for Cultural Relations with Foreign Countries. Initially the agreement was for a period of five years but it has been kept in being. It provides for the exchange of information, of scientific material and of visits between scientists and institutions of the two countries. Annual meetings to review the agreement are held alternately in London and in Moscow.

*Collaboration with the European Communities.* In October 1972, representatives of the Agricultural Research Council and the two Agricultural Departments attended a meeting in Brussels of the EEC Directors-General of Agricultural Research. It was then agreed that the Commission should prepare proposals for the co-ordination of agricultural research. Subsequently a series of "common programmes" was initiated on various research aspects of beef production, plant proteins, farm animal effluents and avian leucosis. Through "co-ordinated programmes" a number of seminars have been held on topics usually related to the subjects of the common programmes and with the participation of many of those involved in the research. The organisation of these activities became the responsibility of a Standing Committee on Agricultural Research of the Commission's Directorate-General VI (Agriculture).

It was also agreed that the member countries would participate in an information system which would lead to the computer storage of all agricultural research projects in progress within the Communities, the Permanent Inventory of Agricultural Research Projects in the European Communities (AGREP).

The four original research programmes were concluded in December 1978, after running for some five years during which ten Institutes of the Agricultural Research Service held contracts from the Commission. The themes for future research programmes are chosen by the Standing Committee, detailed plans for which are drawn up by Working Groups.

The Commission's Directorate-General XII (Science and Education) and the Committee for Scientific and Technical Research (CREST) have been attempting to launch a programme of biomolecular engineering which could be of considerable interest to the Council and about which a number of its experts in this field have been consulted.

*Bilateral arrangements.* Largely through the intermediary of the British Council, bilateral agreements have been made between the Agricultural Research Service and a number of individual countries for example, France, Italy and Brazil. Other contacts have been established with, for example, Bulgaria through the Great Britain/East Europe Centre. Yet other contacts have been established directly without intermediary, or as a result of informal discussions on other occasions, such as are provided by attendance at the meetings of such organisations as the European Science Foundation (ESF), the Organisation of Economic Co-operation and Development (OECD) or the Committee of Senior Officials in Science and Technology (COST).

*International collaboration at Institute level.* The foregoing has referred to the more formal agreements which have involved the Council as representing British agricultural research. Much activity on the international scene takes place at Institute level. In some cases this is the result of a specific arrangement such as the involvement of the Animal Virus Research Institute by functioning as the World Reference Laboratory for Foot-and-Mouth Disease; also the Tropical Weeds Group of the Weed Research Organization and the Overseas Department of the National Institute of Agricultural Engineering. Much more frequently, however, direct contacts are made between scientists or between Institutes and Units and kindred organisations. These are extremely fruitful and often persist over many years.

## Impending Concern about Value for Money

In describing the appointment of the Trend Committee, its findings and the subsequent passing of the Science and Technology Act in 1965, it was noted that although these moves had little immediate effect upon the Agricultural Research Council, a marked influence on the affairs of the Council was to develop. The substitution of the Committees of the Privy Council by a single body, the Council for Scientific Policy, providing advice to the Secretary of State for Education and Science, required that judgement should be made as to the relative claims on a finite provision of funds made by each area of science. One of the first actions of the Council for Scientific Policy on its creation in 1965 was to examine the criteria by which the policy for science was to be justified. It stated its views in the following words: "The practical chances of securing adequate resources for science as an end in itself will be immensely improved, particularly in times of stringency, if the nation as a whole has a full understanding of the kinds of pay-off which are to be expected." Furthermore, the current procedure was instituted of each Research Council presenting annually its statement of proposed forward expenditure. The Agricultural Research Council's response was to publish in its Annual Report (1965–66) its assessment of the value of agricultural research and to set up a Working Party in 1966 to consider the whole forward programme of state-supported agricultural research, to advise the Council on directions in which research could profitably be intensified in, say, the next ten years, and if necessary to advise on the desirability of curtailing research in other directions. The members of the Working Party were Dr. R. E. Glover, former member of Council and formerly Principal of the Royal Veterinary College (Chairman); Professor Sir Ronald Baskett, Director of the National Institute for Research in Dairying; Sir Frederick Bawden, Director of the Rothamsted Experimental Station; Dr. K. L. (now Sir Kenneth) Blaxter, Director of the Rowett Research Institute; Dr. E. E. Cheesman, Acting Director of the John Innes Institute and formerly Scientific Adviser to the Secretary; Professor S. R. Elsden, Director of the Food Research Institute; Mr. W. Emrys (now Sir Emrys) Jones, member of Council and Chief Agricultural Adviser, Ministry of Agriculture, Fisheries and Food; and Mr. W. W. Gauld, Department of Agriculture and Fisheries for Scotland (Assessor).

An excellent report was produced which established guidelines for the development of agricultural research which are as appropriate today as they were more than a decade ago. The Working Party based its recommendations on the assumption that by the end of the twentieth century Great Britain might require at least twice the present net output of home-grown food. It, therefore, recommended support for research that showed promise of contributing to:

(a) increased yield of food or feedingstuffs per acre;
(b) improvement of feedingstuffs conversion by animals;
(c) reduction of waste at all stages of production, storage, processing and distribution;
(d) increased output per man.

Three criteria were chosen for use in assessing the merit of proposed projects:

(a) the probable future importance to agriculture of the chosen objective;
(b) the prospects of success on the lines proposed;
(c) the intrinsic scientific importance of the work.

By no means was all of the report so "mission-oriented" in outlook and due weight was given to the importance of speculative research.

The importance of identifying research priorities came to the fore again following the implementation by Government of Lord Rothschild's recommendation that applied research and development should be done on a customer/contractor basis. This point will be returned to in due course.

## Threat to the Agricultural Research Council and the Dainton Report

The Green Paper "A Framework for Government Research and Development" published in November 1971, contained a report by Lord Rothschild and a report entitled "The Future of the Research Council System" by a Working Party of the Council for Scientific Policy (CSP) under the chairmanship of Sir Frederick Dainton. It is to the second of these reports that reference will now be made.

This CSP Working Party was appointed in October 1970. Its report was submitted to the Secretary of State for Education and Science. The report starts with a statement on why the CSP undertook the enquiry, the first paragraph of which reads:

"The immediate cause of our appointment was the proposal to transfer the Agricultural Research Council to the Ministry of Agriculture, Fisheries and Food. This proposal had not previously been discussed with the CSP who felt that no sufficient case had been made for what appeared to them to be a fundamental and ill-advised change."

The proposal referred to had been made by a Committee of civil servants and its implications were seen clearly by the Council for Scientific Policy as affecting not only the Agricultural Research Council, but the Research Council structure in general. Up to the time of the setting up of the Council for Scientific Policy Working Party, the members of the Agricultural Research Council had received no notice of what was going on although rumour had been strong enough for the Secretary to seek an assurance from the Secretary of State for Education and Science that no change in the status of the Council was imminent. The Council in November 1970, was given an opportunity to discuss the subject with the Secretary of State and a written report of the Council's strong objection to the proposal was subsequently submitted.

The Dainton Report contained a detailed review of the power of science to serve national goals, of the Research Council system, and of the work of the Council for Scientific Policy. It reaffirmed the Research Council principle but identified the need for closer links between the Research Councils. It rejected the idea that there might be advantage in transferring the activities of a Research Council to a Government department even although the least difficulty could indeed be with the Agricultural Research Council. The principal recommendation was that the Council for Scientific Policy should be reconstituted by making the scientific heads of the Research Councils full members and by including representatives from Government departments with major scientific interests.

## A Framework for Government Research and Development and the Rothschild Report

The Green Paper (Cmnd. 4814) published in November 1971 under the title "A Framework for Government Research and Development" included the report by Lord Rothschild, "The Organisation and Management of Government R & D," in his capacity as Head of the Central Policy Review Staff, and a report by a Working Group of the Council for Scientific Policy entitled "The Future of the Research Council System." The White Paper (Cmnd. 5046) published in July 1972, by which Government implemented the principle of the Rothschild recommendations, was called "Framework for Government Research and Development."

In the Introduction to his report, Rothschild identified the objective of R & D organisation and management as being to achieve a logical, flexible, humane and decentralised system with each person in the system having clearly defined responsibilities. The whole of the report which follows is then, in the author's words, "based on the principle that applied R & D, that is R & D with a practical application as its objective, must be done on a customer/contractor basis." The changes recommended in the system of financing the Research Councils were as follows:

1. The Science Research Council was excluded from the new system on the grounds that it was largely concerned with pure, and to a lesser extent applied *science*, not regarded as being synonymous with research.
2. The Social Science Research Council was excluded on the grounds that it was in its infancy.
3. The Agricultural Research Council's customer was identified as the Ministry of Agriculture, Fisheries and Food which would become responsible for 77.54% of the funds then received from the Department of Education and Science. An explanation was included as to why it was recommended that only this amount should be transferred from the Department of Education and Science to the Ministry of Agriculture, Fisheries and Food.
4. The Medical Research Council's customers were to be the Department of Health and Social Security and the Scottish Home and Health Department with a transfer of 25% of funds from the Department of Education and Science.
5. The Natural Environment Research Council's customers were to be the Department of the Environment, the Scottish Development Department, the Department of Trade and Industry and the Ministry of Agriculture, Fisheries and Food, with a total transfer of 50% of the Department of Education and Science funds.

Certain changes were recommended with regard to the composition and duties of the Council for Scientific Policy. It was pointed out that the Department of Health and Social Security and the Ministry of Agriculture, Fisheries and Food must set up Chief Scientists organisations to enable these two Departments to carry out their new responsibilities, in the first case the organisation was judged to be incomplete and in the second case, inadequate.

In presenting this Green Paper the Government announced that it intended to allow time for wide public debate and for discussion with the scientific community of the issues involved.

Although more detailed reference is made elsewhere to the Secretaries to the Council, it is relevant in this particular context to note that Sir Gordon Cox retired from office at the end of September 1971. The then uncertainty about the Council's future made the normal recruitment of a successor impossible and Sir Ronald Baskett, formerly Director of the National Institute for Research in Dairying, accepted the Council's invitation to return from retirement and undertake the Secretaryship for one year with effect from 1st October 1971.

The House of Commons Select Committee on Science and Technology provided another forum for the debate and a delegation appeared before the Committee in February 1972, comprising the Chairman of the Council, the Secretary and the directors of five Institutes, Dr. K. L. (later Sir Kenneth) Blaxter, Dr. W. M. (later Sir William) Henderson, Professor M. Ingram, Dr. H. C. (later Sir Charles) Pereira and Dr. R. Scott Russell. There was, of course, much activity within the Research Councils' community in particular and within the scientific community in general. It can be no surprise that throughout the Agricultural Research Service, great resentment was felt and many were incensed that a drastic change was being proposed which could not but have a most profound effect upon an organisation in which there was much pride and to which many felt it a privilege to belong. A major concern of Council, expressed in a memorandum on the Green Paper, was that no adequate assessment had been made of the proportion of the work of its Institutes which could reasonably be described as being close to application.

Among Institute Directors there was disillusionment. Many had been at pains to make clear to the investigators of the Central Policy Review staff, with whom they had communicated openly and frankly, that they were in close touch with their sector of the agricultural industry. It therefore emerged from their evidence that a large part of Institute programmes could be said to have the expectation in the short- or longer-term of some practical application. This likelihood of practical applications was used by the Central Policy Review staff as a measure of the high proportion of work appropriate to customer/contractor arrangements, rather than, as had been intended, an indication of the extent to which the Agricultural Research Service was already responsive to its ultimate customers, the agricultural and support industries.

Part of the extensive debate that arose following the publication of the Rothschild Report turned on the question of the identity of the customer of research. The Council took the strongest line on this issue. It emphasised that the real customers served by the Agricultural Research Service were the farmers, the growers and the food industrialists. They were the ones who must be consulted, together with the scientists, economists and the representatives of the Agricultural Departments. All these interests were represented in the constitution of the Agricultural Research Council and to an even greater extent on the Council's committees. There was, therefore, much discussion about who was the customer who had to say what he wanted.

In the defensive situation in which the Council found itself it naturally stressed the achievements that had resulted from the research which it had sponsored. As already mentioned it had begun to do this from the time that the Council for Scientific Policy was given the responsibility of judging between the merits of the aspirations of the five Research Councils. It felt it knew what it had to do. This confidence was, to a large extent, based on the strength of the Directors and their staffs at the establishments which formed the Agricultural Research Service. There would be difficulty in accepting that this complex structure with contacts with its real customers at every level could function better just by the wide-scale introduction of commissioning. But others did not see it in this way.

When the White Paper setting out the policy of the Government was published in July 1972, the amounts to be transferred to the Ministry of Agriculture, Fisheries and Food from the Science Budget were less than had been proposed for the Agricultural Research Council in the Rothschild Report. The percentages of the receipts expected by the Agricultural Research Council from the Science Budget that were transferred to the Ministry of Agriculture, Fisheries and Food were to be 26.7%, 40.1% and 53.5% respectively over three years beginning 1973–74. (In the case of the Medical Research Council the amount transferred to its customer Departments in the third year was 24.6% and in the case of the Natural Environment Research Council, 29.4%.) Although no conditions were to be placed on the use of the money transferred to customer Departments, it was stated in the White Paper that the expectation was that it would be spent to commission applied research work from the Research Councils. It was also decided that the Council for Scientific Policy should be reconstituted. A Chief Scientist was to be appointed in the Ministry of Agriculture, Fisheries and Food, supported by two deputies and a small group of other scientists.

The White Paper also defined the rôle of the Department of Agriculture and Fisheries for Scotland as a customer for the research and development work of the eight Scottish Research Institutes and three Scottish Colleges. The Department was to work closely with the Ministry's Chief Scientist's organisation and look to the newly-formed Scottish Agricultural Development Council for the co-ordination of development work within Scotland.

## New Administrative Arrangements

The period of uncertainty about the future of agricultural research from 1970 to 1972 stimulated much critical appraisal of the effectiveness of the whole operation of the Council, its Secretariat and its diverse establishments. One result was that it became apparent that although the structure of the research organisation composed of its Institutes, Units and the support of research in Universities clearly indicated the subjects of the research that was being conducted, there was no central record of projects, their magnitude nor their progress in the detail that would be necessary if any substantial changes had to be made.

The fact that the future was under question emphasised the necessity of ensuring that there was sufficient and correct information being disseminated about agricultural research. The image presented by Council and by the Service needed to be examined.

There was some dissatisfaction with the working of the Committee structure especially at Institute level largely as a result of meagre representation on the Council's Standing Committees. The 1970–71 Annual Report of the Council reveals that no Institute Director was included in the membership of the two principal Standing Committees, namely, those for research on "Animals" and on "Plants and Soils."

The following paragraphs describe the actions that were taken in 1971 and the immediate subsequent years.

## The Planning Section and project costing

A Planning Section was established at the Council's Headquarters, under the headship of Dr. T. L. V. Ulbricht. Its first and principal task was to examine in detail how the Council's current resources were employed. This involved preparing a classification structure and the division of the total research programme into individual projects which could then be related to a project costing scheme. This was obviously a considerable task which proved to become somewhat complex and required repeated visits to the Institutes and Units before a reasonably uniform inventory was completed. The ability to retrieve the correct information was an obvious prerequisite of the system. It was only the persistence of the staff of the Planning Section that produced a workable procedure despite a varied Institute community of "splitters" and "clumpers." A consequence to this priority to establish the project inventory with costings, all on the computer, was that the Planning Section had little time left in which to plan.

This work which was started some two years before the commissioning of research became a reality, provided a major contribution towards achieving a smooth entry into customer-contracting in that the inventory of projects was essential to the construction of commissions. It became obvious during the progress of this activity that the original planning concept for the section was becoming superseded. In 1976 Ulbricht was transferred to the group of Scientific Advisers to the Secretary, the Planning Section was dissolved and replaced by a Programmes Section in charge of Mr. W. S. Wise, formerly of the Planning Section. This reorganisation was appropriate to the pattern of work by which the project inventory, and its computerisation, had been developed under Wise's supervision. An important component in this work was the development of the Agricultural Research Current Information System (ARCIS) which provides the UK input to the EEC Permanent Inventory of Agricultural Research Projects (AGREP). Project costing did not remain as part of the Programmes Section's duties. Its development had been brought to a stage sufficient for routine application by the end of 1977.

## Information services

In implementation of the growing need to increase public awareness of the functions of the Council and to advise and assist the Institutes and Units on communication, the Council, in June 1971, appointed Mr. J. A. Cole-Morgan, previously Public Relations Officer to the Fertilizer Division of Fisons Ltd, as head of a new Information Section. A very successful activity of the Section became the co-ordination of Institute exhibits at major agricultural and horticultural events. A great improvement was achieved by the use of uniform display panels, and by the co-ordinated planning of the total exhibit presented as an activity of the Agricultural Research Council. As part of this presentation of the Council's corporate image to the public the now familiar ARC Symbol was developed by the Information Section for use on stationery, publications, signs, vehicles, etc. Another quite significant, although not necessarily very important, action was to enliven the presentation of the Council's Annual Report by a pictorial cover. This was introduced on the Report for 1972–73 with that year depicting an obvious "Plants" activity and with subsequent years covering "Animals", "Horticulture", "Engineering" etc. This was an innovation as far as the Reports of the Research Councils were concerned and the ARC's example was soon followed.

## Committee structure

The dissatisfaction about the committee structure that was being voiced was discussed at the annual conference of Directors in the autumn of 1971. This structure had remained virtually unchanged for forty years. Council set up a Working Party to advise on modifications that might seem to be more in line with current requirements. This group was chaired by the Secretary, Sir Ronald Baskett, with four Institute Directors as members, Sir Frederick Bawden (Rothamsted Experimental Station), Dr. K. L. (now Sir Kenneth) Blaxter (Rowett Research Institute), Dr. H. C. (now Sir Charles) Pereira (East Malling Research Station) and Professor B. G. F. Weitz (National Institute for Research in Dairying). A report was submitted to Council within less than two months. It should be noted that in the meantime the Rothschild Report had been published. An acceptable and timely recommendation was that a separate Research Grants Board should be established as too much of the time of the Standing Committees was taken up by the discussion of grant applications. More radical and less acceptable recommendations were to have various Research Boards reporting to a Policy and Implementation Board on which there would be Directors' representation. This Board could function as an Executive Committee to assist the Secretary. The Council was not prepared to give its approval to this degree of Director participation, and the report was referred back. The Working Party agreed to dispense with the Policy and Implementation Board and recommended the following structure:

Two Research Boards in place of the two principal Standing Committees.
Research Committees on a commodity basis.
*Ad hoc* Ways and Means Panels composed of Directors, senior staff of Institutes and
    members of the Secretariat.
A Research Grants Board.

The discussion of these proposals took place at the meeting of Council in February
1972, and a Sub-Committee was appointed to study them consisting of Professor K.
(later Sir Kenneth) Mather, Major J. E. M. Dugdale, Sir John Ritchie and Lord
Trenchard. Also on the agenda for that meeting was a discussion on the relations with
the recently identified customer Department. Sir Basil Engholm, Permanent Secretary,
Ministry of Agriculture, Fisheries and Food and Mr. J. H. Perrin, Under Secretary,
attended for that item. It became obvious that the work of the Secretary's Working
Party had been overtaken by events. Wider interests had now to be included and it was
there and then agreed that the Council would invite representatives of the Ministry,
the Department of Agriculture and Fisheries for Scotland, and of the Department of
Education and Science, to form a Joint Working Party, under Sir Kenneth Mather's
chairmanship, with, as members, the remainder of the group nominated by Council to
study its committee structure. This Joint Working Party had to devise a committee
structure to advise the Council and the Agricultural Departments on the whole spectrum
of research and development programmes. It was from this Working Party that the
Joint Consultative Organisation was evolved.

# Chapter 5

# 1972-1980

## Post-Rothschild

The Government's White Paper "Framework for Government Research and Development" (Cmnd. 5046) published in July 1972, affirmed the intention to retain the system of the five Research Councils responsible to the Secretary of State for Education and Science and accepted that, in future, Government Departments should be more closely associated in framing the Councils' programmes through the provision of funds to commission applied research in some areas. Three consequences were listed. Firstly, the Council for Scientific Policy would need to be reconstituted; secondly, Departments would need to be directly represented on the Research Councils; and thirdly, some of the Science Budget would have to be transferred to customer Departments.

The Advisory Board for the Research Councils, which replaced the Council for Scientific Policy, included the Secretary to the Agricultural Research Council and the Chief Scientist, Ministry of Agriculture, Fisheries and Food, who also was appointed, by his Minister, to membership of the Agricultural Research Council. The Council's Charter was amended to provide for not more than four members to be appointed by the Minister of Agriculture, Fisheries and Food and for not more than two members to be appointed by the Secretary of State for Scotland. Since this amendment the Minister of Agriculture has appointed the following officers: the Chief Scientist, the Director-General of the Agricultural Development and Advisory Service, a Deputy Secretary, and the Chief Veterinary Officer; and the Secretary of State for Scotland, an Under-Secretary and the Chief Agricultural Officer of the Department of Agriculture and Fisheries for Scotland. The Department of Agriculture, Northern Ireland has continued to be represented by an Assessor. The financing would, in future, be effected by a transfer of funds to the Ministry which by the third year of operation of the customer/contractor principle would amount to 54% of the Council's share of the Science Budget in terms of constant 1971–72 prices.

The future financing of the research programmes of the eight Scottish Institutes was not made explicit in the White Paper. In the event the Department of Agriculture and Fisheries for Scotland which supported these Institutes by grants-in-aid was recognised as a customer. The same status had not been afforded to the Agricultural Research Council for the fourteen Institutes in England and Wales for which it provided the grants-in-aid. Further reference to the Scottish situation is made later.

## The Chief Scientist's Organisation, Ministry of Agriculture, Fisheries and Food

Inevitably the Chief Scientist's Group at the Ministry of Agriculture, Fisheries and Food to some extent paralleled, in its membership, the staffing of the ARC Secretariat. The Chairman of the Agricultural Research Council when discussing early in 1972, the search for someone to succeed Sir Ronald Baskett in the Secretaryship, said that this could not be done in entire disregard of the search for the Ministry's Chief Scientist, similar qualifications would be required and the two should be compatible. It was a great advantage for the smooth development of the new system that a Director of wide and international experience from an Institute of the Agricultural Research Service was appointed Chief Scientist, namely, Dr. H. C. (later Sir Charles) Pereira, of the East Malling Research Station, He was supported by two deputies, one of whom was Dr. G. A. H. Elton who had been Chief Scientific Adviser (Food) in the Ministry since 1971. The other was Mr. W. F. Raymond (later Professor Raymond), formerly Assistant Director of the Grassland Research Institute, who had been appointed in June 1972. A staff of six Scientific Liaison Officers was subsequently recruited. A supporting administrative staff was provided headed by an Assistant Secretary. Sir Charles Pereira retired in November 1977, and was succeeded by Dr. Bernard Weitz, Director of the National Institute for Research in Dairying.

## The Joint Consultative Organisation

The Joint Working Party under the Chairmanship of Sir Kenneth Mather reported in September 1972, and on the basis of its recommendations the Council and the Agricultural Departments agreed to set up a Joint Consultative Organisation (JCO) consisting of five Boards, covering Animals; Arable Crops and Forage; Horticulture; Food Science and Technology; and Engineering and Buildings. The intent was that this Joint Consultative Organisation should be made up of a balanced membership drawn from the several interests concerned with research and its application in agriculture and food. The membership of these five Boards covered the scientists, agricultural economists, members of the food and agricultural industries, and representatives of the policy, scientific and technical sections of the Agricultural Departments. The membership of each of the five Boards was very carefully considered by the three sponsors, namely, the Agricultural Research Council, the Ministry of Agriculture, Fisheries and Food, and the Department of Agriculture and Fisheries for Scotland. The Boards and the Committees of the JCO replaced the previous Standing Committee, Technical Committee, and Working Party structure of the Agricultural Research Council except as regards research grants and a few special subjects.

The five Research and Development Boards of the JCO each appointed various Committees. The whole organisation had become fully operational by 1973 and the original Board and subsequent Committee structure with chairmen is given in Table 5.

The servicing of the Boards and their Committees was divided between the three sponsoring organisations, thus,

Agricultural Research Council
   Arable Crops and Forage Board
   Engineering and Buildings Board
Ministry of Agriculture, Fisheries and Food
   Horticulture Board
   Food Science and Technology Board
Department of Agriculture and Fisheries for Scotland
   Animals Board

The three sponsors were represented by the Secretary to the Council, the Chief Scientist, Ministry of Agriculture, Fisheries and Food, and the Under Secretary member of Council from the Department of Agriculture and Fisheries for Scotland.

The Boards were asked initially to make a rapid survey of research and development needs, and of the current programme of work. This was completed by 1974 and reports of each Board were submitted to the sponsors. In early 1975 the principal recommendations and the responses of the sponsors were circulated. It was of some satisfaction for the Council to be able to note that each Board had substantially endorsed the existing programme of research in its subject area. A more detailed examination of specific parts of the programme was next undertaken with an identification of priorities. These reports were submitted in the autumn of 1975 and published in December of that year with the response of the sponsors. From the point of view of providing a forum for debate about the research and development priorities within the whole field of agricultural research including horticulture, engineering and food, the JCO can be judged to have been successful. As a means of securing the involvement of many representatives of the users of progress in research and development, the JCO was successful. As a means of enlarging the size of the farming and food industries' communities who were aware of the work of the Council and the Agricultural Departments, the JCO was successful. As an authoritative body, the views of which could be cited by, say, the Secretary to the Council or the Ministry's Chief Scientist in seeking financial support, the JCO was successful. This very success, however, became a source of frustration to the JCO members. The peak of the activity of the JCO coincided with the switch in the growth of the funds available for agricultural research from the positive phase of the previous decades to the negative phase of 1974–75 and 1975–76. This prevented the sponsors responding sufficiently quickly to the recommendations of the JCO for it to become clearly apparent that note of them was being taken. The very thorough examination of agricultural R & D by the JCO had the very positive result of establishing guide lines which could be expected to remain valid for some years. On the other hand there were criticisms that the JCO had led to a proliferation of

Table 5
The Joint Consultative Organisation,
Board and Committee Structure with Chairmen from 1973–1980†

| | |
|---|---|
| **ANIMALS BOARD** | W. A. Biggar, CBE, MC, BSc, FRAGS, Member of Council, Roxburghshire Farmer. |
| Cattle Committee | Professor P. N. Wilson, PhD, FIBiol., BOCM Silcock Ltd. |
| Meat Research Committee | Professor E. F. Williams, OBE, MA, FRIC, Ex-Consultant, J. Sainsbury Ltd. |
| Milk and Milk Products Committee | R. J. M. Crawford, PhD, NDA, NDD, FIFST, West of Scotland College of Agriculture. |
| Pigs Committee | 1. A. G. Beynon*, CB, MRCVS, DVSM, DTVM, Ex-Chief Veterinary Officer MAFF, Ex-member of Council. |
| | 2. R. Braude, OBE, DSc, FIBiol., Formerly Head of Pig Husbandry Department, National Institute for Research in Dairying. |
| Poultry Committee | 1. T. C. Carter, OBE, DSc, FIBiol., FRSE, Director, Poultry Research Centre. |
| | 2. J. A. Calvert, Senior Poultry Husbandry Adviser, ADAS, MAFF. |
| Sheep Committee | J. T. Stamp, CBE, DSc, FRCVS, FRSE, Director, ADRA, Moredun Institute. |
| **ARABLE CROPS AND FORAGE BOARD** | 1. J. S. Martin, CBE, MA., Dip.Agric., Member of Council, Cambridgeshire Farmer. |
| | 2. E. M. W. Griffith, Member of Council, Clwyd Farmer. |
| Grassland and Forage Committee | A. J. Davies, BSc, FIBiol., Chief Agricultural Officer, ADAS, MAFF. |
| Cereals Committee | 1. Professor R. Riley, DSc, FIBiol., FRS, Director, Plant Breeding Institute. |
| | 2. Professor R. C. F. Macer, PhD, Director, Scottish Plant Breeding Station. |
| Potatoes Committee | 1. J. Arbuckle, OBE, Fifeshire Farmer. |
| | 2. A. Q. Hitchcock, Hertfordshire Farmer. |
| Soil Science Committee | Professor E. W. Russell, CMG, DSc, FInstP, FIBiol, FIAgricE., Emeritus Professor of Soil Science, University of Reading. |
| Plant Science Committee | 1. Professor P. W. Brian*, CBE, ScD, FRS, Member of Council. |
| | 2. L. Fowden, PhD, FRS, Director, Rothamsted Experimental Station. |
| From 1975 Sugar Beet Committee | J. N. Holmes, OBE, BA, Suffolk Farmer. |

Table 5 continued

| | |
|---|---|
| HORTICULTURE BOARD | 1. D. G. Frampton, CBE, Chairman, Frampton Nurseries Ltd. |
| | 2. The Rt. Hon. The Earl of Selborne, Director, Blackmoor Estate, Ltd., Member of Council. |
| Field Vegetables Committee | 1. J. D. Lowe, MA., Dip. Agric., MBA, Director David Lowe & Sons, Ltd. |
| | 2. B. E. Bransden, Surrey Grower. |
| Fruit Committee | 1. Professor A. F. Posnette, ScD, AICTA, FIBiol., FRS., Director, East Malling Research Station. |
| | 2. P. J. Smith, Peter Smith (Farmers) Ltd. |
| Hardy Ornamentals and Bulbs Committee | M. O. Slocock, Slocock Nurseries, Woking. |
| Protected Crops Committee | 1. D. Rudd-Jones, PhD, FIBiol., Director, Glasshouse Crops Research Institute. |
| | 2. G. D. Lockie, Surrey Grower. |
| ENGINEERING AND BUILDINGS BOARD | 1. Professor A. R. J. P. Ubbelohde, CBE, DSc, FInstP, FRS, Head of the Department of Chemical Engineering and Chemical Technology, Imperial College of Science and Technology, Member of Council. |
| | 2. Professor Sir Hugh Ford, FRS, Professor of Mechanical Engineering, Imperial College of Science and Technology, Member of Council. |
| Crops Engineering Committee | 1. J. H. W. Wilder, OBE, BA, MIAgrE, Director, John Wilder (Engineering) Ltd. |
| | 2. J. V. Fox, Managing Director, Bomford & Evershed Ltd. |
| Livestock Engineering Committee | J. E. Moffitt, FRAGS, Northumberland Farmer. |
| Farm Buildings Committee | R. G. A. Lofthouse, FRICS, Chief Surveyor, ADAS, MAFF. |
| Since 1978 Farm Waste Committee | Professor J. R. O'Callaghan, Professor of Agricultural Engineering, University of Newcastle-upon-Tyne. |
| FOOD SCIENCE AND TECHNOLOGY BOARD | 1. Professor A. G. Ward, CBE, MA, FInstP, FIFST, Professor of Food and Leather Science, University of Leeds. |
| | 2. W. F. J. Cuthbertson, OBE, PhD, Director of Glaxo Research Ltd. |
| Food Composition, Quality and Safety Committee | A. J. James, PhD, Manager of Biosciences, Unilever Research Laboratory. |
| Food Processing, Distribution and Storage Committee | 1. W. F. J. Cuthbertson, OBE, PhD, Director of Glaxo Research Ltd. |
| | 2. J. Edelman, DSc, ARCS, FIBiol, Director of Research, Lord Rank Research Centre. |

*deceased
†The offices listed are those held by Board and Committee Chairmen at the time of their appointment.

Committees and Working Parties at a time when such bodies were coming under increasing attack. The future of the JCO was, therefore, given careful consideration firstly, by the sponsors' representatives and finally by the Council. It was decided that the Organisation would be continued but in a streamlined form. There would be a single Consultative Board which would set up Special Committees, each for a limited period and for a clearly defined subject as would seem to be indicated.

The various Boards, Committees and Working Parties of the JCO produced, especially during the first few years of its work, many excellent reports as a basis for discussion. The great majority of these were not published although the more important were available on application. One report which had considerable topical importance was published in 1974, namely the report of the Energy Working Party of the Joint Consultative Organisation's Engineering and Buildings Board. This Working Party was set up in late 1973 under the chairmanship of Professor J. R. O'Callaghan of the University of Newcastle-upon-Tyne, to establish budgets of energy use in British agriculture and to indicate potential economies. The main finding of the Report was that British agriculture uses but some three per cent of the national energy consumption.

## The Research Grants Board/Boards

The Council's function as a grant-awarding body to the universities and other institutions was no part of the wide responsibility of the Joint Consultative Organisation and, as originally recommended by the Council's Working Party on Committee Structure, a Research Grants Board was appointed in 1973. The first Chairman was Professor K. (later Sir Kenneth) Mather. There had been considerable debate about whether there should be one Board or two. Two Boards would perpetuate the convenient division of subjects into "Animals" and "Plants and Soils". It had, however, been decided to give the Board/Boards financial autonomy and it was essential that a uniform standard was operated with regard to meeting the criteria for an award. In spite of some foreseeable inconveniences it was judged that one Board should be given the opportunity of initiating the new system.

It was not long before the number of applications received made it necessary for the Board to meet on two consecutive days. Inevitably one day was chosen for the "Animals" applications and the other for "Plants and Soils". Attendance on both days was a very heavy demand to make on the time of those members with very specialised interests. It was, therefore, decided in 1975 to have two Boards from January 1976, with six members appointed to both Boards to ensure effective liaison. In January 1975, Professor P. W. Brian had been appointed Chairman in place of Sir Kenneth Mather who had relinquished that office, although still remaining a member of the Board. At the same time, Professor Henry Harris had been appointed Deputy Chairman. Professor Brian subsequently became Chairman of the Research Grants Board (Plants and Soils) and Professor Harris became Chairman of the Research Grants Board (Animals). Subsequent changes in the membership of Council led to the Chairmanship of the Plants and Soils Board passing to Professor J. L. Harley, then to Professor J. L. Jinks. Professor Sir Andrew Huxley succeeded Professor Harris as Chairman of the Animals Board.

Three types of award are made: special research grants, normally of three years' duration for the support of specific projects of timeliness and promise for agricultural research; block grants of five years' duration, with provision for extension for a further five years, for the support of areas of research of particular interest to the Council not otherwise adequately supported; and equipment grants to provide a particular item of equipment to assist a project in a university department or for more general use. As financial resources became more restricted, the question became relevant of whether the support to research in the universities should be confined to areas of priority as identified by the Council. By that time the reports of the Joint Consultative Organisation and the responses of the Sponsors were freely available to all those seeking support for their research. This was, in general, considered to be a sufficient indication of priorities. There always remained the alternative, as in the Unit principle, for the Council to select particular individuals in the universities or other institutions whose work was of sufficient interest to warrant additional support.

## The Commissioning of Research

In that the transfer of Science Budget Funds to the Ministry of Agriculture, Fisheries and Food had to take effect from April 1973, discussions with the Ministry's Chief Scientist became a high priority as soon as he and the new Secretary to the Council had taken office in December 1972. In the first year the amount involved was 27% of the Agricultural Research Council's allocation from the Science Budget which proved to be £6.55M, and in the second year 40%, which amounted to £11.698M. The limited time available, the necessity for considerable discussion about the application of the customer/contractor principle, and the fact that the Joint Consultative Organisation had just begun its task, prevented the first two years of operation being more than book-keeping transactions.

The system became fully operational in 1975/76. Commissions were constructed by discussions between the Chief Scientist's group and the Council's Secretariat. This task was greatly facilitated by the complete analysis that had been made by the Council's Planning Section of the research programme of the Agricultural Research Service in terms of project units with costs. The selection of the content of the commissions was based upon each having a broad national aim which could be divided into an appropriate number of sub-commissions, based as far as possible, on commodities. For example, the cereals commission had sub-commissions on wheat, barley, oats, etc. The commissioning arrangements made provision for periodical reviews of the work in progress with a procedure for extension, modification and termination.

The formal approval of commissions was by the Research and Development Requirements Board of the Ministry under the Chairmanship of the Chief Scientist and of which the Secretary to the Council and the Chief Scientific Officer were members. Eighteen commissions were approved for 1975/76, the third year of operation of the new system, when 54% was the transferred portion of the Council's resources, amounting to £18.4M.

The build up during 1973 to 1975 to making the system fully operational involved frequent discussions, the overcoming of many difficulties and the reaching of many compromises. The commissions were initially constructed by selections from the project list of the Agricultural Research Council. The commissions were placed with the Council, not with Institutes. The underlying objectives were to make the system work and to do so with the minimum of interference with the work of the scientists.

It was agreed that commissions would normally be reviewed every four years. Changes in the content of commissions might be made, by agreement at any time but one year's notice would be given of the unilateral termination or amendment of a commission.

What, at the time, did not appear to be of overriding importance was the interpretation of Rothschild's dictum that applied R & D must be done on a customer/contractor basis. It appeared to the Ministry and the Council that it would be sensible to avoid artificial cut-offs, within a long-term programme, between research which was and which was not commissioned. Commissions were, therefore, constructed within a commodity framework in which the Ministry funded a flow of strategic and applied research. Correspondingly, because this upset the strict but purely arbitrary proportionment of funds, the Council also agreed to undertake a similar flow of strategic and applied research in another area. These arrangements have not always been approved by external observers, but they nevertheless seem to be the ones which accord best with the aims of ensuring that good and useful scientific research continues.

## The Commissioning of Research by the Department of Agriculture and Fisheries for Scotland

With the passing of the Agricultural Research Act 1956, the Agricultural Research Council, in addition to having its own Institutes and Units and to its overall responsibility for advising on agricultural research, acquired jurisdiction in its own right for agricultural research in England and Wales. It then became responsible for financing the grant-aided agricultural research institutes in these countries. In Scotland, the Council's financial support was limited to its own establishments which, in 1956, were the Animal Breeding Research Organisation, the Poultry Research Centre and the Unit of Statistics. One year later the Unit of Animal Genetics was added.

The jurisdiction granted to the Council by the Act did not extend to the eight agricultural research institutes in Scotland. The arrangement that is extant is that the grant-in-aid to these Institutes is provided by the Department of Agriculture and

Fisheries for Scotland. The rôle of the Agricultural Research Council is that of scientific adviser but with a considerable administrative load, the Council having accepted the responsibility for providing Visiting Groups to the Scottish Institutes and the work of the Scottish Institutes is included in the implementation by the Council of the many management procedures such as promotions, recruitment, conditions of employment etc necessary to maintain uniformity within the Agricultural Research Service. Reference has already been made in this chapter to the financing of the research programmes of the Scottish Institutes, noting that the Department qualified as a customer. As a customer it had, therefore, to commission applied research with its contractors. The Department rejected any attempt at distinguishing between the subtleties of the semantics of the categorisation of research and proceeded to judge the whole programme of each Institute as being commissionable.

## Participation

Within the context of the Council, its Secretariat and the Agricultural Research Service it is, perhaps, more than a coincidence that exactly when the concept of the autonomy of the Council and the Service was so severely jolted, there was a parallel move within the Service to have less autocracy, more democracy and especially, participation in management.

### Management Advisory Committee

Following the 1973 annual conference of Directors during which greater participation in management had been discussed on the basis of proposals put forward by the Secretary, two Committees were established with the approval of Council. One of these was the Management Advisory Committee to which could be referred many aspects of management especially those involving conditions of employment, career management and other management/staff relationships. The chairman was the Under Secretary, Mr. G. M. P. Myers, and the membership consisted of four Directors and two Institute Secretaries appointed by the Secretary. This Committee, together with the Secretary and the Chief Scientific Officer from 1974 onwards, formed the Official Side of the Whitley Council for the Agricultural Research Service which had been constituted at about the same time. (Appendix 7 contains an account of the establishment of a Consultative Machinery and of Trade Union relations in the Agricultural Research Service.)

### Secretary's Policy Advisory Committee

The second Committee established after the 1973 Directors' Conference was the Secretary's Policy Advisory Committee. Its role was to assist the Secretary with the discussion of problems involving decisions to be taken at his level, and to assist the Secretary with the preparation of cases for presentation to Council when decisions were required at that higher level. The Secretary was Chairman of this Committee, and for the first five years the Directors elected their representatives based on "constituencies" of the communities of their scientific discipline. These were "Animals", 2 members; "Arable Crops", 2 members; "Horticulture", 1 member; "Engineering", 1 member; "Food", 1 member and "Units", 1 member. Although there were obviously advantages in such a system from the point of view of achieving participation and of providing an opportunity for greatly strengthening and improving the management/Director relationship, in the long run its deficiencies became apparent. The constituencies were too small in most cases and in the two larger groups (Animals and Arable Crops) the inevitable process of giving each his turn incurred the risk of the resulting group of eight members being less suited for the purpose than if they had been selected. These comments must not be taken as implying any criticism of the Committee's membership. In the beginning, at least, it provided a very formidable body for the counselling and for the support of the Secretary during a somewhat difficult period. Since 1979, the Committee has been reconstituted as the Research and Policy Advisory Committee with the Director members appointed by the Secretary.

## Advisory Groups to ARC Institute Directors

Within the organisation of the Agricultural Research Service comprising the Institutes grant-aided by the Council in England and Wales, the Scottish Institutes grant-aided by the Department of Agriculture and Fisheries for Scotland, and the Institutes and Units financed directly by the Agricultural Research Council, there was until the last few years of this 50-year span, an apparent anomaly. A grant-aided Institute had its Governing Body which was the employer of the staff and which provided advice and support for the Director even to the extent of seeking to modify or, at least, delay the implementation of the more unacceptable edicts from the Council's Headquarters. A Council Institute had no such body. The important consideration was that a Governing Body consisted of a group of important and influential people who had a strong proprietary interest in their Institute. This has always been especially true, for example, of the horticultural Institutes such as the East Malling Research Station and the Long Ashton Research Station, each having been founded by local growers seeking research support.

The question of providing the Council's Institutes with a Committee analogous to a Governing Body had been debated from time to time since as long ago as 1961. On that occasion the point was made that the Visiting Group procedure did not keep the research programme of a Council Institute under the same continuous review as was possible by the Governing Body of the grant-aided Institute. It is recorded that at that time, the Council had hitherto not considered it appropriate to interpose an Advisory Committee between itself and its Institutes. It was noted also that it was through Governing Bodies or Advisory Committees that farmers could most fruitfully be brought into contact with the Council's work. The compromise solution was adopted in 1961 that the Council's Institutes would receive a mid-term Visiting Group, i.e. at three years, for an experimental period. This procedure was continued until around 1972/73 when the pressure of work on the Secretariat became too great to service these additional visits.

In 1973 this subject was again raised as the result of a Management Review conducted by a joint team from the Civil Service Department and the Department of Education and Science. In the then climate of uncertainty about the outcome of the new relationship with the Ministry of Agriculture, Fisheries and Food an Advisory Committee to the Director of each of the Council's Institutes seemed to provide another opportunity for the more direct involvement of the true customers with the work of the Institutes. The first of these Advisory Committees was set up in 1975 when one was provided to the Director of the Institute for Research on Animal Diseases. The procedure was that the appointment of the Chairman and members was made by the Secretary to the Council in consultation with the Director. Once appointed it was left to the Chairman and the Director to arrange how the Committee would operate. No formal links were preserved between the Committee and the Council's Secretariat in the way, for example, of the minutes of meetings being submitted to Headquarters. Informal contacts were made from time to time but the Committee was never an instrument of the Council's management. It did, however, increase the participation of the sector of the agricultural community served by the Institute. Such a Committee was not appointed in the case of the Meat Research Institute until 1980. Previously it had had an Advisory Committee of a different character because of the earlier financial participation of the meat industry and the need to provide for its representation. The Directors concerned came to appreciate the appointment of these Advisory Committees because of the interest shown by the members and by the various ways in which their support and advice was of value.

## Inter-Research Council Collaboration

The proposal to transfer the Agricultural Research Council to the Ministry of Agriculture, Fisheries and Food, which was then followed by the publication of the Rothschild Report, provided a strong stimulus to the Research Councils to ensure that their ranks were closed and that they were standing shoulder to shoulder. Their leader during the early 1970s was undoubtedly Sir Frederick Dainton, as Chairman of the Council for Scientific Policy (1969-72) and Chairman, as it was reconstituted, of the Advisory Board for the Research Councils (1972–73). In addition to their attendance at the monthly meetings of the Advisory Board, the executive Heads of the Research Councils (HORC) met as frequently, informally, in a group, known by that acronym. Inter-Council consultation at other levels has done much to bring the handling of administrative matters into harmony between the Councils. This community jointly fostered other activities, for example, the establishment of the European Science Foundation in 1974 which owed much to the support provided by the British Research Councils in collaboration with the Royal Society and the British Academy.

## Joint ARC/MRC Committee on Food and Nutrition Research

In 1970 the two Councils appointed a Joint Committee under the chairmanship of Professor A. Neuberger to review the field of food and nutrition research and to make recommendations. The Report of the Joint Committee consisted of a most comprehensive and valuable review coupled with indications for future programmes. Its publication coincided with the period when both Councils were much involved in the initiation of the commissioning of research by their customer Departments. An adequate analysis of the Report took some time to complete. The burden of implementation of the findings of the Committee lay with the Medical Research Council, at least as far as nutrition research was concerned. The first move towards this was taken in 1979 by the appointment of a Joint ARC/MRC Nutrition Committee under the chairmanship of Sir John Butterfield, Regius Professor of Physic, University of Cambridge and member of the Medical Research Council.

## Research Priorities

The excellent analysis of the research and development required to increase further the efficiency and productivity of British agriculture that had been completed by the Joint Consultative Organisation by 1976 left two aspects which required further work. Although each of the five Boards of the JCO had listed their priorities, an overall assessment had still to be made with regard to the priorities between Boards. This was the responsibility of the Sponsors. The Joint Consultative Organisation was not constituted to be able to undertake a review of the whole field. On the other hand, the Boards of the Joint Consultative Organisation, except in a few instances, were reluctant to identify areas of low priority. A further fact of some significance for the Council was that the orientation of the Joint Consultative Organisation towards the more applied end of the research spectrum, did not give adequate consideration to more fundamental projects appropriate for support from the Science Budget. For these reasons, the Council established a Priorities Working Party in June 1976, under the Chairman. This Group included members of the Council and representatives of the three sponsors including the Secretary. The choice of the Council members was on the basis of Joint Consultative Organisation Board representation. The meetings of this Working Party were useful and stimulating. For example, the decision for a priority effort in the subject of crop bioenergetics including the genetic manipulation of crop plants was the outcome of one series of discussions. This resulted in the Council receiving a special allocation of £300 000 from the Science Budget.

## Research Groups

In addition to crop bioenergetics, the Council's Priorities Working Party identified other priorities including the causes of variation in crop yields, increasing the efficiency of photosynthesis in plants, the study of the animal's response to its environment and the diseases of animals which prevent the achievement of optimum production and which are still without effective means of control.

In the implementation of these priorities, had it been thought appropriate to seek to form a Unit or Units, the required financial investment and the continuing commitment would have made this approach unrealistic in the 1970s. The formation of Research Groups was accepted as an alternative. Not only would this be financially more bearable but there was the possibility that it might be more successful because of the diversity of facilities that could be made available.

One component of a Research Group may be formed by scientists in Institutes or Units of the Agricultural Research Service. Another component may be scientists in a University Department. The Research Group on genetic manipulation of crop plants, for example, is built on scientific competence at the Plant Breeding Institute, Cambridge; the John Innes Institute, Norwich; the Rothamsted Experimental Station, Harpenden; the Welsh Plant Breeding Station, Aberystwyth; the Unit of Nitrogen Fixation, University of Sussex; and the Botany Department, University of Nottingham. The programme is planned as a whole, is co-ordinated centrally and an annual meeting is held when all aspects of the programme are discussed and evaluated.

## Chairmen and Secretaries, 1968 to 1980

The Hon. J. J. (later Sir John) Astor succeeded the Duke of Northumberland as Chairman of the Agricultural Research Council in 1968. He had already had some experience of the Agricultural Research Service, having been Chairman of the Governing Body of the National Institute of Agricultural Engineering from 1963 to 1968 and he was a practising farmer. After distinguished war service with the Life Guards, he was elected Member of Parliament for the Sutton Division of Plymouth from 1951–1959. His term of office as Chairman covered a very difficult period in the Council's history. There were three Secretaries to the Council during his Chairmanship and with each he quickly established an easy and effective working relationship. This was done by the creation of mutual confidence, by a scrupulous recognition of areas of responsibility, by establishing easy communications and by an insistence upon being thoroughly briefed before undertaking any engagement, however informal. To this was added great wisdom, an ability to analyse the reactions of others, an appreciation of the cares of office of public servants and an astuteness of timing.

Sir John undertook his responsibilities very seriously by attempting to visit all the Institutes in the Service within as short a time as possible after his appointment as Chairman. He also introduced a number of innovations as regards the greater participation of the Directors of the Institutes and Units. It was during his Chairmanship, for example, that the Director was invited to attend the item on the Council Agenda when the Report of the Visiting Group to his Institute was due to be discussed. He initiated a programme by which selected Directors gave a presentation to Council of the work of their Institute. He bullied members of Council to attend, what became during his term of office, the annual residential conference of Directors, not one of which he missed. He was Knighted in 1978.

Sir Ronald Baskett was Secretary to the Council from October 1971, until his death in November 1972. As has already been described, the great uncertainty about the future of the Council and of the Agricultural Research Service had made it impossible for the normal procedure to be followed for recruitment of a successor to Sir Gordon Cox when he retired at the end of September 1971. Baskett had had many years of experience of the Council and of the way in which it conducted its business. Shortly after obtaining a degree in agriculture at Reading he joined the staff of Queen's University, Belfast, and the then Ministry of Agriculture, Northern Ireland. He became Professor of Agricultural Chemistry in 1935 and Chief Scientific Officer of the Ministry in 1947. From that latter position he was appointed, in 1947, an Assessor to the Council. In 1959 he returned to Reading to take up the Directorship of the National Institute for Research in Dairying. He retired from this appointment in 1967 and made his home in County Antrim. It was from there that he was invited to come to London and fill the post of Secretary to the Council for one year from October 1971. His successor was selected in September 1972. Baskett agreed to remain in office until the end of December 1972 to permit time for the necessary consultations and other administrative procedures to be completed with regard to the appointment of the new Secretary. Most regrettably, he was taken ill in October just prior to the Annual Conference of Directors which, thus, he could not attend. He died on the 24th of November 1972. No year of a Secretary's office could have been so packed with such urgency and gravity as that of Baskett's from 1971 to 1972 including, as it did, the publication of the Green Paper (Rothschild and Dainton Reports) in November 1971, and the White Paper in July 1972, in implementation of the customer/contractor principle. No Secretary had previously been asked to bear such a burden, still less when he had attained the age of 70 years. Throughout this period, however, Baskett managed to convey the impression of not being unduly harassed and he never failed to receive his many visitors and carry out his difficult task with great courtesy and patience.

The accounts of the next two Secretaries and one Chairman will, for obvious reasons, be restricted to summaries of biographical information.

Sir Ronald Baskett's successor was William MacGregor Henderson, Director since 1967 of the Institute for Research on Animal Diseases. Because of Baskett's untimely death in November 1972, the new Secretary took office at the beginning of December instead of in January, as had been planned. Henderson entered the Royal (Dick) Veterinary College, Edinburgh in 1931, the year the Council was established, and obtained his diploma of membership of the Royal College of Veterinary Surgeons in 1935. The next three years were spent on the staff of the Royal (Dick) Veterinary College with the promise of research opportunities but, at that time, with no realistic prospect of them materialising. He joined the staff of the Research Institute of the Foot-and-Mouth Disease Research Committee, Pirbright, in January 1939, and remained there until the end of 1956. 1957 to 1965 were spent in Latin America as Director of the Pan American Foot-and-Mouth Disease Center, Rio de Janeiro. On returning to the United Kingdom, he was Head of the Department of Microbiology, Institute for Research on Animal Diseases, until becoming Director of the Institute in

October 1967. He received a Knighthood in 1976 and in the same year was elected to the Fellowship of the Royal Society.

Sir John Astor was succeeded as Chairman of the Council in June 1978, by Lord Porchester who has had a wide experience of public affairs especially in connection with the Hampshire County Council of which he was Chairman and also with the Forestry Commission, Nature Conservancy, Game Research Association, Thoroughbred Breeders Association and as Chairman of the South East Economic Planning Council. Lord Porchester is responsible for the farming and forestry operations of the Carnarvon family estate.

Dr. Ralph Riley succeeded Sir William Henderson as Secretary to the Council in October 1978. After war service Riley obtained his first degree at the University of Sheffield where he was also a postgraduate student. He was recruited in 1952 to the Plant Breeding Institute, Cambridge, by Dr. Douglas Bell, the recently appointed Director, in implementation of his policy to integrate a strong scientific basis into the technology of plant breeding. Within two years Riley was appointed Head of the Cytogenetics Department. He was elected to the Fellowship of the Royal Society in 1967. In 1971 he succeeded Bell as Director of the Institute.

## Other senior staff changes in the Secretariat

In 1971, as has already been recorded, the duties and responsibilities of the Deputy Secretary was divided between a Chief Scientific Officer, Dr. C. C. Webster, and an Under Secretary, Mr. D. J. Parkinson. Parkinson retired in September 1973, and was succeeded by Mr G. M. P. Myers who had been the Assistant Secretary in charge of the Plants and Soils Research Division. Dr. G. W. Cooke, a Deputy Director of the Rothamsted Experimental Station and its Acting Director in 1972–73, succeeded Webster as Chief Scientific Officer on his retirement in 1975. Cooke had been elected to the Fellowship of the Royal Society in 1969. Professor J. A. F. Rook, Director of the Hannah Research Institute, succeeded Cooke in January 1981, his post being re-designated as Second Secretary to the Council.

## A Personal Assessment

It is perhaps fitting and appropriate to finish this historical account by a personal assessment of some of the features of the Agricultural Research Council on the eve of the fiftieth anniversary of it being created by Royal Charter. This assessment must include corresponding references to the Agricultural Research Service for which the Council has the complete scientific responsibility.

As this chronicle has shown, the Council, in its scientific and, initially, largely advisory role, received a heritage of agricultural research in the already established Institutes and other institutions. This heritage was also embodied in the practices of animal and crop husbandry that had been developed. Agricultural research is long-term and the rate of its progress is frequently controlled by the rhythm of the seasons. This scale of time demands continuity among those with the responsibility for leadership and management. This can be found in the organisation of the Council and of the Research Service. A study of the appendices listing the members of Council and the Directors of the Institutes shows that change is not especially frequent. There are, of course, constraints on length of service. The term of appointment for members of Council is five years and re-appointment for another term is permitted and often takes place. Quite apart from providing continuity, this practice has the great advantage of not having to draw too frequently upon the community of, for example, those with qualifications in one of the sciences relating to agriculture or food. It has always proved possible to find candidates for Council, qualified to maintain the eminence and scientific distinction that has characterised its scientific members. Similarly, its lay members, because of their eminence and capability in their particular fields have had no difficulty in working as equal partners with their scientific colleagues. Such is the breadth, in fact, of the spectrum of the activities under the aegis of the Council that it is probable that, on appointment, those on each end had some anxiety about how they could accommodate themselves to what would be bound to be very different masteries exercised by some of their new colleagues.

It is relevant to note that the present Chairman is only the seventh in line and his six predecessors covered forty-eight years. There were more casualties among the Secretaries. Nevertheless the present Secretary is but the ninth in line and his eight predecessors also covered forty-eight years.

The Agricultural Research Service is a convenient term to cover the complex organisation of the fourteen establishments in England and Wales grant-aided by the Agricultural Research Council; the eight Institutes of the Council; its Units and Research Groups; and the eight Scottish Institutes grant-aided by the Department of Agriculture and Fisheries for Scotland, all under the scientific oversight of the Council. The author, in 1978, in the last month of his office as Secretary to the Council, delivered the Golden Jubilee Lecture* of the Hannah Research Institute. The following excerpt represents an attempt to capture the essence of the Service:

"I should like to take this opportunity of commenting upon the organisation and structure of the ARS with its three sources of funds and its mixture of institutes and units dissimilar in age, tradition, degree of independence, local association, etc. There is no gainsaying that it is slightly complex. It is full of differences between one component and another, many of which are more subtle then obvious. It provides a temptation to every new administrator to reorganise it in a simpler way but any attempt to do so should be strongly resisted. The strength and effectiveness of the organisation lies in the directors and staffs of the institutes and units backed by their governing bodies and advisory groups. One of the secrets of this complex service is the maintenance, at institutes, of some degree of autonomy coupled with a sense of predominantly institute loyalty within a corporate organisation headed by the ARC."

Attention has been drawn to various circumstances, especially during the 1930s and the 1940s, that would seem to have steered the Council towards developing an organisation almost wholly dependent upon its own Institutes and Units. The alternative is the procedure used to a very much greater extent by the other Research Councils, namely, to support the relevant research in Universities by means of research grants. The more proprietary policy of the Agricultural Research Council may have simplified the implementation of research priorities but it had the disadvantage, as soon as financial resources became restricted, of a reduction in flexibility. This constraint was due to the high proportion of resources required to retain permanent staff in post. With the cuts in expenditure that were imposed by the Chancellor of the Exchequer, the Council received in real terms, 3.68% less in 1974/75 than in the preceding year. The major item of increasing expenditure was staff costs. Overall, the expenditure on salaries and wages was just over sixty per cent but in some institutes and units this expenditure accounted for up to eighty per cent of their budget. The seriousness of the situation was such that a moratorium was imposed on the recruitment of all but the most essential staff. This was kept on from October 1974 to March 1975, after which recruitment was resumed but subject to central control. This instance is given in some detail because it illustrates how the nature of large scale agricultural research which depends upon the use of complex research facilities cannot readily be adjusted to abrupt changes in the level of financial support. If there were a greater investment in University research this support could be at risk in times of shortage of funds.

---

*Report 1978, The Hannah Research Institute, Ayr, KA6 5HL.

In introducing the previous paragraph, reference was made to the Council having become largely dependent for the implementation of its research upon the Institutes within the Agricultural Research Service. It may also be true to say that the Council may have been surprised by the number of establishments that came to be dependent upon it for their survival. Reference to the section on page 41 entitled "The management of Institutes associated with Universities" illustrates this point as of 1943. All or part of nine of the twelve institutions listed eventually became the responsibility of the Council either as one of its Units or as a grant-aided Institute.

Reference has been made to the rather separate situation of the eight Scottish Agricultural Research Institutes which are funded solely by the Department of Agriculture and Fisheries for Scotland, which had to adopt the rôle of both customer and contractor. The potential difficulties of this arrangement must not be exaggerated. The responsibility for advice on the science of the Department's research programme lies with the Agricultural Research Council in the same way as does that for the science of the research commissioned with the Council by the Ministry of Agriculture, Fisheries and Food. It is appropriate in this context to point out that the contribution from the Scottish Institutes is not confined to Scotland. Although their programmes are planned with a view to Scottish needs and conditions, they form an invaluable part of the total British effort in agricultural research.

It has not been part of this historical account to describe the successes that can be attributed to these fifty years of research sponsored by the Council. The achievements of British farming are evident enough. Many individuals and organisations both in the public and the private sector have contributed to this. There is, however, no question that many of the new technologies, many of the improved plant varieties and much of the healthy state of our flocks, herds and crops are based upon the results of scientific research. The Agricultural Research Council has been successful as a sponsor of research. To a great extent this success has resulted from its policy of delegating as much responsibility as possible. The strength of the Agricultural Research Service lies in the Directors and staffs of its Institutes and Units. It is a high priority for the Council and especially the Secretary, its executive head, to protect and foster this powerful force. When referring to the strength of the service lying in its Directors and their staffs, it is as well to remember the part played by the "founding" Directors who, practically without staff and facilities, so planned what was required that it provided the excellent Institutes which form so much of the Service today.

The most significant changes during the recent years of the history of the Council and of the Agricultural Research Service have been the implementation of the customer/contractor principle and the commissioning of research. In terms of the writing of an historical account, these events are still too recent to permit the making of a definitive assessment. There can be no doubt, however, that the high proportion of the Council's resources that was transferred to the customer Department greatly reduced the Council's scope for initiative. The early years of the new system clearly demonstrated the necessity for a continuing dialogue between customer and contractor, represented by those with the widest ranges of responsibility.

The research policy for agriculture must be to enlarge scientific knowledge so as to provide the options for meeting the changing social, economic and political situations as they arise in the future. The achievement of this objective demands the fostering of good science within centres of excellence. The research programmes must be relevant to the anticipated needs of the population. It is already urgent that the boundaries of our populations are effectively extended beyond national limits and that in this respect, for example, the higher aspirations of the European Economic Community are more rapidly achieved. The development of an international policy for food production in terms of providing an adequate diet for all has long been a pressing need. One can feel confident from the past record that the potential contributions from British agricultural research will be forthcoming when required. To-day's research must be planned not for the needs of to-morrow nor for next year but for the next decade. To-day's problems are urgent and of vital importance for those with the unenviable task of negotiating agricultural policy for the protection of British farming. This, regrettably, is still the stage of European economic co-operation that is imposed by the response of the members of the Community. There is one certainty, however, which is that by the end of the century the policies for food production, storage and distribution will have to be very different. The Agricultural Research Council has a responsibility in each of these sectors but with the major effort being in production. One difference that must be achieved is the wise distribution of regional surpluses. The research priority, therefore, is to find the means to increase the efficiency and productivity of agriculture. It is against this background which makes the priorities selected by the Council's Priorities Working Party so apposite. By determining the causes of variation in crop yield, the current basic farming practices can be made to be more productive. By overcoming the difficulties of applying the new technology of genetic manipulation to crop plants, it will be possible to introduce biological characteristics into new varieties now beyond the capability of the most skilled plant breeder. The greatest achievements are most likely by increasing the knowledge of the subject of bioenergetics in such areas as photosynthesis and nitrogen fixation. A successful outcome to research in these two fields would permit crop yields to be increased without making yet further demands on the dwindling sources of energy from fossil fuels. Crops must be thought of in the widest sense, for example, those suitable as feedstuffs for animals, not solely as the staples for human consumption.

Is this applied research? It could not have been planned without a recognition of the importance of achieving success. While avoiding such a well-used phrase as "for the survival of mankind", there is no doubt that agricultural research is of vital importance in attempting to ensure that food requirements and food production remain in balance. One of the characteristics of all agricultural research is that it belongs to the environment of practicality. It is undertaken by people, many of whom are motivated by hoping to be able to make some contribution towards improving the availability of food in all parts of the world.

# Plant Breeding

## RALPH RILEY

Agricultural Research Council, London

### Establishment of Plant Breeding in the Agricultural Research Service

Plant breeding is the technology which has the practical purpose of producing material objects — varieties or cultivars — which offer advantages over pre-existing varieties in terms of absolute yield, stability of yield, agronomic convenience or in the quality of the marketable produce. As a technology it exploits and integrates knowledge drawn from several scientific disciplines but, since new varieties are differentiated from their predecessors by inherited attributes, genetics is the discipline that is central. Consequently a discussion of the place of plant breeding in the activities of the Agricultural Research Council must refer to the development of plant genetics in the UK.

Appropriately the term "genetics" was coined by W. Bateson (Plate 1) and appears to have been first used by him in 1905, in a letter to Professor Adam Sedgwick, to refer to the study of heredity and "variation and cognate phenomena". Subsequently, in 1910, Bateson was appointed Director of the John Innes Horticultural Institute — now the John Innes Institute — which was the first institute among those which subsequently came under the aegis of the ARC to have a programme including plant breeding and genetics.

As is implied by this, William Bateson was the founder of genetics in Britain. Indeed in the biography, written by his wife, Mrs. Beatrice Bateson, there is a description of his reading, for the first time, Gregor Mendel's paper on inheritance in peas while on the train from Cambridge to London where he was to deliver, on 8 May 1900, a lecture to the Royal Horticultural Society entitled "Problems of Heredity". He at once incorporated in his lecture reference to Mendel's work on the particulate nature of inheritance.

Bateson was aware from the beginning of Mendelian genetics in Britain that the new scientific developments could have considerable practical consequences. In his inaugural lecture on election to a Professorship of Biology at Cambridge in 1908 Bateson said, "There is no lack of utility and direct application in the study of Genetics. If we want to raise mangels that will not run to seed, or to breed a cow that will give more milk in less time, or milk with more butter and less water, we can turn to Genetics with every hope that something can be done in these laudable directions."

Bateson's efforts to establish genetics in the University of Cambridge had been largely frustrated so he eagerly grasped the opportunities offered when he was invited to be the first Director of the John Innes Horticultural Institute at Merton in 1910. In the first four years of the Institute's life work was initiated on bolting in sugar beet and cabbage, blight resistance in potatoes, pollen incompatability in fruit trees, interspecies relationships in strawberries and several other subjects which were to have practical consequences in the future. In this way the foundations were laid for the subsequent involvement of the Agricultural Research Service in plant breeding and in research on plant genetics. Bateson also established at Merton a centre for basic genetic research in the UK at a period when little attention was paid to the subject in the Universities.

During his period in Cambridge, Bateson had influenced R. H. (later Sir Rowland) Biffen to study the application of Mendelian genetics to crop plants. Biffen described how in the season of 1903 he grew the second generation derived from a cross between

*Plate 1* Dr. William Bateson, FRS, Director of the John Innes Institute from 1910 until 1926, and the founder of the science of genetics in Britain.

the wheat forms Rivet and Red King, respectively resistant and susceptible to the yellow rust fungus, and obtained a ratio of plants with different reactions to the disease which would currently be ascribed to the parents having different alleles at a single gene locus. Biffen amplified the work on disease resistance subsequently, and this and other studies gave him confidence that more rational methods, than hitherto, could be introduced into cereal breeding. Partly as a consequence, in 1910 Biffen introduced the successful wheat variety Little Joss to agriculture. No doubt influenced by this the Board of Agriculture decided to give financial support to Biffen, and in 1912 the Cambridge University Plant Breeding Institute was established and in due course this also became an institute of the Agricultural Research Service. Biffen's second important wheat variety Yeoman was launched in 1916 and the success of the Cambridge University Institute was such that in 1919 the National Institute of Agricultural Botany was set up to test, multiply and market its varieties. This Institute supplied, and still supplies, great service to agriculture but never became part of the Agricultural Research Service.

However, Biffen also played a part in the formation, in Cambridge in 1922, of the Horticultural Research Station which, in 1949, developed into the National Vegetable

Research Station which was established at Wellesborne. The numbered cultivars of brassicas and onions developed in Cambridge were transferred to Wellesbourne where vegetable breeding was continued and extended.

Biffen also influenced the establishment in 1927 of the Plant Virus Research Station, in Cambridge, to study potato viruses under the leadership of R. H. Salaman. In 1939 Salaman's potato breeding material was taken over by the Plant Breeding Institute.

The lineage of that part of plant breeding activity in the Agricultural Research Service that has taken place in the John Innes and Plant Breeding Institutes and at Wellesbourne originated with the work of Bateson and with his follower Biffen. The development of two other stations with major responsibilities for plant breeding lay outside the ambit of these two perceptive and powerful men. However, an equally influential figure, Sir George Stapledon, was the first Director of the Welsh Plant Breeding Station on its foundation in 1919. The stimulus to the creation of this Station was the need to improve grassland production, especially in those areas where much land had been ploughed up for arable crop production in the 1914–18 War. The need was for supplies of seed of certified stocks which would establish productive swards. The Station immediately worked to develop such stocks and to investigate related agronomic problems.

The foundation of the Scottish Plant Breeding Station arose from the need, identified by Scottish farmers and agricultural societies, for research in variety and seed production relevant to local conditions. Stimulus came from the Highland and Agricultural Society, the National Farmers' Union of Scotland, the Scottish Seed Trade Association, and the Scottish Chamber of Agriculture, and they found a ready response in the Board of Agriculture for Scotland. In part those who sought to establish the Scottish Station had probably been stimulated by the success of the Cambridge University Plant Breeding Institute and by the Swedish Seed Association Station at Svalöf. The Scottish Society for Research in Plant Breeding was registered in 1921 and the Station established to work at the improvement of plants and crops in Scotland and on the conditions affecting their production. First, Montague Drummond was the Director but after four years he was succeeded by William Robb.

Breeding and associated research on fruit in the ARS is undertaken at the Long Ashton Research Station which was founded in 1903, and at the East Malling Research Station founded in 1913. The improvement of varieties was among the initial objectives of Long Ashton and was started by B. T. P. Barker in 1909 and considerably expanded in 1916. Work on the selection of apple rootstocks was an early part of the programme at East Malling and this led to breeding for rootstock characteristics in association with the John Innes Institute.

In 1947, partly because of the disease problems facing hop growers the ARC together with the Hops Marketing Board and the Society of Brewers, assisted Wye College, University of London, to establish the Department of Hops Research. A major part of the remit of the Department is to breed new varieties of hops.

In 1953 the Glasshouse Crops Research Institute was established at Littlehampton, and the Scottish Horticultural Research Institute was founded by the Department of Agriculture and Fisheries at Invergowrie. Both institutes accepted responsibilities for plant breeding in their specialist sectors.

There are, therefore, nine institutes and the Department of Hops Research involved in plant breeding in the ARS.

## Process of Variety Production

Variety production is a technology which integrates knowledge from several scientific disciplines. It has the practical purpose of enabling farmers and growers to produce crops which are genetically adjusted to provide high yield, yield stability and agronomic and seasonal convenience. It also aims at a better match between the nature of the harvested produce and the purposes for which it will be used on the farm, by the housewife or by processors in the food and feedstuffs industries. In attempting to achieve such improvements the breeder must pay attention to many plant characters which may be changed positively or negatively in the breeding process. The changes affect morphology and physiology, response to temperature and day length, the time of sowing and harvesting, responses to diseases and pests, ease of harvesting, storage and transport, and the quality of the produce. Clearly the breeder cannot be equally successful in bringing every character in a selected genotype to its most useful expression. Consequently every variety is a compromise over the entire range of attributes and the creativity of the breeder lies in his decision as to where the compromise shall be drawn. It is the apparent subjectivity of this decision that leads some to describe plant breeding as an art. It is true that, although considerable rigour will have been applied to the measurement and selection for individual characters, there may be no means by which an objective determination can be made of the relative optimal expressions of the many characters of the plant that may be important to crop production. Judgement of the compromise in plant breeding only becomes possible when it is made by those with profound knowledge of the crop and of the system of agriculture in which a new variety is to be used.

If breeding is an art, the art is analogous to that of diagnosis in medicine, involving the application of science and technology to the provision of many kinds of evidence which must be put together to provide an understanding of plant genotypes and in predicting their usefulness.

In variety production, as in much technology, a logically ordered and rigorously applied decision sequence must precede the initiation of a programme. The course of this will often be as follows:-

*Define objectives* — in terms of the agricultural system in which the crop will be grown and the physical and biological factors of the environment as well as the nature of the outlet for the produce.

*Define the critical characters for selection* — in terms of those having overriding or high orders of significance.

*Determine the selection criteria* — in terms of the processes by which selection is to be practised for or against important attributes or their reciprocals.

*Assess the range of genetical variation available for incorporation in the breeding material* — possibly involving surveys of living collections or literature studies and gaining access to the collections of others.

*Decide on the form of genetic action most likely to lead to the attainment of the objective* — an important element in this decision will be the natural breeding system of the crop concerned, whether it is normally self-pollinated, cross-pollinated or vegetatively propagated. The decision will also be influenced by the generation time of the crop, and by the rate of multiplication of each generation.

The result of the decision on genetic action could be technically complex. Expressed briefly it could be to:

(i) hybridize and practise pedigree selection
(ii) inbreed and produce hybrid varieties from the inbred lines
(iii) produce synthetic varieties composed of predetermined mixture of different genotypes
(iv) practise mass selection
(v) follow one of a number of alternative methods of recurrent selection
(vi) induce gene mutation
(vii) induce polyploidy

(viii) induce rearrangements of chromosome structure

(ix) modify chromosomal make-up by aneuploid methods

(x) exploit haploidy

No elaboration of these available actions is necessary, but it is important to recognise that a diversity of procedures is available to the breeder, some of which may be used in combination.

In order to provide some notion of the numbers needed to follow an effective variety producing programme, and also to show a typical time scale, Figure 1 illustrates the current organisation of the winter wheat breeding programme at the Plant Breeding

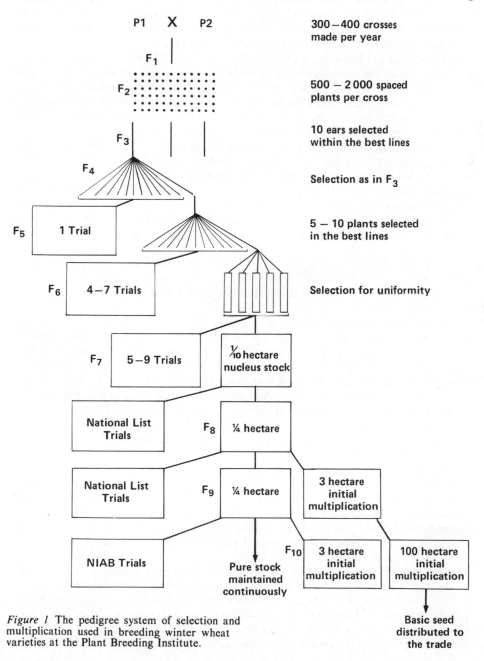

*Figure 1* The pedigree system of selection and multiplication used in breeding winter wheat varieties at the Plant Breeding Institute.

Institute. This is characteristic of the simplest procedures used, which can be applied to self-pollinating annual crops. It involves the hybridization of 300–400 pairs of parents (often established varieties) each year. As a consequence, in each year selection is practised amongst about half a million second generation ($F_2$) derivatives of the first generation hybrids grown in the previous year. Selection is continued until the seventh generation, at the earliest, when possibly a derivative of two or three of the half million or so $F_2$ plants will be submitted for the National List Trials of the Plant Variety Rights Office of the Ministry of Agriculture, Fisheries & Food. Ten years after the original hybridization was made, at the earliest, a resulting new variety may be distributed to the seed trade. Usually there will be less than 500 tonnes of wheat seed to be distributed by the National Seed Development Organisation Ltd. This might plant about 4000 ha and with a multiplication rate of about 40 it will still be another two years before seed becomes readily available to farmers.

A few lessons can be drawn from this example, the first being that the scale is large and, since many characters relating to plant physiology and pathology and to grain quality are being simultaneously investigated, the programme makes considerable demands on labour, land and glasshouse and laboratory resources. In addition there is a lead time exceeding 12 years between the decisions having been taken on the objectives of a programme and its products reaching the generality of farmers.

The lead time is affected by the generation time; annual in the case of wheat, biennial in sugar beet and between 5 and 10 years from seed to seed in apples. The rate of multiplication and the seed rate also affect the lead time. Even though wheat and oil seed rape are both annuals, and can be treated as self-pollinating, multiplication and seeding rates are very different, being about $\times 40$ and 130 kg ha$^{-1}$ in wheat, and about $\times 400$ and 6 kg ha$^{-1}$ for oil seed rape. Consequently when an elite genotype has been identified it can be supplied to farmers more speedily for oil seed rape than for wheat.

## Consequences of Plant Breeding for Crop Production

The consequences of the availability of new varieties on crop production are not readily separable from other changes such as modifications in cultivation and harvesting methods due to new machinery, the use of new agrochemicals in the control of pests, diseases, weeds, or crop growth, and particularly the application of larger quantities of fertilizer with greater precision. Indeed these agronomic changes may give rise to, or originate from, the provision of varieties better able to respond to new inputs. There is, therefore, a continuing interaction between varieties and cultivation practices.

In some crops comparison between old and new varieties is not possible because the variety is not a fixed entity. For example in sugar beet, which is an outpollinating species, prior to the use of hybrids, varieties were resynthesised each year and continuously improved by selection. Consequently comparison could not be made between varieties introduced at different times because those first introduced were no longer in their original state. The prolonged preservation of seed stocks has become available too recently for time comparisons to be possible. A further complication is that the environmental conditions to which an older variety was well adjusted may no longer prevail so that, at a later date, its original advantages may not be displayed.

Nevertheless comparisons of the relative yields of newer and older varieties are possible in some crops. For example the Potato Marketing Board records the mean yield in agriculture of varieties and Table 1 shows the data for King Edward introduced in 1902 and those for Pentland Crown and Maris Piper introduced respectively in 1958 and 1963. From 1965 until 1979 Pentland Crown and Pentland Dell, from the Scottish Plant Breeding Station, taken together have had mean yields 13 per cent greater than that of King Edward. In addition, over the period 1971 to 1979 Maris Piper from the

Plant Breeding Institute and Desiree (1962), taken together have had mean yields 5 per cent higher than King Edward. New varieties have contributed to the increase of yields from 21.6 t ha⁻¹ in 1959 to 30.2 t ha⁻¹ in 1979, and so to the reduction of the area in potatoes from 291 000 ha in 1959 to 203 000 ha in 1979.

Table 1

Total maincrop yield of potato varieties (t ha$^{-1}$) for England and Wales
(Potato Marketing Board)

|  | King Edward and Red King | Pentland Crown | Maris Piper |
|---|---|---|---|
| 1977 | 28.9 | 28.7 | 28.0 |
| 1978 | 31.3 | 35.1 | 34.4 |
| 1979 | 32.0 | 35.5 | 35.3 |

King Edward was introduced in 1902, Pentland Crown in 1958 and Maris Piper in 1963.

Wheat yields have increased from 2.6 t ha⁻¹ in 1948 to 5.26 t ha⁻¹ in 1978 at an average rate of increase of 0.088 t ha⁻¹ yr⁻¹. Using data on the proportion of the crop made up of each variety and their relative yields and comparing this with the rolling five year average for wheat yields, Mrs. Valerie Silvey of the National Institute of Agricultural Botany has calculated the extent to which increased yield has been due to variety or to other factors (Figure 2). This analysis indicated that wheat yields had

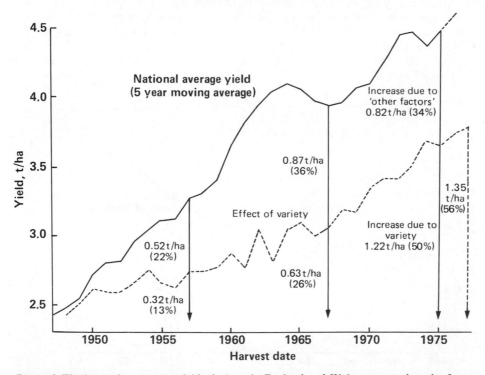

*Figure 2* The increasing average yield of wheat in England and Wales expressed as the 5-year moving average (t ha$^{-1}$) and the estimated effect of variety on the increase (after Mrs Valerie Silvey, National Institute of Agricultural Botany).

Table 2

Comparisons of varieties of wheat of different ages in a trial at the
Plant Breeding Institute in 1977/78

| Variety (Year of introduction) | Grain yield (t ha$^{-1}$) | Height (cm) | Harvest index % |
|---|---|---|---|
| Little Joss (1908) | 6.2 | 142 | 36 |
| Holdfast (1935) | 5.9 | 126 | 36 |
| Maris Huntsman (1972) | 7.8 | 106 | 46 |
| Norman (1980) | 9.0 | 84 | 51 |

increased by 2.04 t ha$^{-1}$ over the period 1947 to 1975, and of this about 60% was due
to varieties. Analagous estimates for the same period suggest that about 0.70 t ha$^{-1}$
(45%) of the 1.47 t ha$^{-1}$ increase in mean barley yield was due to variety.

More recently, due to the availability of broad spectrum fungicides, old and new
varieties of wheat can be compared directly in trials. The fungicides control races of
pathogens which are currently prevalent but which were unimportant when the older
varieties were first introduced. In addition the disadvantages due to the weaker straw
of the older varieties can be obviated by supporting them with coarse netting to prevent
lodging. Under these conditions of trial, and irrespective of the level of nitrogen
fertilizer, the modern varieties yield 40–50% more than their pre-war predecessors
(Table 2). This yield difference discounts the effect which the stronger and shorter
straw of the modern varieties has on resistance to lodging, and the addition in yield
consequential upon greater tolerance of high nitrogen applications. Table 2 shows that
the advance in yield has been achieved principally by increasing the harvest index
(percentage of the total aerial crop product that is harvested as grain). The extra grain
may come from increased numbers of ears per unit area or from increased grain weight.

Whether determined by experimental comparison or by inference from increasing
national yields and the relative yields of replacement compared with old varieties, it

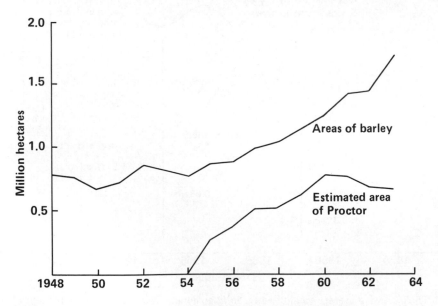

*Figure 3* The area occupied by barley nationally and the association between the
increase in area and the availability of the variety Proctor.

appears that more than half of the increase in wheat yields since the 1939–45 war can be ascribed to breeding. Similar conclusion may be drawn about barley, and the increase in potato yield due to variety has also been considerable, but is not quantified. If half of the increase of yield of wheat between 1948 and 1978 is ascribed to variety, then breeding increased the return per hectare by about £100 at 1980 prices. However, the results of breeding on agriculture are not solely expressed in terms of yield since consequential effects on overall production may also arise from changes that are induced in the crop area. Thus the decline in the area of potatoes, which had reached its maximum during the war, has taken place steadily since 1948, but the demand has been satisfied from the smaller area partly as a consequence of the better yields provided by new varieties.

The effects of improved barley varieties have been in marked contrast to those for potatoes. When the high yielding spring variety Proctor was provided from the Plant Breeding Institute in 1953 the area in barley was 898 000 ha, by 1966 it was 2 411 000 ha, and in 1979 it was still 2 347 000. The availability of Proctor and Rika which, in addition to their yield advantage and stiffer straw, had resistance to *Rhynchosporium*, contributed to the spread of barley, as a substitute for the declining oat crop, into areas where pH had been raised by liming (Figure 3). In 1956 the area in barley exceeded that in oats for the first time since 1879, and by 1966 it occupied more than half the tillage. Never previously had one crop so dominated British agriculture.

## Scientific Basis of Plant Breeding

### Genetics

Use is made of knowledge drawn from a number of scientific disciplines in plant breeding, and this knowledge must be integrated in defining attainable varietal objectives, and in determining the breeding methods to follow in any programme. Genetics is foremost among the sciences used in plant breeding, and the building of the complex structure of knowledge now available was commenced in the early years of the Twentieth Century in Britain by Bateson and his collaborators. While still at Cambridge they discovered the complementary action of genes and proposed the terms "epistatic" and "hypostatic" to describe the relationships in expression of non-allelic genes. Bateson and his colleagues also discovered linkage between genes ("coupling" and "repulsion" as they called it), while Doncaster and Raynor, working in the same group, described sex linked inheritance, and Bateson also took part in the interpretation of this phenomenon. Of importance to breeders was the demonstration by T. H. Morgan and others in the USA that "crossing over" in hybrids could produce new linkage arrangements in their progeny. From this arose the notion of genetic maps.

Thus when Bateson went to the John Innes Institute in 1910 he had already contributed considerably to the development of genetics beyond the base established by Mendel. Plant genetics continued to be elaborated at John Innes, and under Biffen at the Cambridge University Plant Breeding Institute.

It was much influenced by the concept of the "pure line" proposed by W. Johannsen to describe lineages produced by repeated self-fertilization. This led to the recognition of the distinction between the "genotype" (hereditary constitution) of an individual, and the "phenotype" (the appearance arising from the interaction of the genotype and the environment). These are ideas which have been of profound importance to geneticists and breeders ever since their introduction in 1903.

The development of an understanding of quantitatively inherited characters was of crucial significance to breeders since many differences of commercial importance, such as yield or height are not inherited in the discrete manner of the discontinuous features used to illustrate Mendel's Laws. As early as 1902 Bateson and Saunders suggested that characters which show a continuous range of variation might be determined by a number of Mendelian factors. Experimental work by E. M. East, H. Nillson-Ehle and R. A. Emerson confirmed that quantitative inheritance was explicable on the basis that several independent pairs of alleles, each of relatively small effect, were responsible for determining expression of the character. The extension of this work continues to provide a framework for breeding for characters displaying continuous variation. The most detailed analysis has been provided by K. Mather first at the John Innes Institute and subsequently with J. Jinks and others at the ARC Unit of Biometrical Genetics at the University of Birmingham. The contribution to the variance in selfed and back-crossed progenies could be assigned to dominance, interaction between allelic or non-allelic genes, additive effects, linkage and the environment. An analytical procedure using diallel crossing systems, in which every parent of a set is crossed reciprocally with every other parent, has been of especial value in studying quantitative variation; enabling the breeder to estimate the likelihood of progress under selection from the progeny of particular hybrids. The Mendelian factors each of small effect operating in such systems are called "polygenes", and a useful outcome of biometrical genetical analysis is the assessment of the number of effective factors segregating. This permits the complexity of the task facing the breeder in dealing with a quantitative character to be estimated.

Until the emergence of work on the molecular biology of DNA, work on the nature of the genetic determinants — the genes — was undertaken by the study of mutation (i.e. genetic change) or by the study of gene action. Induced mutation by X-irradiation was demonstrated almost simultaneously in the USA by H. J. Muller in *Drosophila* and by L. J. Stadler in maize. Maize was subsequently used as a convenient experimental organism by many workers and mutation was used to investigate many other systems. For example, at the John Innes Institute the self-incompatibility system of *Oenothera* was studied using mutagen treated pollen and this led to the use of mutant pollen to produce self-compatible cherries. Indeed mutation has subsequently become another tool in plant breeding.

The understanding of gene action is now comprehensive deriving particularly from the study of biochemical mutants in fungi and bacteria. The plant breeder works within this immense panorama of biochemical genetics, but it is worthy of recall that among the earliest work in biochemical genetics was that explaining the sequence of synthesis of flower pigments, commencing in the 1930s by Rose Scott-Moncrieff and W. J. C. Lawrence at the John Innes Horticultural Institute.

## Chromosome cytology

In 1903 W. S. Sutton expounded the first clear formulation of the chromosome theory of Mendelian heredity. It was confirmed and elaborated in the United States by T. H. Morgan and particularly by C. B. Bridges. An important centre for chromosome research in Britain was the John Innes Institute where C. D. Darlington worked from the late 1920s. The theory that, in chromosomes paired at meiosis, chromatids from different chromosomes broke and joined had been initially proposed by F. A. Janssens in 1909. The view was supported by J. Belling and comprehensively proven on the basis of cytological evidence by Darlington as part of his detailed description of meiosis. This and other work led to the publication in 1932 of a remarkable synthesis by Darlington of the evidence from chromosome cytology in "Recent Advances in Cytology" (London, J. & A. Churchill).

For the plant breeder the value of chromosome cytology lies in the understanding that it provides of the physical basis of inheritance. It comprehends linkage, the relationship between crossing over and chiasma formation and also chromosome structural change, including many kinds of interchange, inversion, duplication and deletion of the genetic material, all of which may interfere with, or provide benefit to, a breeding programme. All of these changes occur when the chromosome number of an individual is the same as that expected of its species. Also important to breeders are instances, in individuals or lines, where the chromosome number is changed to a multiple of the original either in polyploids (where there is an increase) or in haploids (where a sporophyte has the gametophytic number). Individuals and lines may also be deficient for particular chromosomes or have them in excess — such plants are called aneuploids and the new number may be stabilised in the formation of a new lines or species. Alternatively their occurrence may be sporadic within a crop species and valuable for genetic analysis, or a nuisance which creates genetic instability.

## Physiology

The notion that breeding for efficiency in crop production required attention to be given to the efficiency of physiological processes was strongly advocated in the mid-1920s by R. H. Biffen and F. L. Engledow as a result of their early wheat breeding experiences at the Cambridge University Breeding Institute. They pointed out that grain yield in wheat is a complex character among whose components are the number of ears per unit area of land, the size of the ears, and the size of the grain. The application of these ideas was limited by the capacity of the plant physiology of the time. Nevertheless the concept was clearly appropriate, and it has since been considerably elaborated.

In the 1980s the breeder seeks assistance from the plant physiologist about the physiological criteria to be used in selecting for higher and more stable yield. The criteria so far employed have mostly had a morphological basis. Thus the higher yield of modern wheat varieties has been achieved not by increasing photosynthesis efficiency, nor by increasing the production of aerial dry matter by the crop, but by increasing the proportion of the photosynthate that is deposited in the grain. There has also been selection for so called "tiller economy" in wheat — that is for varieties with fewer tillers a greater proportion of which carry ears, so that water and energy loss from the growth of non-productive tillers is diminished.

The better appreciation of the subtleties of plant physiology now permits selection in grasses, for example, for improved water use efficiency and for low levels of dark respiration, with consequential yield increase. Plant breeding is beginning to make use of information from functional as opposed to morphological physiology, but much further progress is necessary in this direction. We are faced with the "Evans' paradox" in crop photosynthesis. Lloyd Evans of Canberra has shown that, in many instances, although yield is higher in advanced varieties or crop species and the leaves larger or more numerous, often the rate of photosynthesis per unit area of leaf is less than in more primitive forms. An important task facing photosynthesis research is to explain to the breeder how this correlated response to selection for increased leaf area can be overcome.

## Pathology

Under the heading of pathology reference will be made to the infection of crops by fungi, bacterial and viral pathogens, and infestation by pests of all kinds. Clearly the cheapest way of protecting crops from disease and pests is by the use of inherited resistance. Biffen described the reality of such inherited resistance as early as 1905. Much research on the exploitation of genetic resistance has been concerned with the description of the genotype × genotype interactions involved in the occurrence of infection or infestation on the one hand and resistance or immunity on the other. J.

Eriksson showed in 1894 that the stem rusts of grasses and cereals exist in a number of genetic forms each restricted to a particular host species. From 1917 onwards E. C. Stakmann showed that "physiologic races" of the pathogen existed which were differentiated from each other in terms of the ranges of host varieties that they could infect. Subsequently this led to the construction of sets of differential varieties by which physiologic races can be recognised.

The relationship between physiologic races and hosts was conclusively demonstrated by H. H. Flor of North Dakota in the mid-1950s to be due to complementary gene-for-gene relationships in host and pathogen. Allelic variation for resistance/susceptibility at a single locus in the host is matched by complementary allelic variation for virulence/avirulence in the pathogen. Often the only interaction giving resistance occurs when a host with the resistance allele is confronted by the pathogen genotype without the virulence allele.

Breeders have learned by severe experience that major gene resistance of this kind is rarely of prolonged value in the provision of resistance to air-borne fungi. Heavy selection pressure is placed on the pathogen which will result in the multiplication in the population of virulent forms capable of infecting the hitherto resistant host. A major contribution to this field was provided by the comprehensive understanding of the resistance of potatoes to the physiologic races of late blight developed by W. Black at the Scottish Plant Breeding Station where the limitations to reliance in varieties on major gene resistance was quickly learnt.

By contrast major gene resistance to virus infection often appears to be stable and durable, as is that to some forms of soil-borne fungi, like eyespot of wheat, and to soil-borne pests like the cyst nematodes of potato or barley. However, major gene resistance to some insects in varieties has selected out virulent biotypes, as in the greenbug biotypes infesting wheat in the Great Plains of the USA, or the brown planthopper biotypes infesting rice in South East Asia.

Where major gene resistance has provided inadequate or impermanent protection, breeders have sought to use other forms of resistance. This has been described as field resistance which, while not affording the total protection of some major genes, nevertheless markedly reduces yield losses while placing little selection pressure on the pathogen in favour of greater virulence or aggressiveness. Such resistance is often assumed to be polygenic but there is generally no rigorous evidence in support of this. There are also attempts to exploit "durable" resistance which, irrespective of its genetic basis, is recognised on the basis of its efficacy when in wide scale use in varieties in agriculture over a long period.

## Application of Science to Plant Breeding

### Morphology

There have been striking changes in the morphology of crops as breeders have sought to adjust them to match new or modified environmental requirements. Table 2 shows that the wheat variety Norman introduced in 1980 has a height of just over 80 cm, while that of Little Joss (1910) is more than 140 cm. Huntsman (1972) at just over 100 cm was the culmination of selection for height reducing polygenes. The shorter wheat varieties — like Norman — now carry one or other of the major height reducing genes $Rht_1$ or $Rht_2$ introduced from the Japanese variety Norin 10, whose effect is caused by interference with gibberellic acid metabolism. Genetic tolerance of high levels of nitrogen fertilizer application has been incorporated in this way in British wheat varieties without creating any disadvantage, relative to other varieties, when lower amounts of nitrogen are used. Plate 2 shows changes in the height of wheat varieties produced at the Plant Breeding Institute.

*Plate 2* Wheat varieties produced at the Plant Breeding Institute, Cambridge; from left to right – Little Joss (1910), Yeoman (1916), Holdfast (1935), Maris Widgeon (1964), Maris Huntsman (1972), Maris Hobbit (1977), Avalon (1979) and Norman (1980).

The use of *Rht* genes in Britain derived from the earlier demonstration of their effectiveness first in Washington State by Orville Vogel and subsequently in Mexico by Norman Borlaug. Their work on wheat had paralleled that on rice by T. T. Chang and P. R. Jennings, at the International Rice Research Institute, which resulted in the production of the IR8 variety and its successors, following the incorporation in the breeding material of a major gene for dwarfing from Dee Geo Woo Gen. Selection was then practised for short plants with stiff erect leaves that would allow light penetration into the canopy, and the easy run off of rain, in the monsoon season. Varieties like IR8 have profoundly affected crop production in South East Asia.

Another fundamental restructuring of the crop is currently being carried out with peas. Major gene mutants are being used which have no leaves, or in some cases have neither leaves nor stipules. Adequate photosynthesis for normal levels of seed yield is provided by the stems, tendrils and pods. Plants of the crops are held together by their tendrils and, because of the absence of the weight of the leaves, lodging is infrequent. Consequently ripening is early, seed blemishing is diminished and combined harvesting is possible. This new plant model seems likely to have a considerable impact on the agronomy and mechanisation of the pea crop (Plate 3).

Morphological change in the sugar beet crop has had a dramatic effect on its mechanisation. Sugar beet flowers and fruit normally occur submerged together in clusters. Consequently, with old-fashioned untreated seed, at each point in the field, where a cluster was placed at drilling, several seedlings could emerge. These had to be reduced, by hoeing, to one adequately spaced from its neighbours. Seed could be rubbed and graded and so separated from the cluster, but uniformity adequate for the crop to be planted "to a stand" by precision drilling, without need of singling, was not attainable until the major gene character of monogermy was bred into the crop.

In monogerm sugar beet the flowers are single so that each isolated fruit contains only one seed. Such fruits are pelleted to a standard size to facilitate precision drilling. Most of the British sugar beet crop is now monogerm with considerable benefits to speed of drilling and reduction in labour costs. Calculations from the Netherlands show that the introduction of monogerm seed, with the use of associated herbicides and full mechanisation, has reduced the 290 man hours formerly needed for each hectare to 13 man hours. In addition, whereas immediately after the 1939/45 war 23 kg of sugar were produced per man hour, with full mechanisation it is now 550 kg per man hour.

## Induced mutation

In 1976 A. Micke of the International Atomic Energy Authority claimed that 197 varieties had been developed from induced mutation on a world-wide scale, and of

*Plate 3* A mutant form of pea lacking leaves, in which photosynthesis is carried out in the tendrils, stems and pods. The crop is not prostrate like those with leaves. Varieties incorporating this mutation are produced from a research programme at the John Innes Institute.

these a third were in ornamental crops. This is not an outstanding record for a method to which much breeding research has been applied internationally. Mutation breeding has been employed rarely in Britain and no reference would have been made to it here were it not that an important spring barley variety, Golden Promise, was produced by ionising radiation by Miln Masters Ltd. Golden Promise is a short-stemmed variety in which mutation to the recessive condition has occurred at one of the numerous *erectoides* loci known in barley which affect the length of stem internodes. The mutant allelle present in Golden Promise has been incorporated in several other barley varieties of which it was a parent. However, it is not possible to assess the extent to which the value of Golden Promise can be attributed to its *erectoides* allele or to other beneficial attributes, unrelated to induced mutation, prominent among which are its earliness, malting quality and wind resistance.

## Hybrid varieties

Maize was the first crop in which hybrid varieties were used and it is still the most important in world terms. The inventor of hybrid maize was G. M. Shull in the USA who, in 1914, described as "heterosis" the unusual vigour and high yield of the $F_1$ hybrids resulting from the crossing of two inbred lines. Typically commercial maize hybrids are 30 per cent more productive than their inbred parents. The precise practical method of exploiting hybrid vigour was devised by Donald East of Connecticut, who suggested that commercial quantities of hybrid seed could be made available at realistic prices if the final hybrid were to be a double cross produced by intercrossing two unrelated single cross hybrids which had themselves originated by the crossing of inbred lines. Thus the grandparents of a double cross hybrid are four unrelated inbred lines. More recently, in the United States, inbred lines of improved vigour have become available, and it was estimated for 1977 that 80–90% of the hybrid maize grown consisted of single crosses or some modified form of single cross.

Trials of maize hybrids representative of those used in each of the decades from the 1930s to the 1970s show that about half of the yield gain in the Corn Belt over the 40 year period is attributable to genetic advance. This is similar to the benefit from wheat breeding in the UK discussed earlier. Of course, the yield advance in maize has depended on the use of successively improved inbred lines, and the addition to the yield of these of an increment for heterosis. Moreover, it may be held that in addition to heterosis, importance should be attached to the opportunities, offered by the hybrid maize system, of comparing stable and reproducible genotypes. These contrast with the genetically heterogeneous and shifting populations which preceded hybrids in this out-pollinating crop. Maize hybrids could be compared and tested over years and sites just like candidate pure-line wheat varieties. Therefore, genetic advance by selection among potential varieties became possible in maize, just as in wheat, once the hybrid system had become established.

Another trick introduced into the production of hybrid maize seed in the United States was the use of cytoplasmically determined male sterility. This had the effect that in a seed production field, where two parents were grown together, all the seed in the parent with male-sterility resulted from its having been pollinated by the other parent which carried a nuclear gene restoring fertility in the resulting hybrids. Thus hybridity was forced. Male sterility derived from the use of the so-called Texas (T) cytoplasm and is now known to be caused by mutation in the mitochondrial genome. In 1970 a race of the Southern Corn Leaf Blight fungus, which was virulent only on hybrid maize having the T cytoplasm, became widespread in the eastern United States. It had devastating consequences, with the result that hybrids made using the T cytoplasm can now only be grown in the western, drier, end of the Corn Belt, where the disease is unimportant.

By analogy with maize, hybrid varieties are now common in kale, Brussels sprouts, cabbage, onions, sugar beet and other crops. Hybridity is forced in sugar beet using cytoplasmic male sterility in a way similar to maize. However, in kale a method was developed at the Plant Breeding Institute which depended upon the use of the range of alleles at the locus determining sporophytic self-incompatibility. In species such as *Brassica oleracea*, in which kale, cabbage, Brussels sprouts and several other brassica crops are all placed, the self-incompatibility of the gametophyte — pollen grain or embryo sac — is determined by the genotype of the parental plant on which it is produced. As a result a pollen grain will not germinate on the stigma of a plant having either of the two self-incompatibility alleles present in the plant from which it derived. The production of the hybrid kale variety Maris Kestrel, therefore, required the production by bud pollination, which evades the self-incompatibility barrier, of six inbred lines each homozygous for a different self-incompatibility allele. Hybridity was forced throughout the seed production procedure by making, first, two single crosses then by crossing each of the two single cross hybrids by one or other of the two different inbred lines not yet used. Two unrelated three-way cross hybrids were thus obtained and these were crossed together to produce the triple cross hybrid commercial seed. In 1975, the year in which the Institute received a Queen's Award for its work on hybrid kales, it was estimated that Maris Kestrel added about £1M/year to the value of the UK kale crop.

The methods devised for the use of self-incompatibility in making hybrid kale have subsequently been employed in Brussels sprouts, cabbage and other diploid brassicas.

In the 1960s and 1970s much research effort was devoted in many parts of the developed world to attempts to devise methods for use in the production of hybrid wheat and barley varieties. In wheat they centred around the use of cytoplasmic male sterility and nuclear restorer genotypes, while in barley it was anticipated that use might be made of male sterility determined by recessive nuclear alleles. The interest in these systems is rapidly fading, principally because of the achievements of conventional breeding. The extension of the use of hybrid varieties into new crops, and even its more effective development in those in which it is already employed, awaits the recognition of a cheap, easily used gametocide which will make pollen grains inviable without affecting the capacity of the treated crop to produce seed. As yet no suitable chemical has been discovered, but the best clues may lie in the biochemical description of the causes of inherited male sterility.

## Polyploidy

Manipulation of entire sets of chromosomes in breeding may be of three kinds: (a) reduction from the diploid (2n) number to the haploid or gametophytic number (n) but to have that number present in a sporophyte; (b) increase from the diploid number to a higher multiple such as triploid (3n) or tetraploid (4n) and so on; (c) the combination in a new natural or synthetic species of the full complements of chromosomes of two distinct parental species.

Tetraploid forms of perennial, Italian and Westerwolds ryegrasses have been synthesised using the drug colchicine which inhibits spindle formation and so permits chromosome division without cell division. Tetraploid varieties have been produced and are in wide-scale agricultural use. Forage yields are generally higher than in the corresponding diploid forms when expressed as fresh weight but dry matter yields are comparable. The seeds of tetraploids are about 70% heavier than those of the diploids, but seed yield is lower when expressed as the number of seeds per unit area. Polyploid ryegrasses appear to offer some advantage over diploids, in part perhaps because of the preferred intake by stock.

Most European sugar beet varieties are triploid hybrids the seed having been produced from the pollination of monogerm, male-sterile diploids by multigerm, male-fertile synthetic tetraploids. The seed harvested and sold commercially is that from the diploid parent and it is consequently monogerm and triploid. This enables the greater root yield of the polyploid to be exploited in crop production and the double dose of genes from the tetraploid pollen parent covers the effects of any deleterious genes linked to those determining monogermy or associated with the source of male sterility. In the sugar beet crop of Britain, knowledge of polyploidy, its induction and manipulation has had a powerful commercial effect.

## Haploidy

There are two purposes for which haploids can be useful in plant breeding. The first is to accelerate breeding programmes by enabling homozygosity to be approached more speedily in the production of inbred lines. This applies to maize, in which hybrid varieties are cultivated commercially, or to crops in which pure line varieties are cultivated where haploidy permits the fixation of homozygous second generation ($F_2$) segregants from hybrids between varieties.

The second use is to simplify segregation and genetic analysis in tetraploid crops, such as potatoes, when the normal crop is autotetraploid. The haploids are therefore more properly called "dihaploids" since they have the diploid number of chromosomes, which is also the gametophytic number in *Solanum tuberosum*.

In maize and potatoes haploids are isolated by genetic selection which uses a pollinator genotype with a dominant marker which is displayed in hybrid seeds or seedlings. Absence of the marker displays a seed or seedling which was produced without fertilization and which may, therefore, be a haploid sporophyte. In barley use is made of the phenomenon of the elimination, in the first few cell divisions in the embryo, of the chromosomes of *Hordeum bulbosum* when this wild barley is used to pollinate the crop species *Hordeum vulgare*. As a result only the haploid set of chromosomes of *H. vulgare* remains in the seedling. The barley system seems to be that which is most likely to be used for the accelerated production of varieties in the immediate future. *H. bulbosum* is being used to pollinate intervarietal $F_1$ hybrids from which the first products of recombination and segregation are fixed.

A more general method for the isolation of haploids is by the culture, in artificial media, of isolated anthers. The pollen grains in such anthers may grow into haploid sporophytes which can subsequently be transferred to soil and used for breeding purposes. Although some species are more amenable to this treatment than others there is no reason in principle why it should not be applied to any species.

However, it may be recognised that, irrespective of the method used to isolate haploids, the rate of production is slow and they are unlikely ever to be available in large numbers. This must be set alongside the scale-dependence of much variety production research. Haploid breeding methods are, therefore, only likely to find a use in certain special fields of high economic or scientific importance.

## Alien genetic variation

In some breeding programmes desirable genetic variation for particular characters may not be available within the crop species concerned, but it may be present in related species. Where meiosis is normal in interspecies hybrids there is no obstacle to the introgression of genes into the crop, but difficulties arise when the chromosomes of the parental species do not pair and recombine. A sequence of methods has been developed to resolve these difficulties. The methods employ further and further limitations on the amount of alien genetic material that is transferred from one species to another in order to introduce the useful information that is sought.

The sequence starts with the combination, in a synthetic allopolyploid or amphiploid, of the complete sets of chromosomes of two distinct species. Triticale is a 42-chromosome amphiploid which combines the 28 chromosomes of macaroni wheat (*Triticum turgidum*) and the 14 chromosomes of rye (*Secale cereale*). The advantage of triticale over its parents is principally that the high spikelet number of rye is combined with the greater number of fertile flowers and the greater grain size of *T. turgidum*. Other benefits may include the complementary types of disease resistance derived from the two parents. Although triticale varieties have been released in Canada, Hungary and Mexico, there are difficulties with chromosome stability, endosperm development, grain sprouting and yield which make it, as yet, unsuitable for release as a grain crop in Western Europe.

Hybrid ryegrass is already in agricultural use, for example, in the form of the variety Augusta from the Welsh Plant Breeding Station. It is a tetraploid combining the full chromosome complements of perennial and Italian ryegrass. It has the rapid early growth and high nutritive value of Italian ryegrass and the persistency of perennial ryegrass. It also has greater genetic stability than is found in interspecies hybrids and their derivatives at the diploid level.

The next stage after the transference of entire sets of chromosomes is the inclusion of a single alien chromosome pair in a crop species. In these circumstances an alien chromosome pair may be additional to the full complement of chromosomes of the recipient species or it may substitute for a genetically related pair of chromosomes of the recipient. Such genotypes are called respectively alien chromosome addition and substitution lines. Wheat varieties such as Orlando, Zorba and Clement have a pair of IR chromosomes of rye, determining rust resistance, replacing the IB pair of wheat.

A refinement on this process is the incorporation of a segment of an alien chromosome, determining a useful character, into a chromosome of the recipient species. E. R. Sears of Missouri showed how this could be accomplished through the induction by X-irradiation of an interchange of segments between an alien chromosome and one of the chromosomes of a recipient wheat variety. He used a selection procedure that allowed the appropriately modified plants to be detected. The advantage of this procedure is that irrelevant and perhaps deleterious genetic information carried on the donor chromosome is largely eliminated.

In a further development, that applied specifically to wheat, research at the Plant Breeding Institute showed that the absence of recombination between wheat chromosomes and those of other species is determined genetically. Interference in this genetic determination creates conditions in which recombination occurs so that alien genes can be incorporated in wheat chromosomes by meiotic recombination. This was demonstrated by the transference of stripe rust resistance from the goat grass *Aegilops comosa* to bread wheat.

In the future the transfer of foreign genetic information into crop plants may be accomplished by protoplast fusion or by recombinant DNA technology. These techniques will be referred to later.


## Compound plants

Considerable effort has been made over the years in institutes of the ARS on the breeding of fruit crops, particularly in top fruit species. This has resulted in the development of unique technologies in which different parts of the plant may be derived from separate breeding programmes. This work arose from the study of the interaction between rootstock and scion in apples initiated by R. Wellington at the Wye College

Fruit Experiment Station which was the nucleus from which East Malling grew. The study of the compound tree, and of rootstock research, led to collaboration between East Malling and the John Innes Institute in breeding rootstocks for resistance to woolly aphis. Rootstock breeding subsequently extended to the consideration of other characters such as ease of multiplication, firmness of anchorage, induction of precocity in the scion and, perhaps most importantly, the selection of dwarfing rootstocks in apples, pears, plums and cherries. Such apple rootstocks accelerate the breeding of scion varieties by reducing the juvenile (pre-fruiting) period of seedlings worked on them.

The separate but interactive breeding of stock and scion gives the opportunity for distinct arrays of plant characters to be selected independently and provides for a greatly extended range of phenotypic diversity. Despite the slow turnover of generations breeders of other crops will often envy the opportunities available to top fruit breeders to consider distinct arrays of characters in isolation.

## Disease control

Reference has been made earlier to the limitations of attempting to protect crops against air-borne fungal diseases by the use of major gene resistance. Heavy selection pressure is placed on the pathogen population to evolve to a condition where there is a high frequency of the allele giving virulence against the resistance gene present. The pressure of selection is heavier when the resistance gene is present over large areas and in uniform stands of the crop.

There are major agronomic advantages in the uniformity of crops and in fields being sown to genetically homogeneous varieties. However, increased disease susceptibility may militate against this advantage and increasingly consideration is being given to means by which heterogeneity for disease resistance may be exploited. Two systems have been used. In the first, several genetically distinct forms of resistance to a disease are isolated, and then by a sequence of backcrosses each is introduced into the same varietal background which is already superior in most characteristics except disease resistance. After five to ten generations of backcrossing a series of lines will have been produced that are genetically very similar but each will carry a different form of resistance to the disease. The product is called a "multiline" variety and the lines may be assembled for cultivation in accordance with the forms of resistance that are necessary to provide the most effective protection against the currently prevalent virulence structure of the pathogen population.

The notion of the multiline variety is that the genetic heterogeneity of the crop delays the spread and reduces the severity of disease epidemics so limiting yield losses. Multilines also reduce the selection pressure placed on the pathogen. There is clear evidence of the efficacy of the system, indeed the oat crop of Iowa in the 1970s was largely in multiline varieties. However, there is also a sluggishness in the multiline system. First the construction of a multiline variety is slow and laborious and, by the time it is accomplished, the yielding ability of the base variety used may well have been superseded by subsequent advances due to conventional breeding. Second, the genetic make-up of the pathogen population may well change much more rapidly than is possible for readjustment of the line composition of the multiline variety, since several years of seed multiplication must precede the release of a newly mixed supply of seed. For these reasons it seems necessary to conclude that the use of multiline varieties is unlikely to be widespread.

As an alternative it has been proposed that mixtures of existing varieties, with different forms of disease resistance, should be cultivated as heterogeneous crops. This solution has been proposed for spring barley in Britain where the only form of effective resistance to powdery mildew is of the major gene type. The spread of, and the damage due to, powdery mildew has been shown to be reduced in mixtures. Consequently some of the benefits of multiline varieties are provided in the form of genetic heterogeneity with the additional benefit of quick response to the state of the pathogen population since, if the varieties to be mixed are in any case in commercial production, seed is readily available for mixing. The disadvantages may be in the incompatibility of the components of mixtures in agronomic, or quality terms, or in such simple matters as differences in the time to maturity and harvest of components. Nevertheless farmers should understand the hazards of crop uniformity and the potential benefits from heterogeneity. Then each can make his own genetic decision either to use a few uniform varieties, to diversify using different forms of disease resistance in different fields, or to put together within fields a range of resistances by growing variety mixtures.

## Quality of the produce

Breeders have for long been concerned to develop varieties that satisfied the needs of the ultimate consumer, either the on-farm user, the housewife or caterer, or the industrial processor. Often using empirical methods, considerable benefits have been provided, for example in the form of potatoes suitable for boiling or frying, barley that was efficient and economical in malting, or hops with appropriate alpha acid.

The involvement of the breeder in adjusting crop quality was changed in principle by the discovery, at Purdue University in 1965, that allelic variation at major gene loci in maize could lead to striking differences in the proportion of lysine in the storage protein of the grain. Consequently, since lysine is the first limiting essential amino acid in cereal diets for some monogastrics, it was possible to set nutritional goals for maize breeding. Equally important was the recognition from work in Saskatchewan that allelic variation at two gene loci in oilseed rape (*Brassica napus*) could lead to the presence in the seed of either negligible quantities of erucic acid or to its comprising more than 40 per cent of the total fatty acid content. Consequently varieties of oilseed rape could be developed giving oil with very different nutritional and processing qualities.

These developments were made possible by the availability of apparatus giving precise and rapid chemical analyses on a scale necessary for large scale screening in genetical and breeding programmes. Increasingly, where a quality objective can be defined in chemical terms and where there is simple inheritance, it will be possible for plant breeding to provide varieties giving produce close to the customer's requirements.

Thus in the late 1970s and in 1980 investigations of the storage proteins of wheat promise to provide evidence as to the components associated with the physical properties of gas retention in dough in bread making. If this is successful the previously used empirical methods of selection will be replaced by chemical assessment. Such a new method will only be of value, however, if it can be used on a large scale to screen the numerous progenies which breeders must handle to maximise the probability of successful selection.

## Future of Plant Breeding

Genetic amelioration has been a potent contributor to improvement of quantity and quality in crop production. This must continue and the demands on plant breeders will be, as always, to sustain the level of productivity already attained by countering new, or newly significant, limitations on production. In addition, genetic increments to crop produce will still be expected. However, in the 1980s we may be at a point of change in agriculture where agrochemicals will be employed with greater discrimination and precision than previously, partly out of consideration for environmental protection but also because of the high energy and economic costs. It seems likely that such changes will bring genetical crop protection into greater prominence. Increasingly crop protection will depend on the combination of good cultural practice, carefully tailored agrochemicals applied with discrimination and by genetic resistance. The resistance will often be incomplete but set at a level that complements other forms of protection.

Descriptions have been given earlier of the kinds of genetic resistance used by breeders and of strategies for their deployment. Clearly, however, sources of resistance are finite and every effort must be made to ensure that sources of resistance are not rendered ineffective by their careless deployment in varieties. Resistance can also be lost by the erosion of genetic variation in primitive crop forms, or in the wild relatives of contemporary crops. As a counter to this a campaign is necessary to conserve germplasm. Seed banks are being constructed so that the genetic resources, upon which the future of agriculture depends, are not wantonly lost or wasted.

Some of the disease and pest resistance used by plant breeders in the future will have come not from within the crop species, but from an alien source. Reference has been made earlier to the means, some of considerable refinement, already available for the transfer of useful alien genetic variation to crop species. The 1980s will see considerable growth in this research as knowledge from plant cell and molecular biology is brought to bear on practical problems. New opportunities will be presented to plant breeding technology.

These opportunities will arise because of scientific developments which commenced in the 1970s. An important element was the recognition that plant protoplasts — cells from which the walls have been digested enzymatically — could be used for genetic purposes. This development arose as an analogy of earlier research on the fusion of cells of different vertebrate species. Chemical promoters of protoplast fusion were discovered and, in parallel, it was shown that single protoplasts could be stimulated to regenerate first into normal cells, then into entire and normal sporophytic plants. Protoplasts could also be fused to combine genetic contributions from different parental species within the same cell and from this a hybrid plant could be produced.

Peter Carlson and others in the USA produced the first interspecies hybrid by this method, combining the chromosome sets of *Nicotiana glauca* and *N. langsdorfii*. These species are sexually compatible, so the hybrid had already been produced sexually, but the particular attraction of hybrids arising from protoplast fusion is that they might be produced between species from which sexual hybrids cannot be made. In a remarkably short time such hybrids were indeed produced, for example, between tomato and potato, *Datura* and *Atropa, Arabidopsis* and *Brassica*, and, at the ARC Plant Genetics Manipulation Group at the University of Nottingham, between *Petunia parodii* and *P. parviflora*.

From these methods access will be obtained to the genetic variation of species that are phylogenetically distant from our crop plants. Genetic diversity will be extended in many characters, among which may be those affecting resistance to pests and diseases. However, much remains to be learned about the science of these systems, and it would be over optimistic to believe that there will be significant practical returns in the form of crops in agriculture until towards the end of the century.

Alongside this flowering of plant cell biology there have been developments in molecular biology which will have a significant impact on plant genetics and breeding. They arise from the recognition that restriction endonucleases can be used to modify genetic systems by creating openings in DNA molecules into which other DNA sequences can be inserted. The recipient and the donor molecules may come from genetically unrelated and phylogenetically distant species. The DNA molecule so modified can be recaptured in a viable cell and so form a cell lineage in which the inserted sequence is multiplied in parallel with the genome in which it has been placed. Thus an inserted sequence can be cloned.

The relevance of this to plant breeding is that a plant protoplast can be a recipient for engineered DNA molecules carrying inserted sequences. Since a normal plant can be produced from a protoplast, a way appears to be opened by which novel genetic information could be transferred to crop plants. This potentiality for the extension of genetic variation could clearly be of great practical importance and the ARS will be heavily involved in the early 1980s in co-ordinated research in this field which extends from plant breeding to molecular biology. The research is along a number of lines which must converge for the practical success to be achieved some 15 to 20 years after the programme was started in 1978/79. The lines of work are:

(a) the establishment of controlled protoplast technology (production and regeneration) in the crop species, like grasses, cereals and legumes, in which protoplast methods are not yet efficient.

(b) the development of knowledge of the molecular structure of the DNA of the genomes of crop species and of the alien forms from which variation might be sought.

(c) development of systems, probably by the identification of messenger RNA sequences, and their reverse transcription into DNA, to enable desirable information to be cloned and multiplied in a bacterial vehicle as a preliminary to its incorporation in the cells of crop plants.

(d) the development of vector systems which will carry the useful DNA sequences into plant cells. In 1980 *Agrobacterium tumefaciens* and cauliflower mosaic virus are being studied as possible agents for the incorporation in protoplasts of the desired information sequences.

(e) determination of the means by which appropriately modified protoplasts can be selected. Yeast provides a useful model for plant cells in this work.

and (f) the resolution of the problem, yet to be faced, of whether alien DNA sequences are transmitted through meoisis and fertilization to the offspring of the plant which was the initial recipient.

All of these lines of research must come together before we have a practical technology. A considerable but not insurmountable challenge is presented. The rewards for meeting it will be that the genetic advance of our crops is unlikely to be stopped by the inadequacies of the available genetic variation.

The incorporation of new genetic variation in crops by the application of methods from molecular and cell biology will, however, only be the first step towards bringing novel characteristics into practical use. The first products will be parental material which will need to undergo modification by established cytogenetic techniques and by conventional breeding before agricultural varieties are released.

The challenges of the new technologies are not greater than those that faced Bateson and his colleagues in the 1900s. Like our predecessors, ARS plant geneticists and breeders will not overcome all of them, but they should gain sufficient knowledge to ensure that in the future methods of greater and greater genetic precision will be applied to the betterment of crop production.

## Further Reading

Bateson, Beatrice (1928). *William Bateson, FRS*. Cambridge: University Press.

Lewontin, R. C. (1974). *The Genetic Basis of Evolutionary Change*. New York: London: Columbia University Press.

McLeish, J. & Shoad, B. (1962). *Looking at Chromosomes*. London: MacMillan & Co. Ltd.

Mather, K. & Jinks, J. (1971). *Biometrical Genetics*. London: Chapman & Hall Ltd.

Novak, F. J. (1977). *Use of Tissue Cultures in Plant Breeding*. Prague: Czechoslovak Academy of Sciences, Institute of Experimental Botany.

Phillips, R. L. & Burnham, C. R. (1977). *Cytogenetic, Benchmark Papers in Genetics 6*. Stroudsburg, Pa.: Dowden, Hutchinson & Ross Inc.

Russell, G. E. (1978). *Plant Breeding for Pest and Disease Resistance*. London: Butterworths.

Silvey, V. (1978). The contribution of new varieties to increasing yield in England and Wales. *Journal of the National Institute of Agricultural Botany*, **14**, 367–384.

Simmonds, N. W. (Ed). (1976). *Evolution of Crop Plants*. London & New York: Longmans.

Sneep, J., Hendriksen, A. J. T. & Holbeck, O. (Eds.) (1979) *Plant Breeding Perspectives*. Wageningen: Centre for Agricultural Publishing & Documentation.

Whitehouse, H. L. K. (1965). *Towards an Understanding of the Mechanism of Heredity*. London: Edward Arnold (Publishers) Ltd.

Yeoman, M. M. (Ed.) (1976). *Cell Division in Higher Plants*. London: Academic Press.

# Science in Crop Production

## L. FOWDEN

Rothamsted Experimental Station, Harpenden, Herts.

John Bennet Lawes (1814–1900), the founder of Rothamsted Experimental Station, and Joseph Henry Gilbert, his lifelong collaborator, are regarded widely as the fathers of agricultural research; without doubt they were the first to apply rigorous scientific methods and thinking to agricultural problems. Their work relating soil chemistry and mineral nutrients with the growth and yield of crops led directly to the principles of plant nutrition and nutrient cycling still accepted today. Indirectly, their work was the touchstone from which a new era of scientific investigation in agriculture stemmed; one that encompassed a far wider range of problems and scientific disciplines (see Russell, 1942).

What motivates scientists to investigate agricultural problems and how can crop production benefit from scientific enquiry? There is, first, the intellectual challenge and satisfaction deriving from the search for a fuller understanding of the physical, chemical and biological phenomena encountered in a world in which agriculture and food production hold a key position. Of more importance, a greater understanding of scientific principles may lead to new agricultural practices. Lawes' early work provided an excellent illustration of this. He had been attracted by a remark made by a neighbour (Lord Dacre of Kimpton Hoo), who pointed out that on one farm bones were invaluable for the turnip crop whilst on another they were useless. His chemical reasoning suggested that the variable crop responses were caused by differences in soil acidity, which resulted in different rates of solubilization of nutrient phosphate from the bones, whilst his entrepreneurial flair recognized an opportunity to produce a consistently effective form of phosphate by dissolving bones in sulphuric acid. So the manufacture of superphosphate and the era of mineral fertilizers began. Other examples abound, and some will be described later in this essay.

In presenting this account of science in crop production, I have been aware of the complementary relationship existing between my topic and those discussed in other essays in this volume, especially the descriptions of work on soils and fertilizers, plant breeding, and horticultural production. The potential for growth and yield of crop plants is determined by the genes they contain. The plant breeder's continuing aim is to bring together, often by empirical approaches, new combinations of genes which will permit improved crop performance. However, the potential inherent in any genetic line is only realized in practice if growth is free from constraints. It is important that the soil should provide not only a suitably-structured matrix within which the root system of the crop can develop unimpeded, but also sufficient water and amounts of both major and minor nutrients necessary to sustain the full biosynthetic activity of the plant. It is the task of soil scientists to define this ideal situation, and to recommend how it may be achieved in farming practice. Against this framework, my objective will be to review advances in our knowledge of plant physiology and metabolism, especially how plant processes are influenced by both external environmental and internal biochemical and genetic factors. From such information, physiological models may be constructed for different crops to serve as guidelines for breeders; agronomic practices may be modified to permit crops to exploit more fully their physical and chemical environment; and, with increased biochemical understanding of how genes regulate metabolic processes, new techniques for the selection of cell lines possessing desired characteristics may emerge. The vigour and yield of crops can be reduced markedly as a result of pest and disease attacks, and further post harvest losses can occur due to these causes. Scientific investigation of the biology, especially the life-cycles of important fungal pathogens and pests, of the epidemiology of diseases and the population dynamics of insects, and of the opportunities for chemical and biological control has provided much fascinating information and some outstandingly successful protection methods.

## Science in Crop Production: a Retrospective View

The achievements of the last half century can be illustrated by reviewing the status of the sciences bearing on crop production about the year 1930. At that time, knowledge in many fields was very rudimentary if set against that of today.

Fifty years ago, plant nutrition was an intensely active field of research. In fact, by the mid-1920s, plant physiologists realized that in order to understand the effects of experimental treatments on yield it was necessary to study the pattern of crop growth throughout the whole period of development. A field laboratory was built and equipped at Rothamsted in 1925 to make measurements on the growing plant, and E. J. Maskell and W. O. James performed the first investigations, studying the effect of potassium fertilizers on the physiology of the potato plant. A. R. Clapham conducted a similar experiment on wheat a year or two later, the forerunner of a long series of wheat productivity measurements undertaken by D. J. Watson and colleagues. The underlying aim was the assessment of photosynthetic efficiency. Measurements of crop growth in terms of net assimilation rate (the ratio obtained by dividing net photosynthesis by total leaf area) and leaf area index (the area of leaf per unit area of land) separated the effects of change in the efficiency of photosynthesis from the effects of change in the size of the photoactive system. This approach prospered at a time when the photosynthetic process was still described, most inadequately, by the equation:

$$6CO_2 + 6H_2O \rightarrow (CH_2O)_6 + 6O_2$$

and when photorespiration, as a process counterproductive to photosynthesis, was completely unknown.

All ten major nutrients necessary for crop growth had been described by 1930, but the essential role of some micro-nutrients remained to be established. Manganese and boron were identified as essential elements in the 1920s, zinc and copper were shown to be indispensable micro-nutrients in 1930–1931, but the essential character of molybdenum (about 1939), sodium (about 1960) and chlorine (about 1965) was still to be recognized. The function of trace elements as either activators for or components of enzymes was unsuspected.

The idea that enzymes were proteins was still novel and not universally accepted in 1930; Sumner had crystallized the first enzyme (urease from jack bean seed) only four years earlier. There was likewise little appreciation of the three-dimensional shapes of protein molecules or of how the sequence of constituent amino acids within individual proteins gave each a unique spatial conformation, responsible in turn for the specificity of action exhibited by enzymes. Even the number of amino acids recognized as invariable components of protein was not final, for threonine remained to be discovered in 1935. Indeed, molecular biology as a discipline was unknown. There was no conception of the way in which DNA molecules of living cells ensure both their own replication and the inheritance of genetic characters or of how RNA molecules provide an imprint for the directed synthesis of highly specific proteins. Similarly, viruses were not recognized as being giant nucleoprotein molecules, and the mechanism now accepted for their self-replication was not contemplated.

Last century Darwin suggested that the phototrophic response of plants was due to the presence of chemical stimuli in the stem apex. Subsequently, biologists sought intermittently for endogenous chemicals (hormones) that govern the growth and differentiation of plants, but no natural growth substance had been characterized by 1931. In that year, however, indoleacetic acid (auxin) was first isolated from urine and shown to be active in the *Avena* growth test; shortly afterwards, it was identified in yeast and in fungi, and finally in 1942 in maize. Our knowledge of other types of plant growth hormone is derived from studies in the last 30 years.

The decade beginning in 1930 saw parallel developments in our understanding of insect physiology, especially of factors controlling behaviour. Uvarov's classical work with locusts showed how interactions between weather and physiology could initiate build-up and dispersal of insect pest populations, presumably through the mediation of behaviour-controlling chemicals. Wigglesworth studied moulting in the blood-sucking bug *Rhodnius* and laid the foundation for investigation of the endocrine system of insects and of the complex patterns of hormonal control of insect development, colour changes, diurnal rhythms and other activities. Meanwhile, experiments with *Drosophila* and *Ephestia* mutants having abnormal eye pigmentations provided early evidence that each step in a biochemical sequence was effected by a specific enzyme, itself the product of a specific gene. The first demonstration that female insects are attracted by highly volatile chemicals (scents) to oviposition sites was made in 1937, but the major advances in this area are post 1960 — it is perhaps surprising to recall that the term pheromone was not coined until 1959.

Chemicals have long been used to protect crops against diseases and pests, but early preparations such as those based on copper, arsenic, mercury or chlorate lacked selectivity and were very poisonous to man and animals. The new era in pest control did not begin until the insecticidal properties of DDT were described in 1940: the discovery of the selective herbicidal action of 2,4–dichlorophenoxyacetic acid (2,4–D) in 1942 provided the first opportunity for the successful control of weeds by methods other than fallowing or hand eradication. In retrospect, the developments of the last 30 years have provided a range of highly active crop protection chemicals with properties that would have seemed utopian in 1930.

## The Impact of New Techniques

The development of new instruments or techniques has profoundly influenced the advancement of scientific knowledge and completely new fields of endeavour have stemmed from their introduction.

The availability of the light microscope in the seventeenth century undoubtedly changed the face of biology: the development of the electron microscope, initially as a transmission instrument providing high resolution two-dimensional images and subsequently in the scanning form providing apparent three-dimensional images, has been almost as important in refining biological enquiry. Electron microscopy has provided a versatile method for examining many types of structure or structural association in extremely fine detail since its resolving power is approximately a thousand times greater than the light microscope. Examples of its application include studies of the surface characteristics and mode of aggregation of soil particles, of the differences encountered in the structural features of nematodes as an aid in their classification, of the manner in which fungal pathogens or symbiotic *Rhizobia* infect plant cells and tissues, or of the detailed anatomy of insect antennae involved in sensing pheromones. More generally, electron microscopy has advanced the study of viruses by providing critical evidence for the presence of virus particles in plant tissues and details of their fine structures important in their characterization.

As new physical techniques have been developed, the chemist has progressively adapted them to study the structures of molecules of biological interest with increased precision and facility. Infra-red and ultra-violet spectroscopic methods provide a means of recognizing specific functional groups within molecules in favourable circumstances. X-ray diffraction provides a powerful technique for the complete solution of molecular structures, and enables the spatial geometry of all atoms ($<$ about 300) within a molecule to be precisely determined. For some large protein molecules, X-ray diffraction information, together with amino acid sequence data, has led to explanations of biological function in terms of three-dimensional molecular configurations. The technique has one serious limitation — substances investigated must be crystalline. Two newer techniques, mass spectrometry (ms) and nuclear magnetic resonance spectroscopy (nmr), have been described as the chemist's seven-league boots and together have had an enormous impact on biological chemistry. When coupled with gas chromatography, ms can give, in favourable circumstances, the molecular formula of an unknown substance initially present in only ng, or even pg amounts in a complex mixture. Nmr, by providing exact information about the environments of all hydrogen atoms (protons) within a molecule, normally enables the full structure to be derived quickly: 10–100 $\mu$g of material are needed. The technique is also invaluable in organic syntheses by providing quick confirmation that the intended product has been obtained, e.g. in work with synthetic pyrethroid insecticides.

Chromatographic and isotopic techniques, developed mainly since the mid-1940s, have revolutionized the study of crop plants at the molecular level: they have conferred degrees of precision and sensitivity on the determination of chemical composition and metabolic change within living cells and tissues that would have been quite undreamt of 30 years ago.

Chromatography has developed in many forms (paper, thin-layer, ion-exchange, molecular sieve and gas-liquid phase separations), but all have the common feature of allowing small amounts of material to be separated from complex mixtures in which they naturally occur. Initially, chromatographic methods had their greatest impact on the separation of low molecular weight constituents, but the advent of column packings with controlled cross-linkage and pore size provided a means for resolving mixtures of macromolecules, especially proteins and enzymes. Electrophoretic procedures, alone and in combination with chromatography, have further refined the separation of charged molecules; in particular, the techniques of polyacrylamide gel electrophoresis and isoelectric focussing permit the fuller description of the individual components of the protein complex of plant tissues, and they have been used to characterize the subtle differences existing between the storage proteins of cereal seed varieties and thereby to check varietal identity.

Radioactive or heavy isotopes of an element provide a tag that can be employed to follow the fate of a nutrient or an organic constituent in plants. Labelled atoms allow processes (e.g. ion uptake, assimilate translocation or metabolic interconversion) to be established unequivocably; they also permit their sensitive quantitative description. Most major nutrient elements have radioactive isotopes with half-lives suitable for biological investigations; nitrogen is a conspicuous exception and usually is used as the heavy $^{15}$N form and assayed, most accurately, by mass spectrometry. Radioautographic techniques are often used in association with radioisotopes. For example, such techniques have been employed to study uptake by and transport within plants of nutrient elements whose radioactive isotopes have suitable energies of emission; the radioautographic methods can be adapted to study the distribution of isotope either within the intact plant or at tissue or cell level. Radioautography has also been crucial for the elucidation of many complicated metabolic sequences, such as the pathway of carbon during photosynthesis. Calvin and his colleagues made a time-course study of $^{14}$C distribution among the early products of photosynthetic $CO_2$ fixation by first separating the putative products on paper chromatograms and then using radioautographic assay to establish the sequence of their formation. This investigation will remain a classic in the field of plant biochemistry, but it represents only one of many deriving importance from the combination of chromatographic and radioisotopic procedures.

## The Determinants of Crop Productivity

### General considerations

The efficiency of crop production can be defined in thermodynamic terms as the ratio of energy output (plant dry matter) to energy input (solar radiation). Conversion efficiencies are low due to a combination of factors, some internal and some external to the plant, but each associated with an energy loss. For a high yielding U.K. wheat crop producing 10–11 tonnes grain $ha^{-1}$, the economic yield is equivalent in energy terms to only 0.5–0.6% of the total annual solar radiation; the corresponding value for the total crop dry matter is 1.0–1.2%. Expressed as percentages of the solar energy intercepted by the crop foliage, these values increase to about 1.3 and 2.5 respectively. The principal factors causing the cumulative energy loss and their individual contributions (given in parentheses and expressed following Monteith as loss factors) include the incomplete interception of radiation by the crop foliage (0.4), the quantum nature of light and the photoactive ineffectiveness of certain wavelengths (0.1), the light saturation of the photosynthetic system which is constrained by the low ambient carbon dioxide levels (0.7), and the dissipation of photosynthetically fixed carbon by the counterproductive processes of dark respiration (0.6) and photorespiration (0.7). The economic yield is always less than, and for barley and sugar-beet as well as wheat is normally about half of, the total dry matter: this so-called harvest index is considerably higher for potatoes ($\geqslant 0.8$). National average yields of wheat in the last few years have hovered about 5 t $ha^{-1}$, and so an additional loss factor ($\sim 0.5$) may be ascribed to the combined effects of adverse weather, infertile badly-structured soils and poor crop husbandry, including inadequate control of weeds, diseases and pests (see Monteith, 1977, for a fuller account).

Tropical species are potentially more productive than temperate crops, and some very high annual dry matter yields are recorded, e.g. $>60$ t $ha^{-1}$ for sugar cane and $>80$ t $ha^{-1}$ for napier grass. The increased productivity can be attributed mainly to higher levels of solar radiation and its more efficient interception by crops having all-year growing periods: the $C_4$ mechanism of carbon dioxide fixation (see later) found in many tropical species markedly raises their light-saturation thresholds, and so further facilitates the efficient utilization of incident radiation.

### The crop canopy and light interception

Field experiments performed in the 1960s by Warren Wilson and by Monteith and their colleagues showed that crops during the vegetative phase of growth assimilated carbon and accumulated dry weight at rates which were proportional to intercepted radiation. These studies also established that the maximum amount of dry matter accumulated was strongly correlated with the total amount of radiation intercepted by foliage during growth. The relationship is strikingly similar for a range of crops, including barley, potatoes and sugar beet, that received an adequate supply of fertilizers and water: the efficiency of conversion of intercepted radiant energy to crop dry matter had a mean value of 2.4%, and individual values for the three arable crops were within about $\pm 15\%$ of the mean. Other experiments indicate that greater variation in photosynthetic efficiency may be encountered between crops grown under widely different conditions; it is known that plants subjected to water stress or infected with diseases exhibit lower photosynthetic efficiencies. No definite evidence for intra-specific variation in net assimilation rates has been obtained in experiments comparing cultivars.

The leaf area index of a plant (L), i.e. the area of leaf per unit area of soil, governs the proportion of the incident radiation that is intercepted, and so the rate of dry matter accumulation. Optimal leaf area index, i.e. the value of L producing maximum increase in dry matter per unit of land area and time, occurs when almost all (85–90%) of the incident radiation is intercepted and the lowest leaves are near the light compensation point for net photosynthesis. This value is probably about 9 for wheat and barley, 4–5 for sugar beet and about 3 for potatoes. That the optimal value differs considerably between crops is a reflection of the fact that leaf area *per se* is of lesser importance than other factors such as leaf size, shape, angle of orientation and age (or degree of senescence). Watson measured the increase of L during the seasonal growth of several arable crops and found maxima to occur about a week before the date of 50% ear emergence in winter wheat, coincident with it for spring wheat, and a few days after it for spring barley. In these cereals L decreased rapidly during July to zero in August. Maximal values of L are attained later in the season in sugar beet and potatoes: foliage is retained longer into the autumn with sugar-beet than with the other crops resulting in higher seasonal percentage light interceptions for beet (about 50% compared with about 40%). The graphs in Figure 1 show how seasonal light interception by the sugar-beet crop is related to L.

Studies of the foregoing type in environmental physics and physiology have provided models indicating the most desirable architecture (growth habit) for individual plants and for crop stands, and breeders have sought, and still seek, new varieties partly on the basis of this knowledge. In addition, the goal of higher thermodynamic efficiency in crops could be achieved by (i) lengthening the growing season (extra dry matter production of up to $1 \text{ t ha}^{-1} \text{ week}^{-1}$ could result from extension into early spring or late autumn), (ii) producing varieties whose leaves expand more quickly and senesce more slowly, (iii) seeking crops with a faster rate of photosynthesis in bright light, and (iv) still further increasing harvest indices.

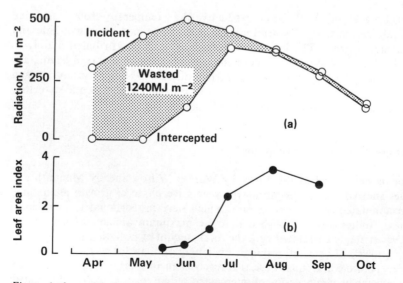

*Figure 1* shows (a) the seasonal variation in incident solar irradiation and the interception of radiation by the foliage of a sugar beet crop, and (b) the increase of the leaf area index of the crop during growth.

## Water, crop growth and irrigation

Penman's work at Rothamsted in the 1940s laid the foundations for our present understanding of potential evaporation from open surfaces and the transpiration loss from leaf surfaces. By developing the theory of turbulent diffusion at boundary layers, the Penman formula was derived to describe the transpiration of a crop as a function of its physical environment, mainly of the radiant energy and the saturation deficit of air (see Penman, 1948).

Water stress can develop in a plant in two ways: by a shortage of water to the root system (determined by the soil's moisture status), or by excessive water loss from leaves (occurring to a warm, dry and turbulent atmosphere). The plant responds to water shortage by growing more slowly, apparently as a result of an increase in endogenous levels of the growth inhibitor, abscisic acid; leaf expansion and stem internode extension are reduced or stopped at the moderate water stresses encountered after a few rainless days in a British summer. Further rainless weather leads to higher water stress and photosynthesis may be seriously reduced; since photorespiration is not so sharply affected, the effect of water stress on net photosynthesis can be more dramatic.

Some crops, e.g. sugar beet, are particularly sensitive to water stress induced by rapid transpiration, and the leaves of this plant wilt on bright, dry days even when the soil is moderately wet. The leaves grow faster in humid air than in dry air, and the rate of leaf photosynthesis diminishes when the humidity of the air decreases, probably as a result of partial closure of leaf stomata. These considerations underlie the interest in applying irrigation in the form of a mist to crop foliages.

Knowledge acquired from field experiments at Woburn and Rothamsted about evaporation, water use and the microclimate surrounding crop canopies have brought major benefits to conventional irrigation practices. We can now describe the yield response of arable crops to irrigation in terms of two crop-specific parameters: the limiting soil water deficit, $D_l$, which is the deficit that must be exceeded before any additional plant growth will result from irrigation, and the incremental gain, k, in crop yield per unit of water used. For three crops (beans, potatoes and barley) extensively investigated, the ratios between $D_l$ at Rothamsted and $D_l$ at Woburn are roughly equal to the ratio between the amounts of water held in the top metre of soil between the water potential limits of −0.1 to −15 bar. The $D_l$ for a particular crop on some other soil can then be predicted provided only that the water holding capacity of the soil is known or measured. $D_l$ can range from almost zero for early potatoes to about 100 mm for deeply-rooting sugar beet, and the yield response, k, ranges from about 0.2 t ha$^{-1}$ of cereal grain (85% dry matter) to 2.5 t ha$^{-1}$ of potato tubers (fresh wt.) for each 10 mm of applied water.

Studies of the incidence and duration of water stress on the growth of field crops are rendered difficult by vagaries of weather, but the recent development of mobile rain shelters has provided an opportunity for more precise investigation. Farming lore has indicated that cereals are particularly sensitive to water stress occurring at anthesis, but new studies with the Rothamsted mobile shelter shown in Plate 1 suggest that the yields of barley crops are equally sensitive to drought regardless of timing. However, the mechanism of yield loss depends on when the stress is applied — early drought affects the number of grains per ear, mid season drought the number of ears per unit ground area, and late drought the mean grain mass, i.e. the components of yield are differentially affected.

## Temperature, crop growth and photosynthesis

Plant growth is affected in a complex way by temperature because it is not independent of other atmospheric variables (irradiance, humidity and turbulence). In the field, the

*Plate 1* Mobile rain shelter for experimental work at Rothamsted.

effects of temperature and humidity counter each other because hot air (stimulating growth) is usually dry air (retarding growth) and *vice versa*. In spring and early summer in Britain, temperature is probably the dominant factor; the rate at which leaves of temperate crops appear and grow increases almost linearly in the temperature range 15–20°, but the rate normally reaches a maximum at a temperature between 20 and 25°, *i.e.* on days when humidity will tend to be low. For tropical species, these temperature ranges are about 10° higher.

The processes of leaf expansion and leaf senescence are both dependent upon temperature and the pattern of light interception by the foliage of a crop throughout the season shows a complex relationship with temperature. Therefore the relationship between temperature and canopy photosynthesis (and crop productivity) must also be complex; furthermore, photosynthetic rates reflect not just the temperature during measurement but also the previous environmental history of the leaf material. This is well illustrated in Figure 2 which records rates of net photosynthesis (determined at 13, 18, 23 and 28°) of young leaves from wheat and maize plants grown in chambers maintained at the same four day temperatures. For wheat, it is clear that photosynthesis proceeded fastest at 18° irrespective of the temperature of plant development, and that plants grown at 18° synthesized better than plants grown at any other temperature. For maize, the rates of photosynthesis measured at 23 and 28° were almost identical, but 23° appeared to be the most favourable temperature for growth. These experimental results were consistent with field experience in suggesting that maize is quite unsuitable as a crop for northern Britain and even in the south summer temperatures may be too low for good growth in some years.

## Fixation and assimilation of carbon dioxide

Carbon is an indispensable component of all organic matter and constitutes almost half the dry matter of plants. It is assimilated from the atmosphere by leaves via the process of photosynthetic carbon dioxide ($CO_2$) fixation. Under most circumstances the process

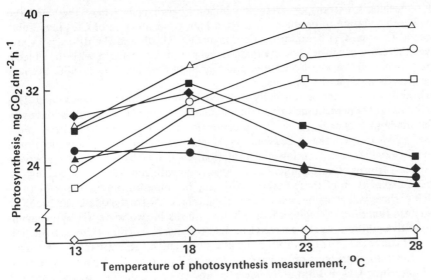

*Figure 2* shows the rates of photosynthesis, measured at 13, 18, 23 and 28°, of wheat and maize leaves, grown at the same day temperatures. Data for photosynthesis measured at different temperatures are shown as:
  wheat grown at, 13° ◆—◆, 18° ■—■, 23° ▲—▲, 28° ●—●;
  maize grown at, 13° ◇—◇, 18° □—□, 23° △—△, 28° ○—○.

seems surprisingly well adapted to the relatively low concentrations of $CO_2$ in the atmosphere (about 0.034% or 340 ppm by volume), but the rate of photosynthetic fixation in temperate crops on bright summer days may be limited by partial deficiency of $CO_2$ at the chloroplast due to the low levels in ambient air and the restricted nature of diffusion into and within leaf tissues. This situation is recognized clearly by the glasshouse industry, and the use of enhanced $CO_2$ levels in horticulture is now an accepted practice producing increased plant growth (see p. 174 in the essay by D. Rudd-Jones). Experiments with arable crops in the field must be performed in plastic enclosures and $CO_2$ effects then are confounded by inevitable changes in the micro-environment, but most experiments have shown positive growth effects from enrichment and cereal grain yield increases have varied between a few per cent and 50%. The experiments take on greater significance when it is appreciated that atmospheric $CO_2$ levels are increasing slowly as the world burns its fossil fuel reserves for energy purposes. Using a model relating crop growth rates with ambient $CO_2$ levels, Monteith (1977) has suggested that, between 1976 and the end of the century, growth may increase 4.6% per decade as a consequence of a predicted rise of $CO_2$ levels to 400 ppm by the year 2000.

Photosynthetic carbon assimilation in temperate plant species normally involves an initial reaction in the chloroplast between $CO_2$ and a $C_5$ compound, ribulose bisphosphate (RUBP), catalyzed by the enzyme RUBP-carboxylase. Two molecules of 3-phosphoglyceric acid (a $C_3$ compound) result from this reaction, and plants employing this primary fixation process are termed $C_3$ plants. However, an alternative mechanism for initial $CO_2$ fixation exists and is encountered mainly in certain tropical and sub-tropical species (e.g. sugar cane, maize) that have a high potential for dry matter production at high light intensities and at temperatures above 25°. $CO_2$ first reacts with $C_3$ organic acid molecules present in leaf mesophyll cells to produce $C_4$ dicarboxylic acids; species possessing this mechanism are called $C_4$ plants. The leaves of $C_4$ plants are characterized by a sheath of specialized cells surrounding the vascular bundles (the transporting tissues); these cells are rich in chloroplasts and RUBP-carboxylase. The

$C_4$ acid molecules are transported to the bundle-sheath cells where they undergo enzymic decarboxylation to produce a localized high concentration of $CO_2$ favourable to the second (normal $C_3$) fixation reaction, involving RUBP and RUBP-carboxylase. The leaves therefore produce photosynthate in cells in direct contact with the phloem transport system. The review by Chollet and Ogren (1975) provides a fuller account of photosynthesis in $C_3$ and $C_4$ plants.

Growth and photosynthesis normally proceed in an environment containing 21% oxygen (the usual $O_2$ percentage in air), but some measurements of plant productivity have been made at higher or lower $O_2$ concentrations; for example, when beans were maintained in 5% oxygen, the increase in dry weight over short periods was more than in controls in air. Plants kept in lower than normal $O_2$ concentrations for long periods show changed patterns of development and comparison with controls is less meaningful. A simplistic explanation of these observations may be found in the dual specificity of the RUBP-carboxylase enzyme, which can use either $CO_2$ (carboxylase function) or $O_2$ (oxygenase function). Oxygen affects photosynthesis in two ways: (i) by behaving as a competitive inhibitor of the carboxylase activity and so causing a direct reduction of photosynthetic carbon fixation, and (ii) by also serving as a substrate for the enzyme's oxygenase function, it triggers off a series of reactions (described as photorespiration, see Fig. 3) in which $CO_2$ is ultimately liberated and so acts indirectly by reducing net carbon assimilation. The photorespiratory processes produce ammonia in an amount equal to that of $CO_2$ released. Since ammonia is toxic to plants, it must be reassimilated rapidly into organic nitrogen compounds and we now recognize that the rate at which ammonia is recycled after photorespiration may be far higher than the rate of initial assimilation following nitrogen uptake by the root system.

Photorespiratory activity differs greatly between species; it cannot be detected with certainty in maize (and other $C_4$ plants behave similarly) but may exceed 50% of the rate of true photosynthesis in sunflower. Photorespiration in wheat increases relative

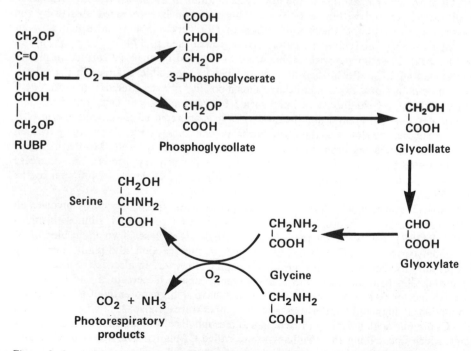

*Figure 3* shows the metabolic steps of photorespiration leading to the production of $CO_2$ and ammonia from ribulose bisphosphate.

to photosynthesis under conditions of high nitrogen supply, high temperature or marked water stress. The existence of the photorespiratory process is seen by some as forming a penalty on yield, and calculations suggest that if it could be inhibited or otherwise eliminated from wheat, then grain production might rise by as much as 50%. A contrary view sees photorespiration as a mechanism for disposing of surplus light energy and therefore avoiding photochemically-induced tissue damage when $CO_2$ levels are limiting.

Three research opportunities for improving photosynthetic efficiency by reducing the photorespiratory activity of $C_3$ temperate species are feasible. The first would seek natural variability in RUBP-carboxylase as a pre-requisite for the selection of types in which the oxygenase function is less important. This approach does not hold much promise because the available evidence suggests that there may be little natural variation. The second would seek to transfer the essential features of the $C_4$ mechanism to temperate species, but information about the number and character of the genes controlling $C_4$ acid synthesis, translocation and decarboxylation is lacking and we are ignorant about the ways in which genes specify structural elements such as bundle-sheath cells. This approach is then highly speculative. The final one involves the possibility of identifying a specific chemical inhibitor of photorespiration. Ideally, the compound would act at the level of RUBP-carboxylase by reducing the enzyme's oxygenase function, but would not interfere significantly with other metabolic processes, especially photosynthesis. No compound exhibiting these properties has been found as yet, and more detailed information about the properties and molecular conformation of RUBP-carboxylase, and the manner in which it catalyzes reactions between ribulose bisphosphate and $CO_2$ and $O_2$ as alternative substrates is clearly necessary if we are to progress logically, rather than empirically, in the search for an effective inhibitor. For the present, then, we must attempt to achieve the best balance between photosynthetic and photorespiratory activity by adopting favourable agronomic practices, i.e. by avoiding water stress where practicable, by avoiding 'luxury' nitrogen applications, and, ideally, by growing crops in areas with suitable temperature regimes.

We have already seen how photosynthetic efficiency is related to the development of the leaf canopy throughout the life of a crop, but it is important to recognize that the economic yield (and harvest index) depends upon processes effecting the translocation and partitioning of photoassimilates between the different plant organs. Plant growth hormones are ascribed a special role in directing the flow of assimilates and in governing the extent to which they are deposited in storage organs, or sinks (i.e. cereal grains, potato tubers, etc.). The capacity of sinks is affected by external environmental factors and by internal regulatory mechanisms; it also seems probable that if sink capacity is limited, then photosynthetic activity may decrease through feed-back mechanisms. More fundamental information is needed to explain how plant growth hormones act at the cellular level to influence plant development and ultimately harvest indices and eventually it may be possible to change, with greater certainty, the form of crop plants in advantageous ways by treating them with growth regulators.

## The uptake and assimilation of other nutrients, especially nitrogen

*General principles* Crops acquire their nutrient elements, other than carbon, mainly by uptake from soil via their root systems. Whilst the lack of any one of the essential elements will, by definition, prevent the normal growth of a plant, there is no doubt that in agricultural practice the element whose deficiency most frequently restricts crop growth is nitrogen (for a more detailed account, see Fowden, 1979). Lawes and Gilbert quickly realized this fact from the yields of the Broadbalk wheat experiment: yields were small unless nitrogen was given, and other mineral nutrients produced yield increases only when given with nitrogen. The experiment stands as a model of Lawes' objectivity. He began it to show the value to crops of superphosphate, from which he derived much of his income, but he devoted progressively more effort and money to establishing the greater importance of nitrogen in crop production.

Crops take up most of their nitrogen in the form of nitrate, but ammonium ion serves as a nitrogen source under some circumstances. The concentrations of the two ions in soil are governed by many factors that jointly determine the populations and activities of soil micro-organisms that cause mineralization of nitrogen (i.e. the production of inorganic forms of nitrogen from soil organic matter) or bring about nitrification (or denitrification under anaerobic conditions). Forage and grain legume crops possess an additional mechanism for acquiring nitrogen being endowed with root nodules that have the ability to fix molecular nitrogen, i.e. to use nitrogen present in the soil air, to reduce it to ammonia within the nodule tissue, and finally to export it to the main root system of the plant. The formation of nodules is a response to infection of root hairs by *Rhizobia* bacteria present in the soil, and the nodule and its enclosed bacteroids represent a symbiotic system.

Physiological studies of ion uptake by plant root systems have a long history. Many investigators adopted nutrient solution or hydroponic techniques to simplify measurement and to give better reproducibility; nutrient film and flowing culture techniques are seen as more recent developments. Ion uptake is essentially an active (energy-coupled) process, and specific proteins (permeases) facilitating the passage of particular ions across cell membranes have been characterized recently: nevertheless, there is clear evidence for competition in uptake of pairs of ions, e.g. $K^+$ and $NH_4^+$. Many factors influence the amount and rate of ion uptake by crops. The available nutrient concentrations in the soil are of paramount importance. The root architecture is also a decisive factor; a highly branched, fine root system enables a plant to explore a larger volume of soil and so facilitates the better uptake of nutrients even when the soil nutrient status is low. In turn, soil type, structure and moisture content strongly influence root penetration and proliferation at different depths; also the diffusion of $O_2$ and $CO_2$ and hence the aerobicity of the soil-root interface. Micro-organisms in the rhizosphere are also believed to influence root differentiation and growth, possibly because they release substances active as plant growth hormones. A special group of soil-inhabiting fungi form mycorrhizal, symbiotic associations with many crops: the fungi derive metabolizable carbon compounds from the host plants and, in return, transfer phosphate, and probably certain trace elements, to the roots and so enhance the phosphorus status and growth of the plant. The mycelia of the fungi are very ramified within the soil and, in some senses, act like an extended root system, able to scavenge phosphate from large volumes of soil of low-phosphorus content. Finally, there is evidence for interspecific variability in the affinity of root systems for particular ions, and it would be interesting to learn whether such genetic variability extends to cultivars, thereby presenting new opportunities for breeders.

**Biological nitrogen fixation and mycorrhizal phosphate uptake** Hellreigel and Wilfarth announced their discovery of biological nitrogen fixation in 1888. Now this subject is one of the most vigorous study areas in plant science. Problems and challenges abound in the more fundamental fields of genetics and enzymology, whilst agriculturalists seek greater practical benefits from fixation to reduce the demand for nitrogen fertilizers, especially in the farming economies of poorer countries.

The ability to fix nitrogen extends beyond the symbiotic Rhizobia-legume systems and into a group of free-living soil organisms that includes the aerobic *Azotobacter* and anaerobic *Clostridium* spp., the blue-green algae (also called cyanobacteria) and bacteria such as *Aspirillum* that colonize the rhizosphere and effect associative nitrogen fixation. However, the quantities of nitrogen fixed by nodulated legumes, which in Britain may reach 300 kg N ha$^{-1}$ for a forage legume and about half this amount for a grain legume, considerably exceed those derived from the non-symbiotic systems, e.g. blue-green algae add only a few kg N ha$^{-1}$ to agricultural systems under temperate conditions, but when inoculated into rice fields in India they may contribute 25–30 kg ha$^{-1}$ of biologically-fixed nitrogen. For these reasons, the main opportunities for increase in the short-term of biological nitrogen fixation lies in the more widespread and successful cultivation of rhizobial legumes. Concerted research might provide in the medium-term a better understanding of associative systems and the role they might reliably play in integrated nitrogen management systems.

The quantity of nitrogen fixed by a legume plant depends both on the number and on the individual effectiveness of its root nodules; some strains of *Rhizobium* infect roots and induce many nodules, but the specific activity of the nodules (amount of N fixed in unit time divided by nodule weight) may be very low. Such ineffective strains occur in agricultural soils and, since they can be aggressive in the infection of root hairs to the exclusion of other, possibly more effective strains, it is not unusual to encounter legume crops in which nitrogen fixation is poor. Inoculation procedures, in which legume seeds are coated, before planting, with cells of specially selected strains of *Rhizobium* contained in a carrier medium, largely overcome this problem by ensuring that the young roots encounter and are infected by bacteria inducing effective nodules.

The success of infection and nodulation of legume roots by *Rhizobium* is controlled by genetic and molecular factors of both the host and the bacterium, and so the quest for more effective nitrogen fixation requires selection or judicious manipulation of both partners in the symbiotic relationship. Little effort has gone into the selection of legume hosts, but P. S. Nutman at Rothamsted has undertaken a crossing programme with red clover involving more than 8000 plants. The selection procedure gave third generation plants whose average yields were more than 50% higher than those of the original cultivar. High yield was correlated with early nodulation and greater nitrogen fixation. More attention has been paid to the *Rhizobium* symbiont. Many strains have been isolated from agricultural soils and subsequently selected for favourable host compatibility, nodulation and nitrogen fixing characteristics. Desirable strains should be (i) robust so that they remain viable throughout the field inoculation process, (ii) aggressive so that they compete effectively with endogenous strains in soils during the root infection process, (iii) highly effective in inducing the formation of nodules with high nitrogen fixing activity, (iv) capable of surviving and functioning effectively over extended temperature ranges, and (v) reasonably tolerant of low soil pH, especially if selected for use with clovers on marginal hill lands, and of agricultural chemicals. Genetic manipulation procedures may help to achieve some of these goals in the future. Already investigations at the ARC Unit of Nitrogen Fixation and at the John Innes Institute have established the possibility of transferring genes for nitrogen fixation between different bacterial species and between strains of *Rhizobium*. Ultimately, it may be possible to tailor *Rhizobium* strains to attain more effective matches with particular hosts.

The vesicular-arbuscular (VA) mycorrhizal fungi infecting the roots of arable and vegetable crops fall mainly in four genera, one typically tropical, the others temperate in their distribution. The species that are important agriculturally (numbering 6–8) are far more catholic than the *Rhizobia* in the selection of their hosts. Some crops showing growth and yield responses to mycorrhizal infection of their roots (listed in diminishing order of dependence) are: onion, legumes, potatoes, cereals, and temperate grasses. Whilst some differences exist in the efficiency with which mycorrhiza establish themselves on roots, explore the surrounding soil, and translocate phosphate to the host plant, it has not proved possible to classify or distinguish species by these criteria.

Work with VA mycorrhiza is complicated by the fact that no one has yet managed to grow them in axenic culture: they must be maintained and grown in cultures containing living root material. Mycorrhizal root material obtained in this way can then be used as a source of inocula in experiments testing for beneficial effects on crop growth. The nutrient film technique may provide a means for the large scale production of mycorrhizal roots (of lettuce or tomato) and the commercial production of inocula could follow from this development. In practice, crops are most likely to respond to inoculation when grown on low P-status soils containing low levels of natural endophytes. This situation has been confirmed for many crops studied in pot experiments where both P and endophyte levels can be controlled. More interestingly, recent experiments of Barbara Mosse at Rothamsted have demonstrated yield responses in field grown crops following inoculation. The yield of barley grown on a low-P soil (9 ppm NaHCO$_3$-soluble P) treated with mycorrhizal inoculum was double that of a control crop grown on uninoculated soil; in a similar experiment, the yield of lucerne was quadrupled. Most agricultural soils in Britain contain considerably higher levels of P, and under these conditions yield increases following inoculation are likely to be insignificant.

*The regulation of nitrogen assimilation and protein synthesis* Some four-fifths of the nitrogen taken up by crops is incorporated ultimately into plant protein which, in turn, represents the most important nitrogenous component of the food of farm animals and many humans. It has then been important to gain an understanding of the way in which protein is synthesized by plants, and of the factors regulating the process.

The outline pathway followed by nitrogen between its uptake by roots as nitrate and its final introduction into storage protein can be represented as:

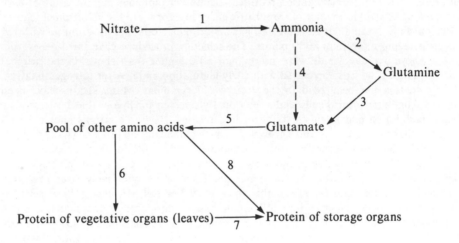

The pool of amino acids also provides the precursors for the synthesis of other essential nitrogenous constituents of plants such as the nucleic acids, chlorophyll and indoleacetic acid.

Nitrate is first reduced via nitrite to ammonia (stage 1) by the sequential action of the enzymes, nitrate and nitrite reductases. Nitrate reductase, as the first enzyme in the assimilation pathway may play an important role in regulating the flow of nutrient nitrogen within plants and it has been suggested that measurement of nitrate reductase levels in young seedlings might be useful in screening genetic lines for ultimate vigour, yield and protein production.

Nitrogen in its fully reduced state of ammonia then enters organic combination. The transition involved in green plants is stage 2; the ammonia-N atom is introduced into the amide-N of glutamine catalyzed by the enzyme glutamine synthetase. Glutamine then transfers the same N atom to a new carbon skeleton to produce glutamate (glutamic acid) in stage 3. Earlier, ammonia-N was considered to enter glutamate directly by a single reaction step catalyzed by glutamic dehydrogenase (stage 4), but this mechanism for ammonia assimilation is now believed to be unique to fungi.

Glutamine synthetase (stage 2) is then seen as the portal through which all ammonia-N passes, whether it arises (i) by reduction of nitrate or molecular $N_2$ (nitrogen fixation), (ii) by the photorespiratory mechanism (see earlier), (iii) by the mobilization of N derived from storage proteins during seedling germination, or (iv) by processes associated with the transfer of N from senescing leaves to developing storage organs. Distinct biochemical differences of the type identified between the N assimilatory mechanisms employed by higher plants and fungi are not common, and this example opens up the possibility for devising a specific inhibitor of the fungal pathway, i.e. producing a fungicide on the basis of known biochemical diversity between plant host and fungal pathogen.

The assimilatory pathway of nitrogen beyond glutamate is very ramified (stages 5–8). Nineteen other amino acids present in protein must be synthesized, some directly from glutamate-N by transamination processes, others only as end-products of long reaction sequences, and all at rates and in amounts matching the plant's needs for growth and development (but not necessarily the nutritional needs of an animal provided with the plant as a feedstuff). It is not then surprising to find situations in which plant cells regulate, within narrow limits, the concentrations of their own constituents. Commonly, enzymes concerned in the early stages of a biosynthetic pathway are inhibited by the end product; since higher cellular concentrations of the product cause progressively more inhibition and therefore reduce new synthesis, the system becomes self-regulatory. These concepts can be illustrated by reference to lysine, which represents, for animals, the nutritionally limiting amino acid in cereal grains. Sustained

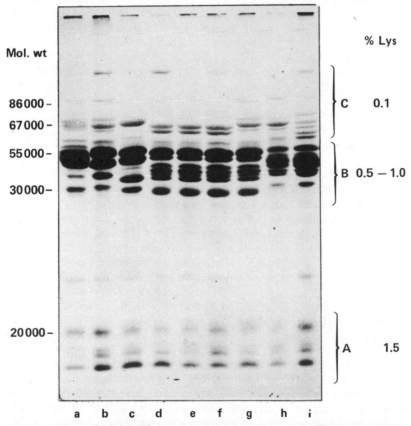

*Figure 4* shows the separation achieved by gel electrophoresis of the hordein polypeptides of nine barley varieties: a, Midas; b, Tyra; c, Ark Royal; d, Maris Mink; e, Aramir; f, Maris Trojan; g, Hassan; h, Senta; and i, Sonja.

effort by biochemists has established that this amino acid is the product of a 7-step synthetic pathway in which the first and especially the third enzymes are inhibited by lysine, which thereby delicately regulates the rate of its own synthesis. Now, Rothamsted scientists are searching for aberrant cell lines in which lysine has lost, partially or wholly, this ability to inhibit its own biosynthesis, i.e. lines that 'overproduce' lysine. At present, the selection techniques use excised embryos of barley treated with a chemical mutagen, but it would be more efficient to screen plant cell or protoplast cultures if the problems associated with their regeneration into whole plantlets could be solved.

Protein molecules are synthesized by the progressive condensation of amino acid residues in unique sequences determined by messenger ribonucleic acid (mRNA) molecules. The mRNAs are themselves transcripts of deoxyribonucleic acid (DNA) genic material. Many individual molecular species make up the protein complexes of leaves, grains or roots used as foodstuffs and so their nutritional value depends not only on the total protein content but also on its mean amino acid composition. Recent developments in gel electrophoresis have facilitated the characterization of the individual components of protein mixtures and the fine resolution of the polypeptide constituents of grain storage proteins such as hordein of barley and zein of maize. The hordein fraction of barley shows interesting varietal differences and the presence of increased proportions of lower molecular weight polypeptides (see Fig. 4) is associated with higher mean lysine contents. Emphasis is now shifting to the molecular mechanisms governing the synthesis of individual proteins within plant tissues; attempts to recognize and purify mRNAs specifying particular proteins are proving successful, and the further step of characterizing individual DNA genes is well advanced. It is then possible to foresee situations in which genes may be systematically modified, by the addition of selected DNA fragments, with resulting changes in gene products, e.g. by attaching additional lysine codons to appropriate DNAs, the lysine content of selected proteins might be increased. Feasibility studies form part of a major ARC research initiative to identify the opportunities for improving crop plants by genetic manipulation techniques.

## Pests, diseases and weeds: their influence on crop production

Disease and pest attacks on crops reduce their productivity either by diminishing the interception or the efficient use of solar radiation by leaves, or by stunting root growth and thereby the effectiveness of root systems to take up water and nutrients. Weeds compete directly with crop plants for light, water and nutrients. Losses vary greatly according to crop and environmental conditions: it is difficult to give a precise measure of damage, especially on a worldwide basis, but sober assessments suggest that weeds, pests and diseases result in one-quarter to one-third of the world's potential crop production being lost before harvest, while a further 15% may be spoiled during storage under poor conditions. By comparison, the situation in the U.K. is relatively favourable — a recent estimate placed total losses at about 10%, equivalent to about £500M per year in 1976. This position has stemmed from the general willingness of British farmers during the past 30 years to test and adopt new chemicals and practices for crop protection.

Until 1940, control measures rested on the use of very few substances. Probably the earliest pesticides used were organic extractives from plant materials, i.e. products such as nicotine, derris and pyrethrum, but inorganic preparations based on copper or mercury salts, elemental sulphur or arsenical compounds were used more widely. The agrochemical (pesticide) industry has developed largely since the war, the modern era beginning with the introduction of DDT and HCH as insecticides and 2,4-D, and later MCPA, as hormone-type herbicides. Now about 200 chemicals appear in the approvals list of MAFF and these are formulated and marketed by the industry in a larger number of approved products satisfying the requirements of the Agricultural Chemicals Approval Scheme. Herbicides form the largest group of approved pesticide chemicals and, in value, their use in the U.K. easily exceeds that of either fungicides or insecticides.

The discovery of new pesticides has followed well tried, but empirical procedures in which large numbers of newly synthesized chemicals are screened for a range of biological activities on representative organisms. Some outstandingly successful compounds have emerged. Herbicides revolutionized cereal growing in the late 1940s and 1950s by permitting the control of broad-leaved weeds, and later compounds have extended control to grass weeds and wild oats — a truly remarkable achievement of selective killing. Certain classes of insecticides and fungicides have been developed to move within the plant and so mimic growth hormones in being systemic; for example, compounds absorbed by the root system and transported in the xylem to kill insects feeding on the leaves, or to control diseases in the stems or leaves. A significant opportunity for future improvement in the control of soil-borne pathogens, or indeed nematodes or other soil-inhabiting pests, attacking the roots and vascular systems of plants lies in a search for systemic chemicals that can be sprayed onto and absorbed by the foliage and then move downwards to the roots. However, with time, it has become increasingly more difficult to discover new pesticides and now it is necessary, on average, to screen about 12 000 compounds to achieve one commercial success. The rate of introduction of new pesticides is then understandably slowing down, while the costs of developing a successful product can be as much as £15–20M, some 40–60% of which may be spent on toxicological and environmental studies.

Scientists in the Agricultural Research Service have complemented this commercial effort by fundamental investigations aiming to establish the principles governing the structure-activity relationships of active chemicals and the efficiency with which pesticide chemicals are transferred to their target organisms. Both of these objectives require an extensive knowledge of the taxonomy and behavioural biology of pest species (weeds, pathogenic fungi, bacteria or viruses, and insect pests and nematodes), and of the circumstances governing the spread of diseases or the build-up and migration of insect populations within crops in the field. The public sector mainly seeks, by these approaches, to provide a fund of information from which novel concepts or improved strategies for crop protection may stem, but occasionally it has itself produced new types of crop protection chemicals. The synthetic pyrethroid insecticides developed at Rothamsted are the most important example, and represent a new class of compound, highly toxic to insects yet safer to mammals than almost all previous insecticides (Elliott, 1979). The compounds now successfully exploited were products of a synthetic programme that sought progressively to modify the structure of pyrethrin 1 (the major active constituent of pyrethrum) and so identify the molecular features associated with its high insecticidal activity and its instability in light. The later synthetic compounds (permethrin, cypermethrin and deltamethrin) possess photostability well suited to their use on field crops, but they are degraded, especially readily in soil, to non-toxic products and so do not pollute the environment.

In comparable studies, R. L. Wain and his colleagues at the ARC Unit of Plant Growth Substances and Systemic Fungicides (now disbanded) sought to identify how substituent groups, usually chlorine or methyl, on the ring or side chain of phenoxyacetic acid modify herbicidal activity. 2,4–D and MCPA (4–chloro–2–methylphenoxyacetic acid) were used as reference compounds, being extremely active because unlike indoleacetic acid they are not metabolized readily within the plant. Another herbicide MCPB (4–chloro–2–methylphenoxybutyric acid) was developed to exhibit a new type of selectivity among dicotyledonous plants that rested upon the biochemical diversity encountered among plants. The principle is logical: susceptible plants including many weed species when treated with MCPB, itself inactive as a herbicide, employ their $\beta$-oxidase enzyme to convert it to the active acetic acid derivative (MCPA); but resistant species, e.g. clovers, possess a modified form of the enzyme that is unable to cleave the butyric side chain of MCPB. Most weeds can then be eradicated from clover pastures by spraying with MCPB.

The speculative suggestion was made earlier in this essay that the biosynthetic dichotomy existing between crop plants and fungi in ammonia assimilatory mechanisms might be exploited to devise new types of fungicide. A similar opportunity could lie in the distinct difference encountered between higher plants and fungi in the pathways used for lysine biosynthesis. In each case compounds acting as specific inhibitors of the fungal pathway are being sought for they might provide a logical basis from which new fungicidal compounds could be developed. Another highly desirable innovation would be the development of chemicals restricting virus multiplication in plants without causing deleterious effects on the host. Interest in this possibility of direct control of viruses has been heightened by recent research showing that a unique complex of proteins is formed in tobacco leaves as a response to infection by tobacco mosaic virus, and that they perhaps serve to limit the further spread of virus. If polyacrylic acid or aspirin is injected into leaves, they trigger the synthesis of the same or a very similar group of proteins. Now it is important to confirm whether, and under what conditions, these induced proteins can confer resistance to virus multiplication; to determine what structural components of the proteins are essential for their biological activity; and to find inducers that will be effective when applied as foliar sprays. The information gained should provide new insights into the prerequisites for a viricide.

For the foreseeable future, the adequate protection of crops grown under intensive agricultural systems must continue to rely in large measure on pesticide chemicals. Yet as the cost of developing new chemicals soars, and concern for their impact on the environment increases, the exact pattern of their future use is uncertain. The seventh report of the Royal Commission on Environmental Pollution (1979) comments on the present situation as follows: "We accept that the continued use of pesticides is essential to maintain food supplies and that much care is taken by manufacturers, and through the existing control machinery, to ensure safety in use and to minimise adverse environmental effects. We are concerned, nevertheless, about the scale of pesticide use." A complementary future strategy anticipates that plant breeders will successfully develop new crop varieties with enhanced resistance to pests and diseases, but success may exact some penalty in terms of other performance characters. Chemical control and host plant resistance suffer a common shortcoming, namely, that their efficacy is frequently transient because of the emergence of strains of pests and pathogens insensitive to the pesticide or virulent against the resistance factors. It is then imperative that future research should (i) facilitate the development of new techniques to improve the efficiency of pesticide application, (ii) expand knowledge of the factors determining the incidence of diseases and pests and of economic threshold levels, (iii) develop strategies to delay the onset of resistance to insecticides in insects, and (iv) seek to apply more broadly the concepts of integrated control. In simple terms, the task is to acquire information that will permit farmers to receive better information about how, when and what to spray, and to know how to incorporate pesticides into farming practices in ways that will maximize the contributions of other factors to the control of weeds, pests and diseases.

Ideally, farmers spray crops with pesticides only when the yield benefit exceeds the economic cost of spraying. Weeds may be distinguished from other damaging organisms because they are always a hazard to crops and some measure of control is therefore invariably required. In contrast, the levels of disease organisms and pests vary capriciously, from season to season, being strongly influenced by environmental conditions, particularly the weather. It is then important to provide farmers with accurate forecasts of potentially damaging attacks if "insurance" spraying is to be avoided, with consequent reduction in the amounts of pesticides entering the environment. By using spore traps, it has been possible to correlate disease levels on foliage with the numbers and probable movement of fungal spores in the atmosphere, i.e. with the likelihood of disease spread to nearby crops, and effective forecasting of the spread of diseases such as barley mildew now occurs on the basis of field symptoms. Suction traps of the type developed by the Rothamsted Insect Survey now provide weekly details of aphid populations and these are used to alert sugar beet growers to potentially damaging infestations of *Myzus persicae*, the aphid vector of virus yellows, and of *Aphis fabae* (black-fly). More recently, pheromones have been employed to provide trapping systems for specific insects pests. This approach has been particularly successful in the U.K. for monitoring pea moth populations using simple, inexpensive equipment readily available to growers. In a well established regime, based upon knowledge of the life-cycle and behavioural biology of the moth, trap catches are used to indicate when and if insecticides need to be applied.

The development of good forecasting procedures for a wider range of pest species must be a priority for future research, because success should provide one of the most effective ways of decreasing the use of pesticides and, in consequence, help to delay the build-up of resistance in insects to insecticides. Better forecasting permitting more timely spraying ideally should be developed in full association with cultural and biological methods that can contribute to the alleviation or prevention of damage to crops, i.e. by adopting the concepts of integrated control. Scientists from the Glasshouse Crops Research Institute and Rothamsted now aim to exploit the long-term observations made by the Game Conservancy at North Farm, Sussex, on the effects of pesticides on the fauna of field crops by initiating a more experimental approach. Some of the components earlier identified as exercising important restraints on pest populations, including entomogenous fungi, insect predators and parasites, cultivations affecting the soil fauna, and weed cover, are now being combined in field experiments designed to quantify the benefits of these methods and to integrate them, through predictive monitoring, with the necessary use of appropriate pesticides.

The biological effect of crop protection treatments depends upon the intrinsic properties of the pesticide and on the manner of formulation and application. Accuracy in application is important; the control agent should be delivered to the target organism with a high degree of efficiency and, ideally, be prevented from reaching unintended recipients. In agricultural practice, the quantities of control agents applied normally far exceed the amounts that would be needed to eliminate damaging infestations of pests if each individual could receive the minimum lethal dose, e.g. in an ideal situation, Graham-Bryce (1978) has calculated that only 0.03% of the dimethoate dose used to control aphids on field beans would be required. There is then great interest in developing methods for obtaining more effective deposition by improving pesticide placement and coverage of the intended receiving surfaces. Theoretical considerations indicate that, for a fixed amount of active ingredient, more effective control should result if it is applied as small, uniformly-sized droplets rather than as larger droplets of variable diameter. Partly as a result of research at the ARC Weed Research Organization low and ultra-low volume methods of application have been developed to meet these requirements, and to reduce the energy consumed during spraying operations. A serious disadvantage associated with smaller droplets is their tendency to drift, but this can largely be overcome by applying electrostatic charges to ensure that droplets follow more direct trajectories from spray orifice to crop foliage. Scientists at Rothamsted and the University of Sheffield have collaborated in the design of prototype equipment producing electrostatically-charged droplets from aqueous formulations, and more recently Imperial Chemical Industries have demonstrated the "Electrodyn" apparatus for electrodynamic spraying using oil-based formulations. By using these methods crop foliage, including the under-surfaces of leaves, can be enveloped by spray droplets more effectively than by conventional spraying techniques, and the Electrodyn can be used with spray volumes as low as $0.5 \, 1 \, ha^{-1}$.

The use of pesticides at high dosage rates and at frequent intervals on crops can enhance the selection of insect strains resistant to insecticides and possibly of variants of pathogenic fungi tolerant to commonly-used fungicides. The problem of resistance in insects is becoming progressively more serious throughout the world and now insensitivity to insecticides has been detected within some populations of most species having agricultural, veterinary or medical significance. In the U.K., resistance in aphids, especially *Myzus persicae*, presents problems of control in both agriculture and horticulture; field populations of this aphid have been detected that are insensitive to organophosphate insecticides at levels a hundred times higher than those killing sensitive individuals, whilst even stronger resistance has been encountered in variant strains from glasshouses. If the risks associated with resistance are to be minimized, we need to understand better the mechanisms of resistance and the ways in which it becomes established in populations. An important factor contributing to resistance is the inherent ability of aphids and other insects to degrade and thereby inactivate insecticides. For a number of classes of insecticides, degradation involves cleavage of an ester linkage within the insecticide molecule; organophosphate, pyrethroid and, to a lesser extent, carbamate insecticides are subject to such hydrolytic breakdown. Resistance levels encountered in *Myzus persicae* show a close relationship with the activities of an esterase (E-4), of broad substrate specificity, found in the aphid. High levels of resistance are associated with the production of multiple copies of the gene responsible for the synthesis of the esterase, and the most strongly resistant aphid populations from glasshouses have 32, or even 64 copies: field populations showing strong resistance often have 16 copies, whilst those showing moderate resistance have 4 copies. Laboratory studies have indicated that populations having 32 or 64 gene copies exhibit chromosomal instability, and if insecticide is withheld, their progeny may revert to having only a single copy of the gene i.e. they become sensitive again. This does not appear to happen with field populations having up to 16 gene copies.

Because resistance once acquired within field populations normally persists the only practicable way of combating established resistance has been to switch to a different insecticide. This may in turn lead to the selection of other resistance mechanisms with the consequence that the range of possible control agents, many of which come from a relatively few chemical classes, may be in danger of becoming exhausted for some pest populations. Therefore, for the future, an essential feature of any policy to avoid escalation of resistance should be the minimization of selection pressures and the withdrawal of selection at a sufficiently early stage to prevent resistant individuals becoming numerous and acquiring increased fitness. Rothamsted has a special concern that the newer photostable pyrethroids should be used to maximum advantage in insect control, and therefore we regret the tendency developing to control houseflies and other domestic pest insects with these moderately persistent compounds; the earlier less stable (non persistent) pyrethroids (resmethrin and bioresmethrin) are still appropriate in this situation and their use probably would delay onset of the build-up of strong resistance to the agriculturally-important photostable compounds.

Problems with fungicides are in many ways similar. Surveys have revealed that considerable variation in the response to systemic fungicides can exist within barley mildew populations. Widespread use of at least one of these fungicides has led to some decline in the overall sensitivity of mildew, but to what extent this has adversely affected yield improvements is not clear. Nevertheless, we must aim to ensure that the most resistant strains do not become abundant within the natural mildew population.

## Concluding Remarks

Because the subject area is so broad and the experimental contributions so detailed and extensive, this account has provided only glimpses of how a variety of scientific disciplines have enhanced crop production over the past few decades. My aim has been to portray to the reader how creative ideas coupled with careful, and often demanding, experimentation on the part of the scientist has led both to exciting new knowledge and to better and more efficient agronomic practices. I hope my efforts have achieved a modicum of success.

## Further Reading

Chollet, R. and Ogren, W. L. (1975). Regulation of photorespiration in $C_3$ and $C_4$ species. *Botanical Review*, **41**, 137.

Elliott, M. (1979). Progress in the design of insecticides. *Chemistry and Industry, p. 757.*

Fowden, L. (1979). Nitrogen: the keystone to plant growth and metabolism, in *Proceedings of the 2nd Long Ashton Symposium on Nitrogen Metabolism in Plants*, p. 1.

Graham-Bryce, I. J. (1978). The need for accuracy. *Agricultural Aviation*, **19**, 107.

Monteith, J. L. (1977). Climate and the efficiency of crop production in Britain. *Philosophical Transactions of the Royal Society of London*, B, **281**, 277.

Penman, H. L. (1948). Natural evaporation from open water, bare soil and grass. *Proceedings of the Royal Society of London*, A, **193**, 120.

Royal Commission on Environmental Pollution (1979). Seventh Report: Agriculture and Pollution, Command 7644, London, H.M. Stationery Office.

Rudd-Jones, D. (1981). p. 174 of this Jubilee Volume.

Russell, E. J. (1942). British Agricultural Research: Rothamsted, publ. for The British Council by Longmans, Green & Co., London.

# Science in Horticulture

## D. RUDD-JONES

Glasshouse Crops Research Institute, Littlehampton, Sussex

Horticulture is variously described as, "the science and art of growing fruits, vegetables, flowers or ornamental plants"; or, "the art of cultivating gardens". Traditionally, it has been regarded as an art or craft rather than a science. In fact, commercial horticulture is a highly sophisticated technology for producing high value crops, nearly all of which can be grown by the home gardener and which characteristically are marketed as fresh produce although they may be stored for quite long periods before sale.

The fascination of horticulture for the scientist is in the wide range of crops. Annual crops such as the majority of vegetables, perennial and plantation fruits, and protected crops which may be short term and leafy like lettuce, or indeterminate like tomatoes where as many as thirty fruit trusses may be harvested from one plant during the season. They provide the scientist with numerous opportunities for applying scientific methods to manipulate growth and development of the crop to increase productivity, to improve quality and to extend the season of production.

The initiative to apply science to horticultural practice came in the first place from the growers themselves. They were responsible for establishing and funding the early research and experimental stations; Long Ashton, East Malling and Cheshunt were all founded by growers before the First World War as Sir William Henderson has described. The horticultural industry has been fortunate too in the determination of growers to use scientific knowledge in improving their methods. Many of them are highly innovative and ingenious in developing new systems, and eager to use the scientists' work, often before the research is complete. But equally, the growers have been fortunate in attracting able and often outstanding scientists to study their problems. During and after the war the Agricultural Departments and the Agricultural Research Council, firstly through the Agricultural Improvement Councils, and later with advice from the Joint Consultative Organisation, have played an increasing role in providing facilities for research, development and advisory work in horticulture so that this country is now extraordinarily well equipped.

## Value of the Horticultural Industry and Trends of Production

In 1979 the value of commercial horticultural production in the United Kingdom amounted to £783M or about 10 per cent of total agricultural production. Table 1 summarizes the value of horticultural crops and imports, and the increase in value of home production achieved in the ten years 1968–78.

Trends of production over the past decade reflect changing consumer preferences and the exploitation of opportunities for reducing imports or promoting exports. Salad crops have become much more popular for reasons of convenience and changing eating habits, and foreign holidays have developed more exotic tastes.

The increase in the proportion of vegetable and salad crops grown under some form of protection — now amounting to over 30 per cent in value — reflects the demand for quality which will have to be maintained to offset competing imports. This is true also for dessert apples where the high eating quality of the Cox's Orange Pippin apple is

Table 1

Value of horticultural output in UK, 1968–78
£ millions

| Crop | 1968 | 1978 | Imports 1978 |
|---|---|---|---|
| **Fruit** | | | |
| Soft fruit | 17 | 69 | 5 |
| Orchard fruit | 36 | 69 | 114 |
| **Vegetables** | | | |
| Field vegetables | 92 | 285 | 89 |
| Protected vegetables | 39 | 140* | 103 |
| **Ornamentals** | | | |
| Protected ornamentals | – | 51 | 15 |
| Bulbs and bulb flowers | – | 28 | 10 |
| Hardy nursery stock | – | 48 | 20 |

* Excludes Channel Islands (£M29)

essential to counter the imports of Golden Delicious. The yield of French orchards can be as high as 60 t ha$^{-1}$, which is more than five times the average yield of dessert apples in the UK. Similarly, the need to compete with early strawberries imported from Italy and Israel (grown outdoors or under protection) has stimulated the home production of strawberries under plastic and the selection and breeding of improved varieties.

In the ornamental sector too, the influence of imports from more Southerly latitudes (notably Colombia and Israel), and high fuel costs, has affected production of protected carnations especially in winter when the quality of home produce tends to be low because of poor light.

The bulb industry has been outstandingly improved by applying research and development. The UK is now the largest producer in the world of narcissus bulbs and a co-operative bulb producers' marketing organisation, Lingarden Ltd., received the Queen's Award for Export in 1979.

Changing trends of production reflect changing demands, but also changing economic constraints, mainly the increased cost and lower availability of labour, particularly skilled labour. Technological innovation in all sectors of horticulture, including mechanization and the use of herbicides, has enabled production to be maintained on a much smaller area and with a greatly reduced labour force. For example, Kent, which had over 37 000 hectares of fruit in 1939, had only just over half the area forty years later.

## Crop Improvement

Since the war, and due largely to applying the results of research, highly sophisticated, intensive production systems have been developed for horticulture. With these systems growers can manipulate crops to achieve high yields of high quality with minimal waste. There are four ways in which growers control growth and development of their crops.

## Environmental control

Light, temperature, atmospheric composition (especially carbon dioxide) and relative humidity are the factors of the aerial environment that need control. In the root environment they are the soil (or other substrate) temperature, water, nutrients and oxygen.

Light is the main constraint on production in Britain. Solar radiation is the one factor that cannot be controlled, and yet the grower must aim to maximize the photosynthetically active radiation reaching the leaves of the crop. The timing of the crop is important in making the best use of sunlight, and this is linked to other factors of the environment such as soil temperature and time the crop matures. There is limited scope for offsetting adverse weather conditions with an outdoor crop, but techniques such as avoiding frost damage, speed up successful propagation and growth. In glasshouses the grower is cropping in a controlled environment; air temperature and humidity can be controlled very precisely and the atmosphere can be enriched with carbon dioxide. The grower can also control precisely the amount of water and nutrients applied to roots through trickle irrigation systems, and he can speed up propagation by artificial lighting. He can control the flowering response of ornamental crops by manipulating the daylength with artificial lighting and blackouts. Environmental control extends also to the post-harvest physiology of the crop including field cooling of vegetables, short- or long-term storage, and conditioning harvested produce for processing.

## Genetic control

The selection and breeding of improved varieties of horticultural crops probably accounts for the major improvements in yield which have been achieved, but it has also contributed significantly to better quality in some. Breeding may achieve earlier, more consistent yields, winter hardiness, better response to fertilisers and, especially important in horticulture, resistance to pests and diseases. The selection and development of apple rootstocks of differing vigour has been vital to exploiting different soil types and climates and different cropping systems. Clones of ornamental hardy nursery stock have been selected for earlier propagation, improved growth habit and better flowering characteristics.

## Chemical and biological control

Plant growth regulators are widely used in horticulture. They can be applied to set fruit blossom or tomato flowers, to inhibit fruit drop, to retard growth, to promote rooting, to suppress lateral shoots, to delay or accelerate senescence and ripening, and to break dormancy in forcing flower bulbs. They may be used to inhibit sprouting of stored crops.

   Chemical pesticides are used to control pests, diseases and weeds, and to reduce the yield losses they cause. Most chemicals now used have been developed since the war; in particular herbicides have had profound effects on horticultural cropping systems and have contributed greatly to improved yields. Within the past decade, however, there has been a dramatic rise in the development of resistance and tolerance to pesticides, especially of systemic fungicides; the development of integrated systems of pest and disease control, in which the use of biological control agents is combined with chemical methods, has therefore become urgent. Developing virus-free stocks of vegetatively propagated crops is another form of biological control which has been vitally important to the top and soft fruit crops, to protected ornamental crops, and prospectively to bulb crops.

## Mechanical control

Cropping may be manipulated to meet specific environmental requirements, and to aid genetic and chemical control methods. The success of methods of mist propagation and trickle irrigation, for example, has depended on the design and development of suitable equipment, as has the use of carbon dioxide enrichment in glasshouses. Similarly the designs of strawberry, raspberry and apple harvesting machines have depended on varieties with particular growth and fruiting characteristics. Other examples are the design of spray equipment needed for applying pesticides in low volumes as fogs or controlled drops.

The different ways in which growers manage cropping can best be illustrated by discussing examples of modern production systems.

## Production Systems and Productivity

### *Fruit:* **Dessert apples**

Top fruit orchards provide the best example of intensification of horticultural production over the past 50 years. Between 1939 and 1970 the total apple acreage fell by about two-thirds, and nearly half this reduction in area occurred after 1962 when the more productive Malling-Merton rootstocks distributed in the 1950s were beginning to come into full bearing. These rootstocks were the result of a joint breeding programme between East Malling and the John Innes Institute (when it was located at Merton). Planting of apples has changed from orchards of large trees, 120 to the hectare, through bush-type orchards with semi-dwarfing rootstocks at 300–400 per hectare, to the present hedgerow plantings of spindle bushes or palmettes of 700–1000 trees per hectare. Plant density is further increased in dwarf pyramids and cordon systems with up to 3000 trees (Plate 1). These systems have reduced the land required and the size of trees with earlier cropping and easier mechanical harvesting.

In 1971 Professor J. P. Hudson, then Director of Long Ashton, put forward his concept of the "meadow orchard" which has been developed by his colleagues to take this progression of very dwarf rootstocks and closer planting a stage further, so reducing unnecessary "scaffolding" as he called it. Trees were to be induced to form fruit buds in the first year so that in the second year they would blossom and fruit and would be "combine harvested" or "mowed" (hence "meadow orchard") leaving a stump from which a new shoot would appear to continue the biennial cycle. In such systems the orchard floor is uncultivated but maintained weed-free with herbicides; overhead irrigation lines can dispense pesticides and growth regulating chemicals as well as fertilizers and water (Plate 2). The meadow orchard remains experimental for apples in Britain but is used commercially for peaches in Israel. Nevertheless it has stimulated ideas for improving the overall economic and biological efficiency of apple production. Simplifying propagation, reducing time from planting to first harvest, and lowering the ratio of vegetative growth to reproductive growth necessary to give a good crop, are all technical advances and have speeded the development of methods of hedgerow and "fruit wall" planting.

*Plate 1* Fifteen-year old trees of James Grieve; left to right – on M27, M9, M26, and M106 rootstocks.

The "fruit wall" uses growth regulators, combined with root competition, and is designed primarily for an "over-row" mechanical harvester. The trees, planted 30 cm apart with 3 m between rows, are supported on wires and trained as vertical cordons 2 m high, allowing maximum light penetration. Measurements at East Malling show well-managed spindlebush hedgerow orchards intercept up to 70% of available energy.

Lateral growth of trees in a fruit wall is controlled by mechanical pruning combined with a growth retardant. The system gives annual crops of high quality fruit from the second year onwards.

Variability of yield is a major problem of apple growing and indeed of fruit crops generally; changes in productivity over the past 40 years are shown in Table 2. Fluctuations occur in all fruits, being most marked in plums where there can be a tenfold variation from year to year. There have been marked increases in average yield between the pre-war and post-war periods amounting to 39% in dessert apples, 69% in strawberries, but virtually no increase in plums.

*Plate 2* A meadow orchard of Egremont Russet; the trees in the foreground have been harvested and cut down according to the meadow orchard procedure.

Table 2

Yields (t ha$^{-1}$) of major fruit crops in England and Wales, showing changes between 1936–37 and 1971–75

| Crop | | 1936–37 | Average 70/71–74/75 |
|---|---|---|---|
| Apples | Dessert | 6.83 | 11.16 |
| | Culinary | | 13.56 |
| Pears* | | 6.05 | 10.37 |
| Cherries | | 2.68 | 3.21 |
| Plums | | 6.93 | 7.06 |
| Strawberries | | 1.83 | 6.96 |
| Raspberries | | 1.90 | 4.64 |
| Blackcurrants | | 1.76 | 5.73 |
| Gooseberries | | 3.20 | 7.28 |

\* excluding pears for perry making.

Weather is the major factor determining differences in yield from year to year. While climate and other environmental factors will contribute to the loss of potential yield in the so-called "June drop" of young fruit, light levels in the previous year will have been the major factor determining the number of fruit buds formed. Another factor that is largely uncontrolled is the level of pollination with certain varieties, notably Cox. When this variety is selfed fruit set is less than 1 per cent, whereas the variety is cross fertile at over 7 per cent. Research at Long Ashton has shown that cold spring weather can reduce cross-pollination, and pollen tube growth, and hand pollination can increase the yield of Cox up to 40 per cent.

Increase in yields of strawberries are due to several contributing factors associated with improved health of stocks, freedom from virus and fungal diseases, and cropping in a weed-free environment by using herbicides (Table 3).

Table 3

Yields of strawberries in England and Wales from 1928–1978

|         | Yield (t ha$^{-1}$) | Reason for increase |
|---------|---------------------|---------------------|
| 1928/37 | 2.5 | – |
| 1938/48 | 3.5 | Healthier stock |
|         |     | Freedom from virus |
|         |     | Formation of Nuclear Stock Association |
| 1950/60 | 4.0 | Improved varieties |
| 1961/70 | 6.0 | Herbicides and Botrytis control |
| 1971/78 | 6.8 | Botrytis control |

## *Vegetables:* Onions

Until the 1950s bulb onions produced in this country had to be marketed within two months for immediate use. The crop did not keep and there was no clear understanding of requirements for field curing and storage. Consequently Britain depended for winter supplies on imported onions costing about twice the price of the home-grown crop.

Improved varieties, and the use of herbicides which remove the need for hand weeding and facilitate precision drilling of seed, contributed to increased yields. Research at Wellesbourne on crop-spacing, row width and the development of a bed system indicated the full yield potential that could be achieved in a weed-free environment. At the same time the development of improved storage methods and the control of neck rot disease caused by *Botrytis alii* enabled the crop to be stored until the end of March at ambient temperatures, and until early June if refrigerated. However, between June and September onions had to be imported from Spain and other countries and research was started to see if home production could provide year-round supply. This centred on the hypothesis that an autumn-sown crop would be earlier maturing, but the varieties then being grown required 16-hour days to start bulbing. The search for improved varieties concentrated on day-length requirements and several Japanese varieties were found

Table 4

Increases in yield of some vegetable crops in England and Wales

| Crop | Yield (t ha$^{-1}$) | |
|------|---------|---------|
|      | 1951/52 | 1973/74 |
| Summer and autumn cabbage | 25.7 | 29.5 |
| Brussels sprouts | 7.2 | 13.1 |
| Late summer and autumn cauliflower | 14.8 | 24.0 |
| Peas (green for processing) | 3.2 | 4.9 |
| Broad beans | 6.4 | 10.4 |
| Carrots | 25.4 | 42.0 |
| Beetroot | 24.0 | 31.4 |
| Onions (dry bulb) | 19.0 | 35.1 |
| Leeks | 19.8 | 22.2 |

which started to form bulbs once the day length had reached 12–13 hours. Yields of bulb onions doubled from about 17 t ha$^{-1}$ in 1947 to about 34 t ha$^{-1}$ in 1973, and in the past fifteen years a fourfold increase in home production has left a gap of only 20 per cent that has to be filled by imports. This represents an outstanding achievement in the commercial application of research and development, which was recognised in 1977 by the Queen's Award for Technological Achievement to the National Vegetable Research Station at Wellesbourne.

The yields of most field vegetables have increased markedly over the past 25 years (Table 4), and improvements in the leading three, Brussels sprouts, carrots and onions, can be attributed largely to inputs of research and development.

### Protected crops

During the past 50 years the design and construction of glasshouses has markedly improved. This has increased light transmission especially during winter and spring, and a one per cent increase in light transmission has been shown to give a potential increase in yield of one per cent. Before 1950 most glasshouses were wooden, with thick glazing bars, built in multi-span blocks orientated North-South. Light transmission in winter rarely exceeded 40 per cent. The change to metal houses with fewer glazing bars and larger panes of glass, orientated East-West, has increased light transmission to over 70 per cent. These improvements have been associated with improved heating systems and the development of highly sophisticated automatic ventilation controls, which also allow the atmosphere to be enriched with carbon dioxide. At the same time better control of the root environment has come from more precise control of water and nutrients applied through trickle irrigation systems.

### Tomatoes

Early tomato crops have benefited from much research and development at the Glasshouse Crops Research Institute at Littlehampton and by the Agricultural Development and Advisory Service (ADAS); the results have been assembled in a "Tomato Blueprint", providing a very precise specification for achieving high yields.

The blueprint specifies the optimal day and night temperatures for the various growth stages, enabling the grower to manipulate the growth and development of the crop by environmental control to avoid problems such as abortion of the first flowering truss, which can happen in dull weather if the temperature is not lowered. Adhering to the blueprint also ensures that the earliest possible yields are obtained — picking starts with quite remarkable precision in the South about the third week in March! The use of $CO_2$ enrichment enables higher temperatures to be maintained before ventilating the house and cropping can continue for 8 or 9 months.

Adding $CO_2$ is, of course, peculiar to protected cropping since only within the closed and controlled glasshouse environment is it possible to enhance photosynthesis and hence productivity in this way; early yields can be increased by more than 30%.

Until about 10 years ago nearly all glasshouse tomatoes were grown in "border" soil which had to be sterilised either with steam or by a fumigant chemical (generally methyl bromide) to control soil-borne diseases, especially *Fusarium* and *Verticillium* wilts and also tomato mosaic virus (TMV). The high cost of sterilization in terms of both labour and steam or chemicals has led to the development of cropping systems out of the border soil. The most rapid change has been the development of fertilised peat filled into plastic bags or "modules". Peat is light in weight and has a high water holding capacity coupled with good aeration. It has however little buffering capacity, and with the small root volume of the modules it is essential that water and nutrients are applied with great precision through a trickle (drip) irrigation system.

The use of peat has increased the precision and productivity of tomato cropping, and has reduced the "turn-round" time between crops (and the same is true for cucumber production in rock wool, a method developed in Scandinavia and Holland). However, peat is a finite resource which will become more expensive as it becomes more scarce. Nevertheless, the more precise control of the root environment provided by a peat substrate now finds its logical extension in some form of hydroponic culture. The "Nutrient Film Technique" ("NFT") was developed at the Glasshouse Crops Research Institute in the 1960s as a research method for studying the physiology of roots, but it was A. J. Cooper who first saw its commercial potential. The basic principle is simple; a shallow stream of solution containing the essential nutrients circulates over the roots of growing plants in a film a few millimetres deep, providing adequate aeration, water and nutrients. The plants are grown in a series of sloping parallel gullies placed directly on a glasshouse floor, graded to a slope of 1 in 75–100, or raised on supports (Plate 3). The nutrient solution is pumped to the upper ends of the gullies and flows along the rows of plants to a catchment tank below ground level (Fig. 1). pH and conductivity are controlled automatically; pH is held at 6–6.5, and conductivity at levels above 2000 micromhos. This allows the nutritional requirements of the crop to be met satisfactorily although imbalances can develop and give rise to deficiency symptoms even though the conductivity readings remain high.

*Plate 3* Nutrient film cropping of tomatoes on a commercial nursery shortly after planting in December-January.

Conventional nutrient solutions used in hydroponics, such as those developed by E. J. Hewitt at Long Ashton, have proved satisfactory for NFT. Research at Littlehampton has, however, demonstrated that tomatoes can be grown in nutrient film culture at surprisingly low levels of nitrogen and potassium provided these concentrations are maintained at the root surface.

It had been thought that the nutrient film technique would provide opportunities for energy saving by heating the nutrient solution and growing the crop at *lower* night air temperatures. Experiments at Littlehampton and on Guernsey indicated that heating the solution to 23–26°C improves growth (and growth is retarded below 15°C); this allows the night temperature to be lowered to 10–12°C without losing yield, although cropping may be delayed. However, the effects of raising root environment temperature appear to be independent of air temperature so there is no energy saving advantage.

The development of NFT has aroused world-wide interest, especially in arid zones where it is possible to grow crops using limited water supplies economically. The

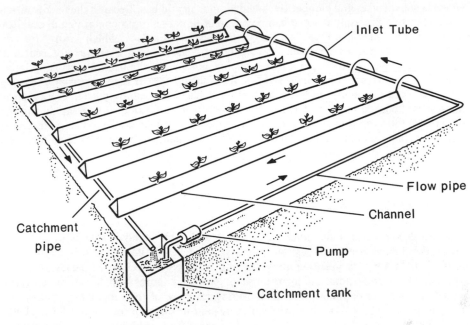

*Figure 1* The main features of a nutrient film system.

technique can also be fully automated, and computerised commercial installations are already producing tomatoes and lettuce in Britain.

Increases in productivity of protected tomatoes are difficult to assess because average yields include both heated and cold-house crops, and crops in different parts of the country. However, yields before the war were about 75 t ha$^{-1}$, and these had improved to 150–200 t ha$^{-1}$ by the late 1950s. In the ten years between 1968 and 1977 productivity increased by 30% on average, and by 40% on some nurseries which reached 350 t ha$^{-1}$.

An analysis of the factors contributing to increased yields on one nursery showed that control of tomato mosaic virus disease, either by using attenuated virus inoculation, or by resistant varieties, could account for 17% of the increase. The switch from growing in border soil to peat bags, and heavier yielding varieties, could account for much of the rest. However, improved environmental control probably contributed significantly, as did introducing biological pest control since chemical pesticides are known to reduce yields. In an experiment comparing NFT and peat bags over three years, NFT grown crops averaged 378 t ha$^{-1}$, peat bags giving a yield of only 310 t ha$^{-1}$.

During the same 10 year period 1968–77, the productivity of protected cucumbers increased by 11%, protected lettuce by 26%, and mushrooms by 27%.

## Mushrooms

Mushroom production has now reached a precision and predictability undreamed of thirty years ago; yet we still know comparatively little about the needs of growing mycelium that makes it switch to reproductive development and form sporophores — the harvested crop. Nevertheless by a largely empirical approach by both research scientists and a technically progressive industry, a highly productive technology has developed. Initially this involves fermenting a compost traditionally based on horse manure, but now increasingly using "synthetic" composts of straw fermented with other animal manures. Carbohydrate and protein supplements are recommended in various published formulae, including two from Littlehampton. The initial fermentation lasting about a week, is followed by pasteurization which lasts a further week, during which pests, diseases and competitive weed moulds should be killed and the fermentation completed to a precisely defined compost free of ammonia, and containing about 70% moisture. The trays are then "seeded" with mushroom spawn, which "runs" for two weeks under controlled conditions before being "cased" with a mixture of peat and chalk. The trays are then placed in cropping houses in which temperature, relative humidity and $CO_2$ are controlled. The first flush should appear three weeks after casing, to be followed at weekly intervals by further flushes. Immediately after cropping the houses are "cooked out" to sterilize them; meticulous attention to hygiene during the growth of the crop and during the turn-round between crops is probably the most important feature of successful production. Pests — sciarid, phorid and cecid flies, and virus and *Verticillium* diseases — are the most serious problems.

## Year-round chrysanthemums

Growing flower crops under glass on a year-round basis involves control of light for flower development as well as for photosynthesis. In Britain, natural daylight is insufficient to keep chrysanthemums growing from November to February; growers supplement natural radiation by the use of powerful lamps which sustain uniform growth and control daylength for the flowering response of the crop. *Chrysanthemum morifolium* is a short-day plant; the varieties used in glasshouses initiate flower buds when the dark period exceeds 9½ hours, and these buds develop into flowers with a dark period of more than 10½ hours. Artificial lighting is used to delay flowering in the winter; blackouts are used during the summer to induce flowering. At our latitudes, the artificial long days needed from early August to the middle of May are usually applied by "night-break" lighting switched on automatically in the middle of the night. Lighting must be applied for 3–4 hours in Southern England, and care taken that the continuous dark period does not exceed 7 hours or flower bud initiation may start. Blackout has to be used from March to September to delay flowering.

The response of chrysanthemums to manipulating light and dark periods — the photoperiodic control of flowering — is highly quantitative. Research at Littlehampton has confirmed earlier work which showed that although flowering is accelerated by short days (8 hours) flowers are eventually formed in long days. This suggests there are two separate processes involved in flowering, and the second appears to be a more gradual process unaffected by daylength. When no short days were given the plant formed 30 leaves on the stem (main axis) before producing one terminal flower in ten weeks. The number of leaves formed before flowering appears to be related to the intensity of the short-day treatment, for, after exposure to 4 short-day cycles, two flowers were produced with 25 leaves below them. As more short-day cycles were given more axillary flowers were formed down the stem (Fig. 2). The predictability of the photoperiodic control of flowering which can be achieved with chrysanthemums enables growers to plan a year-round production schedule very precisely.

The duration of the long- and short-day treatments depends on time of year and the response type (i.e. flowering time) of the varieties used. Growers normally devise a range of varieties in several growing units to ensure year-round production. With November planting of a 10-week response variety, there will be 5 weeks of long-day treatment followed by 11 weeks in short days before flowering, a total of 16 weeks. In summer, the long-day treatment will last only two weeks and be followed by 10 weeks of short days to crop in 12 weeks. This system allows 3–4 crops in one year.

Year-round chrysanthemum production, which started in this country in 1955, depends on cuttings which are generally produced, especially in winter, in southern regions, such as the Canaries, Malta, Kenya and Israel, where with better light, growth of the stock plants and quality of the cuttings is better.

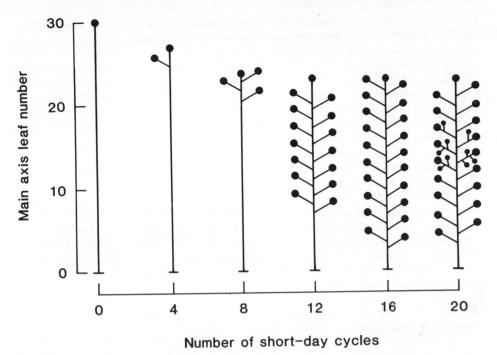

*Figure 2* The pattern of flower production in relation to the number of short day cycles received. Each "flower bud" is represented by a circle.

## Gains from protection

Yields of protected crops are very high when measured as annual yield per unit area. On a dry weight basis, tomatoes and cucumbers yield five or six times the weight of apples that can be produced in the same area, four or five times the weight of cereal grain, and twice the weight of potatoes. Such comparisons are not very meaningful because protected crops are grown in an expensive, controlled environment, with high energy inputs. They do, however, show the yields that can be achieved in intensive production, and they point to the technical objectives of scientific research while indicating economic constraints. In a similar context, when herbicides were first used in vegetable production, J. K. A. Bleasdale achieved a yield of carrots equivalent to 296 t ha$^{-1}$, or more than ten times the national average, from field crops grown without any constraints and with as long a growing season as possible.

## Special Techniques of Horticultural Production

As with any industry in which scientific knowledge is being applied, the specialized techniques of horticultural production provide examples where the scientific basis was established first, and others where scientific understanding came after the practice had been adopted but may have contributed to further improvement. It is convenient to look at horticultural production in the sequence of sowing or planting through to harvesting and post-harvest treatment.

### Seed propagation

Most salad and vegetable crops, whether grown outdoors or under protection, are raised from seed. The introduction of herbicides and minimal cultivation methods has meant that precision drilling of the seed to the final stand required is possible without thinning.

Therefore all seed must germinate and become established as seedlings and cropping plants. The difficulties of field establishment with small-seeded crops have been overcome in various ways, notably by using pre-germinated seed. A recent idea has been to sow pre-germinated seed in a jelly which protects the young seedlings from drying out during establishment. Originally conceived by J. G. Elliott at the Weed Research Organization for grass seeding, it has been adapted for the direct drilling of vegetable seed as the "Fluid Seed Drill" at Wellesbourne and is now being commercially developed. Seeds are pre-germinated in sodium alginate gel which also carries them from a reservoir into the furrow.

While many vegetable crops are directly sown, some are transplanted, as are glasshouse vegetable crops. Specialized seed and potting composts have been developed to facilitate rapid and successful propagation. The formulae for the first standard composts were published by W. J. C. Lawrence and J. Newell of the John Innes Institute in 1936. Their seed compost was based on partially sterilized loam mixed with moss peat and sand, superphosphate, and chalk to neutralise the peat. At Littlehampton, a range of loamless composts has been developed based on mixtures of sphagnum peat and sand; since loam is not used these composts do not have to be sterilized (essential with John Innes composts). However, the base fertilisers need more precise attention and trace elements are supplied as frits.

## Vegetative propagation

Propagating cuttings of carnations and chrysanthemums has already been mentioned, and the propagation of softwood and leafy hardwood cuttings for fruit and hardy nursery stock is equally important. Rooting compounds and artificial lighting have been used for some time to promote the rooting of cuttings, and the introduction of mist propagation in the USA in the early 1950s significantly improved the success rate. The technique provides intermittent misting of cuttings, control being by a clock or by an "artificial leaf" which activates misting when dry. An alternative is to monitor incoming solar radiation so that the periods of misting are determined by a fixed light integral. Contrary to earlier interpretations it has been shown at Littlehampton that rooting is inversely proportional to the sugar concentration of cuttings above a basic level so light is not the sole factor determining successful rooting, even when cuttings are kept turgid and cool. This finding has led to the development of simple shading of the cuttings so that the light levels are optimal for rooting through the year. Ambient humidity can fall steeply in the periods between misting, and the use of muslin or polythene mesh provides shade and traps water droplets, so that a high relative humidity is maintained in the micro-climate of the cutting bench throughout propagation.

## Micropropagation

Tissue culture has also been significant in propagating new varieties and disease-free clones of horticultural crops. This technique is based on the concept of "*totipotency*" in plants — if a single cell or a plant tissue is cultured it can develop into a complete new plant. In practice isolated plant cells or tissues are grown on sterile media containing the necessary nutrients, and differentiation and development may be induced by adding plant growth hormones and growth factors. The cultures are grown in controlled environments with artificial lighting and daylength control. Shoot tips may be used to culture crops such as strawberries and apples, and ornamentals including carnations, gerbera and rhododendron. O. P. Jones at East Malling showed that adding phloridzin or phloroglucinol to the medium promotes internode extension and the production of axillary shoots in apple cultures; this discovery could prove valuable for rapidly propagating new scion and rootstock varieties of apples. (One shoot tip culture of the apple rootstock M. 26 produced 6000 shoots in 8 months).

At the John Innes Institute a number of monocotyledons have been successfully cultured, including gladiolus, freesia and iris. Axillary shoots are dissected out of bulbs and corms, and further axillary and adventitious shoots produced by adding auxin and cytokinin to the medium. Using this technique for rapidly multiplying onions, narcissus and *lillium* bulbs could similarly prove valuable in building up stocks of particular genotypes, especially of virus-free stocks. There is however a risk of genetic variation in stocks raised by tissue culture, although this should be less where an intact shoot is used to start the culture and to produce axillary shoots rather than undifferentiated callus. Nevertheless, before stocks of narcissus are released as true to type, they must be flowered.

Meristem tip culture involves much smaller shoot tips. The technique was first introduced by G. M. Morel in France in 1948, and has been much used for establishing virus-free stocks of many horticultural plants. The "meristem tip" comprises the apical meristem dome, together with the first pair of leaf primordia. The survival rate of such cultures is lower than with larger shoot tips, and M. Hollings and O. Stone at Littlehampton have shown that the leaf primordia are important in establishing successful cultures. They have used the technique to produce virus-free cultures of the narcissus Grand Soleil d'Or. This variety is grown almost exclusively in the Scillies since it is not frost-hardy elsewhere in the UK. The first meristem tips were cut in 1963 but extensive multiplication could not begin until 1968 when the bulbs from these cultures were large enough and had flowered. Although micropropagation is 3–4 times more rapid, Hollings and Stone have preferred a technique of "chipping" or "twin-scaling" because of the risks of clonal variation or somatic mutation. This involves cutting bulbs into small segments or twin scales each weighing about 2 g, which are then planted in sterilized peat-grit composts. Small bulbils develop in the axils of the bulb scale and are grown on to bulbs to repeat the process. In this way the 18 single foundation bulbs were multiplied to over 176,000 in the 10 years to 1977.

Another technique of potential value for horticultural crops is anther culture involving the tissue culture of pollen grains and their differentiation into whole plants from callus. Haploid plants (i.e. with half the normal diploid number of chromosomes) have obvious application in plant breeding to establish homozygous lines, and anther culture is being applied to some ornamental genera including paeony, petunia and saintpaulia. The technique has not been successful with the cultivated tomato *Lycopersicon esculentum* although haploid callus and some differentiation of plantlets was achieved in three out of forty-five cultures tested in Australia. Isolating and culturing of protoplasts from hybrids may offer more promise for somatic hybridization in tomatoes.

## Nutrition, fertilizer use and irrigation

Much of the research on nutrition of horticultural crops has aimed at determining fertilizer requirements, and especially the changes in crop response resulting from introducing new varieties and production systems. An example is work done with glasshouse crops. Having quantified the fertilizers needed by crops in border soils, G. W. Winsor and his colleagues at Littlehampton set about establishing fertilizer responses in peat. With tomatoes they found that raising the level of nitrogen in the liquid feed from 60 to 200 ppm increased fruit yield and the essential role of potassium for fruit quality was determined at the same time. Examples of ripening disorders in tomatoes associated with mineral deficiencies include "blotchy ripening", largely attributable to potassium deficiency, and "blossom end rot", associated with low calcium in the fruit. The latter disorder seems to be due to poor mobility of calcium in the plant, and to be related to "bitter pit" disorder in apples, and "tip-burn" in lettuce, which are also associated with calcium deficiency.

Extensive research on the nutrition of fruit crops has been done at Long Ashton and East Malling. The most notable contribution was from Professor T. Wallace, Director of Long Ashton, on the effects of deficiencies of mineral nutrients and micronutrients on fruit trees. The ARC established a Unit of Plant Nutrition under Wallace's direction in 1952, and this continued until 1959. Wallace published the first edition of his book on the "Diagnosis of Mineral Deficiencies in Plants by Visual Symptoms" in 1943, and a third edition of this valuable handbook is being prepared.

D. J. Greenwood and his colleagues at the National Vegetable Research Station have developed predictive mathematical models to determine fertilizer requirements of vegetables. These have been based on field experiments made at Wellesbourne, using a novel experimental design, to define the nutrients requirements of twenty vegetable crops. The data collected related to yield, nutrient uptake and crop quality, and the predicted responses of each crop on specific soils were then tested by comparison with yield data of fertilizer experiments made in many areas by Wellesbourne, by ADAS, and by commercial organisations. A computer program based on this model was further refined by using additional data from ADAS, and the response curves were summarised into an NPK Predictor, published in 1978, which has been widely adopted by ADAS and growers. A further refinement was a nitrogen calculator, published in 1980, which enables a grower to determine nitrogen losses by leaching during the winter and spring, and hence to decide how much nitrogen fertilizer will be needed for spring dressing. The data on which the calculator is based are water-holding capacity for different soil types, critical rooting depths for different crops, and weekly evaporation data, information that is also useful for forecasting the benefits of irrigation.

## Temperature control and carbon dioxide enrichment

Precise temperature control in glasshouses is essential to make the most efficient use of energy. Energy requirements are high especially in winter and during the night. In daylight, solar radiation provides most of the heat balance and the glasshouse is effectively a solar collector. Thus, in a heated early tomato crop, solar radiation provides 20% of the daytime energy requirement in January, 26% in February, and more than half in March.

Whilst establishing optimal temperature regimes has been a major objective of research for many years, it is only within the past ten years that attempts have been made to link temperature control to solar radiation and enrichment with carbon dioxide. It has long been known that in poor light high temperatures induce tall, weak tomato plants, which fail to flower and fruit normally. By contrast when light is reasonably good, high temperatures hasten development without adverse effect on flowering and fruit set. Fundamental studies by P. Gaastra in Holland in 1959 showed that although at ambient carbon dioxide concentrations (330 ppm) there is little response of tomato photosynthesis to temperature over the range of 20–30°C there was a 30% increase when the $CO_2$ concentration was raised to 1000 ppm. These observations, taken together with developments in glasshouse engineering and instrumentation that derived from work at the National Institute of Agricultural Engineering at Silsoe, led to much more precise and integrated control of environmental factors including carbon dioxide and the development of a light-dependent controller which enables temperature to be modulated in relation to solar radiation. (Experiments on the possibility of increasing yields in glasshouse crops by $CO_2$ enrichment were started at Cheshunt in 1923 but it was not until systems of automatic control of temperature and ventilation in glasshouses were developed that it became a commercial proposition).

In experiments at Littlehampton A. Calvert and G. Slack showed that $CO_2$ enrichment for early tomatoes gave earlier flowering, higher yields and larger numbers of fruit, and confirmed that 1000 ppm of $CO_2$ was the optimum concentration. A dramatic effect of $CO_2$ enrichment is in limiting abortion in the first truss; the most likely explanation is that in low light $CO_2$ increases photosynthesis in the same way as does extra light with consequent benefit to the developing fruiting truss. Net photosynthesis can be increased by 50% in dull light and, if the temperature is raised, by as much as 100% in bright light. Enrichment at three times the ambient level (1000 ppm $CO_2$) corresponds roughly to an increase of 30% in winter light level and a similar increase in yield.

Carbon dioxide enrichment is widely used in early crops of tomatoes, cucumbers and sweet peppers. It is also used for heated winter lettuce where the head weight of lettuce can be increased by 30% and the date of maturity advanced by 10–15 days. Enrichment is not widely used for glasshouse flower crops although it increases the number of vegetative bud breaks of roses. One reason may be that there are pollutants in the fuel used to generate $CO_2$; commercial propane is the principal source, although some growers use pure $CO_2$ from bulk stores, or burn low-sulphur kerosene. When commercial propane is burnt, propylene may be released and at low concentrations it can behave like ethylene and delay flower initiation in year-round chrysanthemums.

## Virus-free stocks

Producing and distributing healthy, disease-free stocks of all vegetatively propagated horticultural crops has been a vital factor in successfully exploiting improved varieties in intensive systems of production. Large quantities of such stocks have to be available to growers if the strategy of diluting the amount of virus infection below significant levels is to be achieved.

The most commonly used and most successful technique for ridding plants of virus has been heat treatment. This can be done by heating dormant plant material such as apple hardwood for periods of a few minutes to several hours at 37° to 54°C. More generally however, growing plants are heat treated for several weeks at slightly lower temperatures of 35–40°C. About half the viruses affecting horticultural crops can be eliminated by heat treatment, the other most widely used technique being meristem-tip culture, referred to earlier. The leading exponents of heat therapy and meristem-tip culture in this country have been B. Kassanis at Rothamsted (potatoes), A. F. Posnette at East Malling (fruit, especially apples, pears and strawberries) and M. Hollings at Littlehampton (carnations and chrysanthemums).

In the 1960s Posnette and his colleagues at East Malling systematically indexed the virus diseases of apples and pears. They found the majority of commercial orchards were infected with virus and quite often with several different viruses. Fruit tree viruses are extremely difficult to investigate, a virus may produce marked symptoms in one variety and remain latent in another. Chlorotic leaf spot virus, for example, is widely distributed but it causes no obvious symptoms on commercial varieties although it can kill some ornamental crab apples. By contrast, apple mosaic is a virus that affects stone fruit and roses, and even in tolerant commercial apple varieties causes losses in yield of 20% or more.

The original Malling-Merton rootstocks were not tested for virus when released, although most of them proved to be healthy. East Malling started by establishing a mother-tree scheme and, as virus-free stock became more generally available, collaborated with Long Ashton in launching the EMLA scheme, East Malling producing the virus-free rootstocks and Long Ashton the virus-free budwood. An EMLA clone may take 5 years to produce and on release it goes to the Nuclear Stock Association (NSA) (Tree Fruits) Ltd. whose members are nurserymen producing apple rootstocks for further propagation. At the same time the Ministry of Agriculture, Fisheries and Food monitors the health of the material through its Special Stock Certification Scheme.

The first Association to be established was for strawberries, and initially it was concerned with freedom from Red Core fungus disease. Other Associations have been established, one for ornamentals which is located at Littlehampton, and another for bulbs.

Virus diseases of hops have long been a problem, especially "necrotic ringspot" which in the past affected about 40% of hopyards. The virus reduces the alpha-acid formed by the hop which is the main bittering component required by brewers. The production of virus-free hops by East Malling, in collaboration with the Hop Department of Wye College, which bred a new hop variety combining tolerance to *Verticillium* with high alpha-acid, was recognised by the Queen's Award for Technological Achievement in 1978.

## Biological and integrated pest control

As long ago as 1927 when damage caused by whitefly in glasshouses posed a serious problem to Lee Valley growers, an entomologist at Cheshunt, Speyer, developed a method of biological control of the pest. This replaced the use of the phytotoxic cyanide (with its attendant hazards to operators!) with a parasite of whiteflies, the chalcid wasp *Encarsia formosa*. This wasp inserts its eggs in the larvae of the whitefly, the so-called "scales" which develop in large numbers on the undersides of leaves of infested plants (Plate 4). Subsequently infested scales turn black and the life cycle is completed in about a month with the release of further parasites. Cheshunt established a service for the breeding and distribution of *Encarsia* in this country and overseas which continued until 1953, when it was replaced by DDT and other more modern insecticides. However, restrictions on the use of DDT and the widespread occurrence of tolerance to other insecticides led to the re-emergence of *Encarsia* as an economic means of whitefly control in the 1960s.

*Plate 4* Biological control of whitefly with *Encarsia formosa*.

The development of the use of biological and integrated pest control since the war has come about as a result of the need to control pests where chemical methods have begun to fail, generally due to the selection of strains resistant or tolerant to pesticides.

The aim of an integrated system is to combine the use of biological control agents, predators, parasites and pathogens with chemicals which are relatively non-toxic to them, to control the complex of pests and diseases which may attack a particular crop. Glasshouses provide an environment where the selection pressure on new chemicals is especially intense, and no more so than in the case of the red spider mite *Tetranychus urticae*. New acaricides produced to control this pest may only remain effective for 4–5 years before tolerant strains appear. This problem had become acute by 1962, and as a consequence N. W. Hussey and his colleagues at Littlehampton started to devise systems of integrated control for this and other pests of glasshouse crops. They were quickly successful in finding a predatory mite, *Phytoseiulus persimilis*, a native of Chile, which can only survive under glass in Britain but effectively controls spider mite.

In practice, the design and development of commercial systems of integrated control have demanded a great deal of ingenuity on the part of researchers and ADAS entomologists and horticulturists, not only in finding the most effective species of predators and parasites and compatible chemical pesticides, but also in maintaining the necessary dynamic balance between pest and parasite to ensure efficient control throughout the long cropping season. Since the predator can only survive if the pest host is present in the crop, the aim of the control programme is not to eliminate the pest but to hold it at low level which will not cause economically unacceptable damage during cropping. This had led to the concept of the "pest-in-first" technique in which crop plants are deliberately infested with small numbers of the pest, to be followed after an interval by the release of the predator or parasite into the crop. Further introductions may have to be made during the season, and if the pest gets out of control a pesticide spray may be needed to restore the balance, as is illustrated in Fig. 3.

## PRINCIPLES OF PEST MANAGEMENT

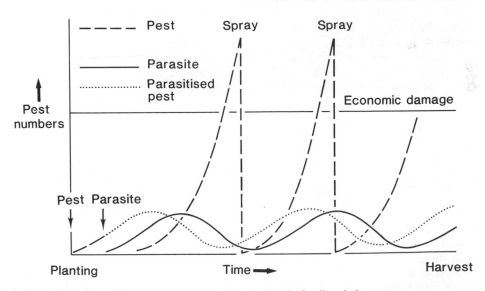

*Figure 3* Principles of pest management using the "pest-in-first" technique.

Another problem is achieving a uniform distribution of pest and parasite throughout the crop. A technique has been devised for using "banker" plants, which are infested with the necessary levels of pest and parasite before placing them at regular intervals among the crop. By suitable manipulation and the renewal of banker plants, infestations can be successfully controlled by the grower himself throughout the season.

Integrated pest control is now being used in more than half the tomato and cucumber glasshouse production in Western Europe, and it is also becoming more widely adopted in protected flower crops, notably year-round chrysanthemums. Not only is it economically viable, but it also relieves the selection pressure on chemical pesticides which should prolong their useful life and reduce the amounts that have to be used. These are important considerations, for a recent report from the UN Environment Programme showed that the number of insect and mite species which had developed tolerant strains increased from 182 in 1965 to 364 in 1977.

The scope for biological and integrated control is not confined to glasshouses, indeed the earliest commercial developments were on orchards of citrus and peaches in California and Australia, and with apples, notably in Nova Scotia, for the control of fruit tree red spider mite. In outdoor crops research has to be directed to the encouragement of natural enemies by using pest control chemicals which are relatively harmless to them since there is unlikely to be scope for introducing artificially reared predators and parasites. A recent development which may have great significance is the selection of predacious mites which can survive the spray programmes which are necessary for the control of lepidopterous pests of apples, including codling moth. If these pesticide-resistant strains can be introduced into orchards, they might control the fruit tree red spider mite without inhibiting the use of sprays for moth control. If, additionally, these strains are tolerant to apple mildew fungicides, then their potential value will be even greater. Incidentally, research at Long Ashton has shown that another important predator of the codling moth is the blue tit!

So far references to biological control have been confined to predators and parasites, but the use of insect pathogens also shows promise. For example, at Littlehampton it has been shown that *Bacillus thuringiensis* controls the tomato moth, and the fungus *Verticillium lecanii* can control aphids in chrysanthemums; this is now being commercially developed. There are prospects too for the use of granulosis virus to control codling moth on apples.

Biological control has extended also to controlling fungal diseases by antagonistic fungi which may be parasitic or may produce antimetabolites toxic to the disease organism. At Long Ashton, it has been demonstrated that implanting cultures of the soil fungus *Trichoderma viride* into the trunks of apple, pear and plum trees infected with silver-leaf disease can markedly reduce symptons, and this use has now been approved under the Pesticides Safety Precautions Scheme.

## Weed control

Weed-free environments in horticultural crops were first established in citrus orchards in California, and by 1963 nearly two-thirds of the total area in the State was kept weed-free by using herbicides rather than by cultivation.

In Britain the earliest uses of herbicides were in soft fruit where labour costs for cultivation and for weed control can account for a quarter of total costs. D. W. Robinson at the Experiment Station at Loughall in Northern Ireland, made some of the early experiments on blackcurrants and gooseberries; he found no evidence of improved yields, but the damaging effects of cultivation on surface roots were avoided and weed competition for nutrients and water was largely eliminated.

Herbicides for soft and top fruit have now become universally adopted; generally diquat and paraquat are used to kill annual weeds, and the more persistent, soil-acting herbicides such as simazine, control perennial weeds. Herbicides for weed control have been evaluated by the Weed Research Organization and possible phytotoxic damage to crops assessed.

## Post-harvest handling, distribution and storage

Most horticultural produce is marketed and consumed fresh, and once produce is harvested it is essential to preserve quality and to extend shelf life until it reaches the consumer or processor, or until it is put into storage.

Certain autolytic and irreversible processes start even before a crop is harvested and continue after harvest. These biochemical changes of ripening and senescence are generally associated with increased rates of respiration and in fruits are accompanied by colouring and the softening of tissues as pectic substances in cell walls break down. These processes can be slowed by holding produce at low temperatures, and research workers at the Ditton Laboratory, and later at the Food Research Institute, have established optimal conditions for storing soft fruit and vegetables. Generally, soft fruit and leafy vegetables can be stored for short periods of 2–3 weeks, or they must be refrigerated, whereas top fruit and vegetables where the crop is a storage organ (e.g. carrots, potatoes, onions, white cabbage) can be stored for much longer — 30–35 weeks. After harvest fresh produce may lose water rapidly but this can be lessened by maintaining high humidity in the store. The optimal conditions for long storage are generally a temperature of 0–2°C and a near saturated atmosphere, but there are exceptions such as runner beans, where the optimum is 8°C, and cucumber and marrow where it is 14°C. Low temperature storage also reduces losses caused by fungal and bacterial rots, although these are favoured by high humidities.

The faster the crop can be cooled after harvest, the longer will be the shelf life. A rough rule is that soft fruit and leafy vegetables will deteriorate as much in one hour at 26°C as in one day at 12°C, or in one week at 0°C. Heat can be removed by using an ice bank cooler or some form of air blast cooling, the rate of cooling being much faster than in a conventional cold store. The so-called "cold-chain" system of distribution involves rapid removal of "field heat", a short time in a cold store, followed by transport in an insulated truck to the shop where it is sold from a cooled counter. Vacuum cooling is another rapid method, where produce is loaded into a chamber in which pressure is reduced so that it cools as it loses latent heat of evaporation. Some glasshouse lettuce growers use equipment developed at Silsoe (the Institute has also developed an ice bank cooler); and the system is used for all lettuce handled through the Dutch vegetable auctions. Long-term stores for vegetables such as onions and carrots are relatively simple and only temperature and humidity are controlled.

In contrast, apples are stored in atmospheres where carbon dioxide and oxygen are controlled. The principles on which storage are based were first established by F. Kidd and C. West, who, in 1922, observed a characteristic rise in the rate of respiration measured as carbon dioxide output when harvested apples were stored at ripening temperatures. They later demonstrated that the same rise in respiration occurred if the apples were left on the tree — a phenomenon they termed "climacteric". Ten years later Kidd and West showed that a volatile substance produced by ripe apples stimulated the respiration of unripe apples into the climacteric phase. In 1935 R. Gane identified this substance as ethylene — the "ripening hormone". The timing of harvesting and putting the crop into store is critical in relation to the climacteric. The optimal time for apples is in the pre-climacteric phase when respiration rates may be depressed, but practical experience with Cox's Orange Pippin indicates greater latitude, satisfactory long-term storage being achieved by picking one week before or after the start of the climacteric.

Recommendations for controlled atmosphere storage of apples have been specified precisely for several varieties by the Ditton Laboratory at East Malling and range from 3.5° to 4.5°C, and gas mixtures of 5% $CO_2$ and 3% $O_2$; this regime allows storage until March but the period can be extended to May if the oxygen level is lowered to the recommended minimum of 1.8% or as low as 1–1.25%, but very low oxygen is associated with a disorder that can occur in fruit stored for long periods. At these levels there is risk of anaerobic respiration and accumulation of alcohol.

## Dormancy and vernalization

Many plants require low temperature treatment either before or after flower buds have been initiated to stimulate flowering; this is known as vernalization. Apples require low temperature during the winter to break the dormancy of fruit buds formed during the previous summer, and bulbs require a period at low temperature to flower. The natural vernalization process can be speeded up or slowed down by appropriate temperature treatments.

Low temperature treatment is used commercially in forcing bulbs to flower for Christmas or early in the New Year, but it is preceded by high temperature storage immediately after lifting. The temperatures used and the duration of warm storage do not appear to be critical, but for narcissus to flower at Christmas recommendations are to lift early and store for 5 days at 35°C; this treatment can bring forward anthesis by 14 days. The timing of warm storage is critical since if applied too late it will delay flowering, and it is only fully effective if applied before flower initiation begins. The warm storage is followed by a period at 17–20°C, and the bulbs are then "pre-cooled", traditionally at 9°C, for 6–8 weeks, after which the bulbs are planted in soil in boxes and held outside before forcing. Recently, however, a direct "five-degree forcing" method has been devised — after 9 weeks at 5°C, the bulbs are planted directly into boxes in the glasshouse and forced at 18°C.

At Littlehampton it has been found that even lower temperatures could be used for a shorter time, the critical requirement for flowering being the number of "cold units" (defined as days multiplied by the temperature below that used for forcing (°C)); 1000–1100 units are adequate provided chilling injury with sub-zero temperatures is avoided. The cold treatment promotes the breakdown of starch and mobilizes soluble carbohydrates which supply the developing shoot.

The plant growth substances known as gibberellins, associated with vegetative growth and particularly stem elongation, are also involved in regulating flowering; they promote flowering of some species and inhibit others. Gibberellins can also replace the cold requirement of many dormant seeds, bulbs and tubers. Research at Littlehampton has demonstrated that the cold requirement of tulip bulbs can be partly, but not wholly, replaced by injecting gibberellic acid directly into bulbs.

## The Underlying Science and Prospects for the Future

So far this essay has concentrated on the technology of horticulture — on the application of science to the improvement of horticultural productivity — and descriptions of the underlying science have been limited to accounts of the technical basis of a system or technique. However, to speculate on the future we need to look more closely at basic science to assess the potential for further improvement.

In his chapter in this volume "Science in Crop Production", L. Fowden has considered the determinants of productivity in field crops. They apply equally to horticultural crops, although in glasshouses we can largely control the environment. However, despite precise control, glasshouse crops seldom achieve more than one per cent efficiency in using light energy to produce energy-rich plant material for harvest. While light interception by the crop may be poor, and while the assimilation process itself may be inefficient, subsequently there are substantial losses of assimilate associated with respiration and utilization.

Enrichment with carbon dioxide increases growth and yield: essentially by eliminating losses caused by photorespiration — indeed $CO_2$ enrichment effectively converts a $C_3$ plant into a $C_4$ plant. L. J. Ludwig at Littlehampton has shown in studies with single leaves that lowering the oxygen level also suppresses photorespiration and there is no further response to $CO_2$ enrichment, indicating that atmospheric levels of $CO_2$ are sufficient to saturate the photosynthetic process at relatively high light intensities. This would suggest that if we are to improve photosynthetic efficiency by a plant breeding programme, it should aim to breed plants with a much reduced sensitivity to oxygen to diminish losses of assimilate due to photorespiration.

Light is the main limiting factor in horticultural production in this country. The differences in productivity in our latitudes as compared with further south are illustrated by the much higher apple yields in France — and G. Stanhill has estimated that tomato production in heated glasshouses in Southern England requires forty times the gross energy input of a comparable crop in an unheated glasshouse in Israel where hours of sunshine are more than double from November to February and a third higher for the rest of the year. Existing tomato genotypes are approaching the limits of productivity that can be achieved by environmental manipulation at our latitudes. Nevertheless there is scope for research into genetic variation in adapting horticultural crops to low light, since in normal cropping most leaves are well below light saturation for carbon assimilation for most of the time. We also need a better understanding of response to low temperatures to reduce energy inputs, and we need to know more about the translocation of assimilate from the leaves, and the partitioning of assimilate between the harvested crop and other parts of the plant.

While there are opportunities for improving our understanding of carbon assimilation, and hence productivity, we also need more research on plant development, on the role of plant hormones in controlling crop processes, and on the mechanisms through which morphogenetic and adaptive responses to light — including photoperiod response — are mediated by phytochrome and other photomorphogenetic pigments. Such studies will lead to a better understanding of natural control mechanisms including the process whereby plants switch from vegetative growth to flowering. They should also increase our knowledge of ways in which the controlling effects of natural hormones might be modulated by using synthetic plant growth regulators. We still have much to learn about the flowering process and about whether there is such a thing as a "flowering hormone".

Turning from crop production to crop protection, the most serious problem for horticulturists is the increasing incidence of resistance and tolerance to chemical control of many pests and pathogens. This can only be countered by developing alternative methods where biological and chemical methods are combined in compatible systems of pest and disease control.

The past fifty years have seen spectacular advances in our knowledge of crop processes, and spectacular improvements in crop productivity. The next fifty years may not see such dramatic improvements, but there is still much to be learnt that could make horticultural production more efficient. Nevertheless, we may find ourselves forced by high energy costs into developing alternative technologies, where lower productivity has to be accepted as a consequence of lower energy inputs and less effective methods of crop protection.

## Further Reading

Bleasdale, J. K. A. (1977). *Britain's Green Revolution.* Presidential Address. Section M. Agriculture, 139th Annual Meeting British Association for the Advancement of Science, University of Aston.

Bleasdale, J. K. A. (1978). Two decades of change in horticulture. *Span,* **21,** 59.

Cockshull, K. E. (1972). Photoperiodic control of flowering in the chrysanthemum. In *"Crop Processes in Controlled Environments"* (A. R. Rees *et al.* ed.) p. 235. London, Academic Press.

Hollings, M. (1965). Disease control through virus-free stock. *Annual Review of Phytopathology*, **3**, 367.

Hudson, J. P. (1971). Horticulture in 2000 A.D. in *"Potential Crop Production"* (Wareing, P. F. and Cooper, J. P. ed). p. 187. London, Heinemann Educational Books Ltd.

Jackson, J. E. (1975). Effects of light intensity on growth, cropping and fruit quality. In *"Climate and the Orchard"* (H. C. Pereira, ed). *Research Review No. 5*, p. 17, Commonwealth Bureau Horticulture & Plantation Crops, East Malling, Maidstone.

Luckwill, L. C. (1978). Meadow orchards and fruit walls. *Acta Horticulturae* **65**, 237.

Ludwig, L. J. (1972). The relationship between photosynthesis and respiration. In *"Crop Processes in Controlled Environments"* (A. R. Rees *et al*, ed). p. 305. London, Academic Press.

Parr, W. J. (1972). Biological control of glasshouse pests. *Journal Royal Agricultural Society of England*, **133**, 48.

Rees, A. R. (1972). *The Growth of Bulbs*. London and New York, Academic Press.

Rudd-Jones, D. (1979). *Environmental control in vegetable crop management*. XXth International Horticultural Congress, Sydney, Australia 1978. Phytotronic Newsletter *19*, 16.

Sheard, G. F. (1979). "Energy and the future of the Glasshouse Industry". 1978 Eric Gardener Memorial Lecture. *Annual Report Glasshouse Crops Research Institute* 1978, 154.

Stanhill, G. (1979). *The energy cost of protected cropping: A comparison of six systems of tomato production*. Contribution from the Agricultural Research Organisation, The Volcani Center, Bet Dagan, Israel, No. 114-E, 1979 Series.

# Soils and Fertilizers

## G. W. COOKE

Agricultural Research Council, London

Soil science began in the first half of last century and most early work was chemical and concerned with crop nutrition. Studies of soil bacteriology and soil physics began about 100 years ago and at that time Russian workers made the first proposals for the classification and mapping of soils. An impressive body of knowledge of soil existed when the ARC was formed. Later progress can be assessed from the successive editions of E. J. Russell's "Soil Conditions and Plant Growth". First published in 1912, this classic reached its Sixth Edition in 1932; the Tenth Edition by E. W. Russell, published in 1973, shows the advances made during 40 years. The Soil Science Society of America (1977) has also reviewed the progress made in 200 years.

Since 1931 few new concepts have been developed which have resulted in major advances in our ability to control soil productivity. The greatest practical gains have come from new understanding of the storage and movement of water in soils, the value and valuation of reserves of nutrients in soils, and the role of cultivations in modern production systems. Most of the work done has been on topics recognised before 1931, and it has strengthened the scientific basis for research and advisory work. British soils now produce much more, but improvements in soil fertility have mostly been due to applying knowledge of the value of manures, fertilizers, and lime, the basis of which we had in 1931. The application of this information on crop nutrition and soil conditions has been aided by new chemical and physical techniques for measuring soil properties and plant composition. We have received much help from developments in optical and electronic instruments, and latterly from computers. But these tools have affected only our ability to analyse quickly large numbers of soils and crops and to use the results.

In field experimentation the new designs of R. A. Fisher and F. Yates gave us experimental methods of tackling problems related to soil management systems that had not been attempted before and altered our approach to work with biological systems. The most notable applications were by E. M. Crowther (1951) who developed the concept of field experimentation as a tool for studying soil fertility problems. Because the precision of results could be estimated the new field experiments had a greater value in research; equally important was the possibility in one experiment of measuring the effects of varying several factors simultaneously and of investigating their interactions. The new experimental methods were a powerful stimulus to work with farming systems in the field. Experiments were first done at research institutes but to give full assistance to farmers, these needed to be repeated on other soils and in other climates. This was made possible by the eagerness of local workers to take part in collaborative work with the institute staffs. Tribute must be paid to the vital role of scientists in the old advisory services attached (before 1946) to Universities and Colleges, to soil scientists of the National Agricultural Advisory Service (NAAS, later to become the Agricultural Development and Advisory Service — ADAS) formed in 1946, and to many other workers in agricultural research and education, in forestry, and in the industries serving agriculture. Their enthusiastic collaboration has made it possible for series of experiments on soils and fertilizers to be done so widely that the results may be applied by farmers in all parts of the country.

This account of advances in our ability to understand soils and to improve their productivity is inevitably incomplete. The emphasis is on advances made in Britain.

Many topics important in other countries, for example soil salinity and soil erosion, have had to be omitted.

## Some Advances in Soil Science

### Soil colloids

Steady progress has been made in studying the negatively charged soil colloids which have an essential role in all cation relationships. Early soil scientists thought clay was amorphous but by 1931 the (then) new technique of X-ray analysis had shown clays had crystalline structures based on layered alumino-silicate minerals. Work during the last 50 years with this and other new techniques has revealed much more about the constitution of soil clays and their reactivity. By contrast the nature of organic matter in soil is still not well understood. Its composition varies greatly in different soils and regions. The importance of "humus" as a reservoir of plant nutrients has become very clear. But more research will be needed on the structure and properties of the humic substances which make up the bulk of soil organic matter before we can fully assess its contributions to the colloidal properties and structure of soils.

### Soil physics

Much was done early in this century on measuring the proportions and arrangements of the ultimate soil particles (sand, silt and clay). The early 1930s marked the end of this productive period in soil physics since the scientific gains from studies of particle size distribution were small. The way the soil is assembled is more important than its components; its properties depend much on the characteristics of the clays and particularly their swelling and shrinking properties. The spaces between the particles are at least as important as the particles themselves; soil should be regarded as a cellular rather than a granular material. Progress has been made since 1930 in studies of water in soil pores, and in flow and diffusion of liquids and gases.

In spite of much work reported in many papers we cannot define and measure soil structure in ways that aid communication with other scientists. Some techniques for measuring physical parameters related to structure, and to mechanical properties, help in agronomic work, but are empirical; often results depend on method of measurement and time of year. The three most useful measurements of physical soil conditions are mechanical composition, bulk density, and the moisture characteristic curve.

### Water in soils

The reduction in free energy, as between water in bulk and that retained in soil by physical and chemical forces, determines the availability of water to crops. This free-energy change is often expressed as a "suction head". Since the limits of this, from soil saturated with water to completely dry soil, cover a very wide range, the convention introduced by R. K. Schofield at Rothamsted in 1935 of working logarithmically (the use of $p$F values) has proved convenient.

The ability of soil to hold water useful to crops is assessed by the *soil moisture characteristic curve* made by plotting moisture content of soil against soil water potential. The pattern of the curve indicates the size distribution of the pores in soil. Measuring water content *in situ* in the field was made possible when radioactive sources of fast neutrons became available; although the technique has limitations, particularly for measurements near the surface, neutron probe meters are now widely used to measure soil water. The absorption of $\gamma$-rays is largely influenced by bulk density of soil, and to a lesser extent by pore water, so $\gamma$-ray meters are used for measuring bulk density in field soils *in situ*.

Until the 1940s the basis for controlling irrigation was crude. Thus in 1937 E. J. Russell wrote "the ideal course is to moisten the soil to its field capacity, and to the depth penetrated by the roots, but no deeper". He said that this pattern of advice had revolutionised irrigation practice in California.

L. Fowden has described in his essay the progress in irrigation which resulted from H. L. Penman's classic study of the energy balance concept for the evaporation of water from soil and vegetation made at Rothamsted in the 1940s. Penman's method has been widely tested and is used in practice all over the world to plan irrigation and in the hydrological management of catchments. In Britain the Meteorological Office calculated potential transpiration from weather data at sites over Great Britain and compared these figures with local rainfall. The maps show that in dry regions of South-East England irrigation will increase yields of some crops in 9 years out of 10, further north and west the frequency is much less.

Work on drainage began at Cambridge in the 1930s with special concern for heavy clay soils. In 1951 the ARC established the Unit of Soils Physics at Cambridge with E. C. Childs as Honorary Director. Childs died in 1973 and E. G. Youngs continued as Acting Director until 1977 when the staff and work were transferred to Rothamsted. The unifying theme of work at Cambridge was to develop a general theory of land drainage by assessing agricultural needs in terms of the soil moisture profile required and then to design a drainage system to achieve this. The soil properties mostly concerned in drainage are: (a) moisture characteristic — expressing the relation between soil water suction and resulting moisture content, (b) hydraulic conductivity of the soil and its dependence on moisture content and (c) the stability of the subsoil. The properties were measured and the Unit elucidated the fundamental laws of soil water equilibrium and movement. They showed that unsaturated flow obeyed diffusion laws and developed an equation in which diffusivity depended on the changing moisture content. This gave new leads and accelerated development and application of water movement theory (Childs 1969).

The Unit under Childs had international recognition for its outstanding work on the theory and practice of soil water movement which has led to a scientific basis for drain installations here and overseas. In Britain the drainage done annually has increased from virtually none in 1940 to 100 000 ha in 1975 (when the cost of the work was about £200 per ha). Nearly 3 M ha in Britain may still benefit from drainage and the present rate does little more than keep pace with the need to replace old systems installed in the last century.

## Mineral nutrients in soils

During the last 50 years work on the forms of nutrient reserves in soils, and on their solubilities and mobilities, has given better understanding of the factors that govern availability. Studies on phosphorus were advanced when the radioactive isotope $^{32}P$ became available; its half-life made it suitable for measuring the fractions of fertilizer-P taken up by crops in pot and field experiments. R. K. Schofield at Rothamsted, and others, applied thermodynamic concepts to the solubilities of nutrient ions. He stressed that it was the work needed to withdraw phosphate ions from the pool in the soil that determines availability — "the availability of soil phosphorus is determined mainly by the appropriate chemical potential and its rate of decrease with phosphate withdrawal". Schofield devised a method of measuring phosphate potential. The labile pool of P (from which the potential in the soil solution is replenished) can be measured by exchange with $^{32}P$ (anion exchange resins are also used).

Schofield also studied the relationships of cations in the electrical double layer involving the charged surfaces of soil colloids and the nearby solutions in equilibrium. His "Ratio Law" proposed in 1947 was a notable step forward in understanding cation exchange phenomena. Schofield's work has been used to express "available" K in terms of the intensity (I) of the potassium ion activity relative to the activities of cations dominating soil solutions (usually calcium and magnesium). The status of a nutrient ion such as potassium in a soil is well expressed by the relationship between I and "Q" (Q is the quantity of exchangeable K held by the soil).

The processes involved in movement of nutrient ions from soil to root have been studied in the last 20 years. Concepts of ion mobility first put forward by R. H. Bray and developed by S. A. Barber in USA, are used in mathematical modelling of processes of nutrient uptake; an account of progress has been given by P. H. Nye and P. B. Tinker (1977).

These developments in knowledge of factors affecting the availability of nutrients in soils have greatly aided understanding and research. But none of the new methods proposed, for example the "potential" of nutrient ions, has been widely used in practical work. Most advice to farmers still depends on empirical methods for measuring soluble phosphate, and on exchangeable potassium.

## Trace elements in soils

Notable contributions to knowledge of the distribution of trace elements in soils have been made by the Macaulay Institute for Soil Research (founded in 1930), and particularly by R. L. Mitchell (1963). Concentrations are related to soil series, particularly as affected by parent materials; Mitchell considers that trace element content can be predicted "with some accuracy" if parent material of soil is known. The solubility of most trace elements depends on drainage status, being higher on badly-drained soils. The minute amounts of some of the essential elements present in soils and crops had needed very sensitive analytical methods and from its foundation the Macaulay Institute has made important advances in spectrographic and other methods of instrumental analysis. Less is known of the distribution of trace elements in the soils of England and Wales. Surveys of stream bed sediments made by R. A. Webb, I. Thornton and others at Imperial College, supported by ARC, have indicated where problems due to excess or to deficiency may arise. Trace element concentrations in crops used for animal feeding depend on type of soil and crop, and on manuring and liming; of the materials normally applied to land only organic manures supply worthwhile quantities.

## Soil biology

In 1941 the ARC recognised the need for a biological basis for understanding soil fertility, and particularly the microbiological aspects; the Council established its first Unit — the Unit of Soil Enzyme Chemistry at Rothamsted in 1941, the Director was J. H. Quastel. (The name of the Unit was later changed to "Unit of Soil Metabolism"; it moved to South Wales in 1945 and was disbanded in 1947.) The Unit's work ranged widely and much was based on a continuous technique for perfusing fluid through a soil column — treating soil as though it was an intact biological entity. Investigations included the microbiological transformations of nitrogen, carbon, and manganese compounds in soil. Microbiological processes which lead to formation of substances which stabilise soil structure were studied and alginates were shown to be effective soil conditioners some years before synthetic conditioners (such as polyacrylonitrile derivatives, "Krilium" etc) were developed. The initiatives created by the Unit were not pursued at the time. It is now recognised that comprehensive work on soil fertility must include microbiological and biochemical studies.

Microorganisms have a profound effect on soil development and the formation of structure. Those that occupy the rhizosphere have complex roles ranging from removal of nutrients or their release, to protecting roots from pathogens. Relevant work is now being done at several Institutes of the ARS.

## Soil Classification and Survey

The principal Soil Groups of the World were established by 1930. Many classification systems have been developed since then, some suit local agricultural purposes, others are designed for regional or world use. A purely taxonomic approach to classification proved inadequate and in recent work classes are defined by intrinsic properties of soils, preferably using criteria that can be *measured* in field or laboratory (Soil Survey Staff 1977).

Systematic study and classification of British soils progressed in the 1930s, much stimulated by the late G. W. Robinson who introduced the soil series concept. In 1939 the Soil Survey for England and Wales was formed and Robinson was its first Director.

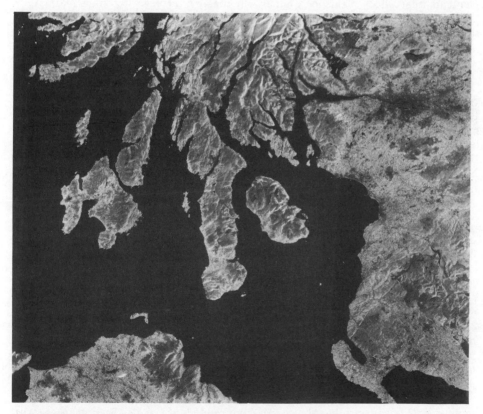

*Plate 1* The Macaulay Institute for Soil Research, Aberdeen uses remote sensing techniques in the mapping of peat resources. This is a Landsat satellite image of the Firth of Clyde and South West Scotland.

In 1946 the Headquarters of the Survey moved from Bangor to Rothamsted and A. Muir, Head of the Scottish Soil Survey, moved to England and became Director. The ARC appointed a Soil Survey Research Board in 1947, this Board advised and guided the two Surveys in Britain until 1972 when the Joint Consultative Organisation took over its functions. B. W. Avery (1973) has described the development of the soil classification now used in England and Wales. Detailed surveys have now covered a fifth of the country. A new programme, started in 1979, will provide maps on 1:250 000 scale and associated memoirs for the whole country and extend some of the benefits of soil survey information to all farmers. The Soil Survey of Scotland was started as a Department of the Macaulay Institute by W. G. (later Sir William) Ogg when the Institute was founded in 1930. Most of the lowland suitable for arable or mixed farming has been surveyed. A rapid survey is now being made of areas not previously covered, mainly the uplands, maps will be published on 1:250 000 scale. Plate 1 shows a Landsat satellite image used in this survey.

Soil survey descriptions and maps must be interpreted for practical application to land-use planning or developments in agriculture or forestry. Land-use capability classifications have been developed in many countries and that used in Britain has been described by T. S. Bibby and D. Mackney (1969); maps have been published by both British Surveys. Because soils classified in the same series behave similarly, surveys are a basis for transferring results of experimental and development work at one site to other farms. Soil information is now used in planning land use and to aid decisions between the options open to farmers so that they may maximise returns from inputs. Among other uses the surveys are applied in forecasting deficiencies or excesses of elements that affect plants or animals, in making fertilizer recommendations, in planning irrigation and drainage systems, in assessing the suitability of soils for direct drilling, and in planning the use of slurries of animal wastes.

## Nitrogen in Soils and Crops

In agricultural systems in temperate regions where other nutrients are supplied by fertilizers and lime, yield is usually determined by the supply of nitrogen. No long-lasting reserve of inorganic nitrogen can accumulate in soil. The large stores of N in soil which are combined with organic matter are released by microbial activity as nitrate for use by crops at rates which may be characteristic of soil type, climate and farming system, but which are not readily altered by the farmer except when he ploughs grassland.

### Available nitrogen

Attempts have been made in the last 50 years to develop laboratory methods for measuring the N which soil may release to the next crop but none have been widely adopted as routine methods to advise farmers on their use of N-fertilizers. In field experiments the responses of crops to N-fertilizers are related to previous cropping and manuring of land. The reserves of readily-decomposable organic matter left in soil after ploughing grassland, growing legumes, or using farmyard manure, decompose to release nitrate which may be sufficient for the next arable crop. Good quality long leys and permanent pasture leave residues that release extra N for several years, release from an annual leguminous crop, or from one FYM dressing, lasts no more than a year; there is little release of mineral nitrogen from residues of cereals. These facts are used by ADAS to establish a "Nitrogen Index" system for advising farmers, used in the same way as soil analysis indices (Shaw 1979).

## Losses of nitrogen

The most important single problem in crop nutrition and soil management in Britain is the large loss of nitrogen, possibly amounting to about half of the N involved in the annual agricultural cycle. Much of the total loss is from animal farming. Losses occur in making and applying farmyard manure and slurries; these may be minimised by careful spreading of manure and ploughing it in immediately. Other large, and inevitable, losses occur from excreta dropped by grazing animals; faeces and urine decompose rapidly on or near the soil surface and much ammonia volatilises.

Mechanisms of loss of N from crop land — leaching of nitrate, denitrification (to release nitrogen oxides or nitrogen gas), and volatilisation of ammonia, had all been recognised by the end of last century but little was done to study their practical extent or to devise ways of preventing loss. Three considerations were responsible for much new research in the 1960s and 1970s — two were environmental concerns, the third was simply that N-fertilizers now cost much more than they did a few years ago. Research to make nitrogen fertilizer more efficient is now a priority topic the world over.

Concern about the "eutrophication" of natural waters began in the 1960s. Enrichment with N and P increased the growth of water weeds and microorganisms to create difficulties for water supply and drainage authorities and damage the amenity value of lakes and rivers. There was also concern about risks to health from increases in nitrate

*Plate 2* Lysimeters at the Letcombe Laboratory with a moveable glasshouse in the background.

in surface and underground waters used for public supply. During the last 15 years we have shown that very little phosphate enters surface waters from properly managed agricultural land unless animal excreta or eroded soil are washed into streams. Most of the P present in rivers comes from sewage effluent, but much of the nitrate in streams and aquifers has "leaked" from farmland. It is difficult to show that fertilizer-N moves directly into natural waters, but the large quantities of N involved in intensive farming inevitably lead to much larger losses than occur from natural ecosystems — where the N is conserved by vegetation and microorganisms. Plate 2 shows how these problems are investigated at Letcombe Laboratory.

The second environmental concern related to nitrous oxide ($N_2O$) released to air by denitrification in soil (but also by combustion in engines and furnaces!). It seemed that $N_2O$ might react in the stratosphere to diminish the ozone layer which protects us from ultra violet radiation but recent assessments suggest that this threat has been exaggerated. Several institutes of the ARS are now investigating the potential for loss of N by denitrification from both arable and grass lands. Plate 3 shows equipment used at Letcombe.

Slow-acting nitrogen fertilizers have been investigated throughout the last 50 years. Many early experiments tested alternatives to natural materials (such as hoof or horn or blood meals); we hoped that rates of release of inorganic nitrogen might match rates of uptake by crops and so improve efficiency. Urea-formaldehyde condensation products have been much tested and some are used in horticultural fertilizers. Isobutylidene diurea (IBDU) improved efficiency consistently but it is expensive. Recently sulphur-coated urea has been widely tested (the sulphur coating at first protects the fertilizer but is later broken down microbiologically to release urea). In most British experiments on arable crops and grassland, no slow-acting fertilizer has had an efficiency greater than that of inorganic fertilizers.

*Plate 3* Collecting gas samples from lysimeters with transparent domes at Letcombe Laboratory to measure the nitrous oxide escaping from pasture.

Other work has been done to check the microbiological transformations of N-fertilizers. Nitrification inhibitors are available, for example "N-serve" (2 chloro-6-trichloro-methyl pyridine); they inhibit nitrification but the increased efficiency they provide has not been sufficient to secure wide adoption. Urea is hydrolysed to ammonia by the enzyme urease; if this transformation could be slowed until the urea had moved from the surface by diffusion or in moving water less ammonia should be lost. Substances that inhibit urease activity have been found, but again their use in practice is not yet established.

## Phosphorus and Potassium in Soils

### Available nutrients

Since the time of Liebig, chemists have analysed soils to determine the amounts of nutrients that may become available to crops, and therefore what extra amounts should be applied as fertilizers. In spite of many papers describing new extraction methods little progress had been made by 1930. Partly this was because the methods were empirical but also because of a lack of *precise* field experiments to standardise them. Even when many results from more accurate experiments were available in the 1950s, and corrections were applied for soil properties and for weather, correlations between soluble P and K in soil, and crop responses to P and K fertilizers, were disappointing. Analytical methods did distinguish between soils with very little or very large reserves, and they were useful in the war-time campaign to grow more food. But for most cultivated soils analyses were not closely related to crop response to fertilizers. Differences in depth and intensity of rooting of different crops, in seasonal variations in weather which affect both microbiological activity and root growth, as well as in other soil characteristics, will always prevent accurate forecasts of nutrient availability. At best we can expect to establish general analytical limits for given crops, types of farming, and soil conditions. This objective was pursued by NAAS (later ADAS); methods were standardised and an "Index" system was adopted for interpreting soil analyses when advising farmers (Shaw 1979).

### The value of reserves in soil

Crops absorb only a portion of the P given as fertilizer, the rest is retained in the soil. This "fixation" of phosphate was long regarded as a disaster because it diminished short-term efficiency. Although in the 1890s B. Dyer demonstrated that the residues of P fertilizers in soils of the Rothamsted experiments were soluble in dilute citric acid, even in the 1930s many regarded fixed P as useless to crops. Much has been done since 1950 to understand both the nature of the reactions between phosphate and soil, and the solubilities and value to crops of the residues. The most important work in Britain has been the modifications by A. E. Johnston, G. E. G. Mattingly and R. G. Warren of the classical field experiments controlled by Rothamsted which are an irreplaceable resource for soil fertility research, not available in any other country. Residues of phosphorus and potassium in soil have been valued in terms of fresh fertilizer dressings. The experiments indicate that the whole of dressings of P or K may ultimately be recovered by crops; but we cannot enhance the solubility of residues to hurry recovery. In fact phosphate "fixation" is a beneficial process that conserves a resource and prevents loss from nearly all our soils; similarly potassium is "fixed", and protected from leaching in soils containing much clay. Equally important has been the proof that soils enriched in phosphate (and potassium) often produce larger yields than soils poorer in P (or K), however much fresh P (or K) fertilizer is used. Gains from residues are most where poor soil structure hinders mobility of phosphate (and K) ions and diminishes root-fertilizer contact.

In the classical experiments at Rothamsted some of the P and K applied has penetrated 60 cm deep during a century. Some K may have leached from the root zone, but no P has been lost. Both P and K have penetrated more deeply into the sandy soils at Woburn which contains little clay. The long-term experiments cannot be modified to test values of subsoil reserves of P and K, but in other recent experiments where P and K fertilizers were incorporated into subsoils crop yields were larger with than without these dressings, even where much PK fertilizer has been applied to topsoils.

## Nutrient Deficiency Symptoms of Plants

Symptoms of nutrient deficiency shown by leaves were much studied in the 1930–50 period. T. Wallace at Long Ashton Research Station pioneered this method of assessing the nutrient needs of crops and produced a colour "atlas" of deficiency symptoms. This method of diagnosing deficiencies was very useful in association with soil analyses when poor soils were being improved, or crops new to an area were being introduced, during the war. Visual diagnosis was usually confirmed by analysing the leaves. Wallace's work in the 1930s was particularly important in showing the need of fruit trees for large supplies of potassium. The method is now little used for advising on the application of major nutrients since, when such symptoms in annual plants are well developed, the crop may already be damaged and it is often too late to remedy the situation by fertilizing. (For permanent crops there *is* opportunity to remedy deficiencies indicated by leaf symptoms for future production.) In intensive arable agriculture shortages of nutrients should never be allowed to become so acute that deficiency symptoms occur; if they do large losses are inevitable. In Britain visual deficiency symptoms are now used for diagnosing shortages of micronutrients. Elsewhere they are of most use for advisers who are aiding the intensification of farming in areas where there is little information on soils or crop requirements, and the initiatives of Wallace and other workers have been invaluable.

## The Use of Fertilizers

Fertilizers have had an essential part in the changes in British agriculture which have roughly doubled output in the last 50 years. Use was assisted financially by the Government by price control from 1940 until 1951. Subsequently subsidies on nitrogen and phosphorus lessened cost to the farmer until these stopped in 1974. In 1979 fertilizers and lime cost British farmers £550 M, accounting for one-eighth of total "input" expenditure; three-quarters of the total is spent on nitrogen.

The plant nutrients applied as fertilizers in UK and the World 50 years ago and now are:

|  | UK | | | | World | | |
|  | N | $P_2O_5$ | $K_2O$ | | N | $P_2O_5$ | $K_2O$ |
|---|---|---|---|---|---|---|---|
|  | thousands of tonnes | | | | millions of tonnes | | |
| 1931 | 45 | 148 | 49 | | (2.2)* | (2.8)* | (1.8)* |
| 1979 | 1186 | 416 | 416 | | 48 | 28 | 23 |

(*approximate estimates)

In UK the use of nitrogen has increased about 20 times in the last 40 years; phosphate used has increased about two and a half times and potassium nearly six times.
Examples of the changes in amounts of fertilizers used on two typical arable crops are

shown below by quoting data from Rothamsted's Surveys of Fertilizer Practice: which have been done on farms in England and Wales since the 1940s with assistance from NAAS and from the Fertiliser Manufacturers' Association.

| | Winter wheat | | | Maincrop potatoes | | |
| | N | $P_2O_5$ | $K_2O$ | N | $P_2O_5$ | $K_2O$ |
|---|---|---|---|---|---|---|
| | | | Kilogrammes per hectare | | | |
| 1943/5 | 19 | 30 | 2 | 79 | 92 | 100 |
| 1950/2 | 33 | 28 | 15 | 117 | 124 | 166 |
| 1966 | 90 | 44 | 44 | 161 | 173 | 241 |
| 1979 | 135 | 46 | 38 | 193 | 195 | 257 |

By the 1950s root crops grown for sale were already well fertilized and there was a rapid increase in the nitrogen used on cereals when varieties with short stiff straws were introduced. Arable crops grown for sale in Britain now receive on average about as much fertilizer as is recommended. By contrast the average dressings of N used on grass, and particularly permanent grassland, are still much less than are recommended (figures are given later). Grass has no direct cash value; returns depend on using it in animal farming systems and some of the problems involved are discussed by W. F. Raymond in his essay in this volume.

## Forms of fertilizers

The forms of fertilizers used in Britain have changed greatly in the last 50 years. Then ammonium sulphate (20.6% N), superphosphate (14% $P_2O_5$) and "muriate of potash" (50% $K_2O$) dominated the market and were sold as powders or crystals, often in poor physical condition. They were mixed to provide N P K compound fertilizers which often absorbed moisture and formed a caked mass which had to be broken down before application. Bad physical condition, which used to be a hindrance to fertilizer use, has been overcome by the development of granular fertilizers which were first introduced here about 1930. Now nearly all N, P and K fertilizers are sold in prilled or granular forms packed in moisture-proof plastic bags. Insoluble sources of P — ground rock phosphate and basic slag — are still sold as powders. Basic slag is much less important than formerly because new steel-making processes do not produce slags with high contents of available P. In Britain most of the N is supplied by ammonium nitrate (34% N); some urea (46% N) is used here but much larger amounts are used in other countries. P is supplied by triple superphosphate (48% $P_2O_5$) and both N and P by ammonium phosphates. These ingredients give mixed fertilizers that are twice as concentrated as those used 40 years ago.

Changes in forms of fertilizers have entailed much research in comparing the newer forms against older standards. For example experiments in this and other countries have shown that urea spread on the soil surface may be inefficient unless the urea is washed into the soil before it is hydrolysed to form ammonia. The efficiency of urea is now a major research topic in developing countries where this fertilizer is the common form made by most modern factories. All water-soluble phosphates have been found to have similar efficiencies. The conditions under which water-insoluble dicalcium phosphate can be as effective as water-soluble mono-calcium phosphate have been established. Much field and laboratory work has been done by Rothamsted, with great assistance from the UK Advisory Services, to value water-insoluble phosphates. The soils and crops for which basic slags and rock phosphates are effective were established by early work. During the War "Silicophosphate", made by incinerating phosphate rock with alkali, was developed by the Building Research Station, evaluated by Rothamsted, and manufactured by the Ministry of Supply. Later research has examined the value of nitrophosphates (made by treating rock phosphates with nitric acid), and novel materials such as polyphosphates, including such concentrated materials as potassium "metaphosphate".

Liquid fertilizers have become common; first developments were in USA where anhydrous ammonia injected deeply into soils was found to be efficient for some crops. Later, aqueous solutions of ammonia and of ammonium nitrate and urea have been used. Liquid-mixed fertilizers have been developed, ammonium phosphates and poly-phosphates supplying the P. Low concentration (and therefore high freight and application costs) have been overcome by developing suspensions stabilized by clays. These new fertilizers have been tested in Britain where liquids now provide between 5 and 10% of the total fertilizer market. Liquids can be as efficient as solid fertilizers; whether their use expands will depend on costs and farming practices.

## Fertilizer recommendations for arable crops

Fertilizer recommendations in the 1930s were based on the results of local field experiments with some assistance from soil analyses and leaf deficiency symptoms. No systematic study had been made until 1941 when Crowther and Yates assembled the diverse results of some thousands of field experiments done in Britain and Western Europe to measure the effects of fertilizers on crop yields. Their classic work resulted in simple recommendations which formed the basis of the rapid expansion in fertilizer use during the war and afterwards. As fertilizer use expanded the advisory services needed more detailed information on the effects of soils, climate, and farming systems on crop responses to N, P and K. The expanded research and advisory services, and commercial firms, quickly developed a greater capacity for field and laboratory experimentation and provided new information that kept pace with the farmers' capacity to use it. Work on the form of the relationship between amounts of fertilizer dressings and their effects on crop yields, initiated by Crowther and Yates, has continued until the present; D. A. Boyd and his colleagues at Rothamsted made notable contributions by showing that often response "curves" were not curvilinear but had the form of two intersecting straight lines. The correct choice of a model to represent response of crop to fertilizer is important as different models provide estimates of optimum dressings which may differ widely. A new approach to defining the fertilizer requirements of vegetables, made by D. J. Greenwood and others at Wellesbourne, has been outlined by D. Rudd-Jones (p. 174).

Recommendations based on the results of field experiments testing fertilizers now also take account of soil series, of "available" P and K in soils, and of previous cropping and manuring on the land for which advice is being given. They also take account of the gains and losses of P and K in the farming system which will be used. Balance sheets for nutrients inputs (in fertilizers, animal feedingstuffs and manures, and other wastes) and outputs (in produce sold from farms) show that British farms as a whole have accumulated phosphate for many years. Consequently it is now rare to measure a response to P-fertilizer with most arable crops in Britain. Inputs to farming supply much less potassium than crops remove and balance calculations emphasise the importance of the K recycled in farm wastes and of that released from soil reserves (which depends on past treatment of the land and on soil series).

## Fertilizers for grassland

Most of the work done to guide the use of fertilizers has been with arable crops. The value of nitrogen for increasing the yield of grass was shown by the Park Grass Experiment begun at Rothamsted in 1856. Experiments later last century tested the (then) new source of phosphate — basic slag. This fertilizer proved valuable indeed in improving grass, particularly on acid soils and the heavy clays of the Midlands and Northern and Western England. Many experiments showed that slag supplied both lime and phosphorus and greatly encouraged clover which fixed nitrogen and upgraded the pastures; an example was the famous "Manuring for Mutton" experiments laid down at Cockle Park by Armstrong College (later Newcastle University) in 1896 which lasted for 50 years. Finely ground rock phosphate was also found to be useful for improving grassland on acid soils.

In the 1930s more research was done to establish the place of nitrogen in systems of grassland management and ICI had a leading role through their Jealott's Hill Research Station (formed in 1928). However, few farmers made use of the results and fifty years ago little fertilizer other than phosphate (usually basic slag) was applied to grassland. During the war the fertilizers available were mainly directed to arable food crops. The subsequent history of grassland manuring has been the slow adoption of an existing body of knowledge; the changes over the last 30 years are shown by these data for average rates of application from Surveys of Fertilizer Practice:

| | Temporary grass | | | Permanent grass | | |
|---|---|---|---|---|---|---|
| | N | $P_2O_5$ | $K_2O$ | N | $P_2O_5$ | $K_2O$ |
| | | | Kilogrammes per hectare | | | |
| 1950/2 | 16 | 35 | 15 | 6 | 24 | 4 |
| 1966 | 66 | 50 | 30 | 29 | 29 | 16 |
| 1979 | 173 | 33 | 37 | 99 | 23 | 20 |

Grass received very little N in the 1940s but the quantities used have steadily increased in the last 35 years. The N used on permanent grass has always lagged behind that used on leys.

As the amounts of N-fertilizer used on grassland increased during the 1960s the need for more information on the responses of grass to N given to cut and to grazed swards was realised. A new series of national field experiments were started. The work was coordinated by the Grassland Research Institute and experiments were done by ADAS, Universities, Agricultural Colleges and Agricultural Research Service (ARS) Institutes. Very good information has now been obtained on the use of nitrogen on grass that is cut. The response to N appears to be linear up to about 300 kg N ha$^{-1}$ — three times the average rate now used on permanent grass and nearly twice that used on leys. Progress is also being made with the more difficult tasks of assessing the value of N for grazed grassland and of making the best use of clover to fix N in swards that also receive N-fertilizers.

## Trace element fertilizers

Experience has accumulated in the last 50 years on the incidence of trace element deficiencies in the soils of this and other countries and on the practical means of correcting shortages for crops or animals. Much is also known about the ways in which reserves of the elements are combined with soil, and the factors that affect their release. Diagnoses of deficiencies are often made from deficiency symptoms on leaves, or from analyses of the plants. Boron deficiencies are common in agriculture and horticulture, affecting root crops, legumes and fruit trees. Iron deficiency can be serious in Britain where fruit trees are grown on calcareous soils. Manganese deficiencies were commonly found on some of the soils reclaimed for arable cropping during the War; many examples occurred on soil rich in organic matter and having neutral or alkaline pH. At present manganese deficiency is often diagnosed in cereals. Copper deficiency is much less common in Britain but there have been many examples on calcareous soils derived from Chalk, on fenland peats, and on sandy soils. Zinc deficiency has been rarely recorded in field crops in Britain, but has occurred in fruit trees. Molybdenum deficiency occurs in some brassicae crops.

## Timing and placing fertilizers

Much has been done to try to make fertilizers more efficient by applying them at the best times and in the best places. Timing is very important with soluble nitrogen fertilizers which may be lost by leaching if they are applied too early before the crop has sufficient roots to take them up. Very many field experiments have been done during the last 50 years to compare N-fertilizers applied at various times before and after sowing arable crops, and in single and divided dressings. This work has intensified in the last 10 years as the costs of fertilizers have risen and the importance of using efficiently the large dressings now given has been realised. The field experiments are now supported by modelling work on the movement of nitrate in soils used for arable and vegetable crops.

Phosphate and potassium fertilizers combine with soil, dressings applied to the surface do not act quickly; these fertilizers are best used when placed in a limited part of the root zone. "Combine-drills" which sow seed and fertilizer together were introduced in North America and Australia to save time and labour. It was found that small dressings of P and K fertilizers placed in bands near the seed of cereals were more efficient than larger dressings broadcast and mixed with soil before sowing. These drills were tested in Britain in the 1940s and it was found that only half as much placed P or K fertilizer was needed to secure a given crop response as was required when the same fertilizers were broadcast. The use of combine-drills spread rapidly when these results became known and they had a vital place in the 1940s in growing cereals on the ploughed grasslands which were often very deficient in P and sometimes in K. The extra efficiency the drills provided was very important as supplies of P and K fertilizers in war-time were very restricted.

The experiments on placed fertilizers were later extended to arable crops other than cereals. Placement improved the efficiency of fertilizers used for potatoes, peas, beans and some vegetables and made all crops grow more quickly in the early stages. Special planters fitted with fertilizer attachments were introduced in the 1950s to place fertilizer and seed for potatoes and arable crops; the importance of placing fertilizers has lessened in Britain as continued fertilizing has built up reserves of P and K in our soils. Direct drilling of crops into an undisturbed soil surface is now becoming common. This technique gives no opportunity to work broadcast fertilizer into the soil and it may become necessary to use drills which place P and K below the surface for direct-drilled crops.

## Liming of Soil

Lime was applied empirically to farmland in Britain for many centuries. By 1930 pH meters had been developed and these replaced the indicators previously used for testing the acidity of soils to advise on liming. Because ions present in the soil solution prevented accurate measurements of pH in poorly buffered soils, R. K. Schofield (of Rothamsted) introduced the method of measuring soil pH in a $0.01M$ calcium chloride solution. Work has continued since 1930 to measure rates of leaching of calcium and to provide better advice to farmers. The role of the aluminium and manganese, which become soluble in very acid soils, in damaging crop growth has been investigated; this problem is particularly serious in tropical soils.

Field experiments have shown that all the common liming materials behave similarly when used at equivalent rates of neutralizing value of calcium. There was no evidence for the old prejudice for calcium hydroxide or oxide as compared with the carbonate, or of fine as compared with coarse products. In war-time experiments blast furnace slags (essentially calcium silicates) were inferior to calcium carbonate as liming materials. Government action to encourage the use of lime began with the Land Fertility Scheme in 1937 and a subsidy on liming was paid from that year until 1976;

it contributed to the success of the war-time food production campaign. The amounts of lime applied in England and Wales in three periods, expressed in million tonnes of calcium carbonate were: 1941–50 2.9 M t, 1951–60 4.2 M t, and 1961–70 3.4 M t. It is estimated than in England and Wales we need to apply 3.0 to 3.7 M t of $CaCO_3$ annually to prevent losses of crops from soil acidity.

## Experiments on Organic Manures

Apart from the extra nitrogen fixed when legumes were grown, manures were the only means of adding extra nutrients to soil, or replacing those removed by crops, until chemical fertilizers were introduced. The "high-farming" systems built up in the first half of last century depended on farmyard manure (FYM) from housed animals, fed liberally on imported products (containing much N, P and K), to increase soil fertility. In the classical experiments begun in the last century at Rothamsted, Woburn, Saxmundham and other centres in England, FYM was compared with fertilizers. At the rates of application used similar yields were obtained from FYM and from complete fertilizer dressings where the latter supplied enough N, P and K. If organic manures had large and specific effects on crops, because they were *organic*, these must have been demonstrated in these long experiments; there were no signs of such effects. In most of the comparisons FYM supplied more nutrients, and particularly more N and K, than the fertilizers tested; and yet in most experiments fertilizers gave yields as good as, or better than, the organics. Nearly all effects of organic manuring in the period up to 1960 were explicable in terms of the nutrients supplied.

The classical experiments at Rothamsted were modified in the 1960s by growing modern varieties (some in rotational systems), by testing new fertilizer schemes, and by improved control of weeds, pests and diseases. In most of the new schemes FYM had some advantages over fertilizers. For example in the Barnfield Experiment on root crops yields of mangolds, sugar beet, and potatoes, have been larger on FYM-treated plots than on plots having only fertilizers. Tests with increasing rates of fertilizer nitrogen suggest that yields with fertilizers would never equal those with FYM, however much N was applied.

Recent experiments on loamy sand soil at Woburn by G. E. G. Mattingly and G. V. Dyke have been planned to detect any superior effects of various ways of adding organic matter to sandy soil; the amounts of P and K supplied by the different systems have been equalised. FYM, peat, straw, grass-clover ley, grass ley grown with N fertilizer, and green manures of ryegrass, trefoil or clovers undersown in barley, have all been tested as sources of organic matter. In these experiments the organically-treated plots have often yielded more wheat, sugar beet and potatoes than fertilizer-only plots, however much N was applied. As in the modified Classical experiments discussed above it seems that the gains from organic treatments are associated with the provision of N for crops in ways that are not fully imitated by fertilizers used in conventional ways.

## Alternatives to farmyard manure

From the 1930s onwards many annual and short-term field experiments were organised by H. V. Garner and others at Rothamsted; they were greatly assisted by workers in the advisory and educational services. The experiments compared FYM with composts, sewage sludges, town refuse and other wastes. A. H. Bunting (1963) found that sewage sludge was no more than a source of nitrogen and phosphate. All sludges contained very little potassium that was useful to crops. Composts of sewage sludge and rotted straw were superior, (the straw they contained supplied more K). On an equal weight basis FYM was superior to sewage sludge, to composts and to other organics, because it supplied more nutrients and particularly more potassium. Fermented town refuse, and composts of sewage sludge and town refuse had from one-third to two-thirds of the effects of a similar weight of FYM. Screened dusts from town wastes were variable and generally inferior to all the other wastes tested. The main value of all the organics tested in this period was in the nutrients they contained, content of organic matter as such was not important.

Toxicities of heavy metals contained in sewage sludges and other wastes applied to land now cause concern. Large quantities of zinc, copper, lead and chromium may accumulate if sludges from industrial areas are regularly applied. The risks of toxicities have been investigated by the Macaulay Institute and by ADAS. Guidelines have now been prepared to advise farmers on the amounts of sewage sludges of known compositions which may safely be applied.

## Animal manures

The place of fertilizers in farming systems involving livestock must take account of the large amounts of nutrients in animal manures and crop wastes which should be recirculated. The amounts in animal excreta in UK total about 850 k t of N, 200 k t of P and 700 k t of K — that is two-thirds as much N, as much P, and twice as much K as fertilizers supply. Whether these nutrients play a full part in producing more crops depends much on the evenness and efficiency with which the wastes from housed livestock are returned to land. Research has been done on the semi-liquid slurries which result from modern methods of housing livestock to recycle the nutrients efficiently and to avoid environmental pollution. Models developed by J. R. O'Callaghan at Newcastle University with ARC support guide the application of slurries by taking account of land use, soil characteristics, local climate and recent weather.

## Soil Fertility

The term soil fertility is widely used but has different meanings for different people. Usually it indicates the capacity of the soil to produce biomass — whether under undisturbed climax vegetation, or under intensive agriculture. G. V. Jacks (1963) said soil fertility was a biophysical rather than a physico-chemical phenomenon, and defined fertility as the capacity to support the climax population of plants and animals above ground and the associated flora and fauna below ground. The most extensive debates on factors concerned with the fertility of soil, which have continued through the last 50 years, have been on the role of soil organic matter, and on cultivations.

## Soil organic matter

Soil organic matter increases when land is not cultivated, for example under natural vegetation or grass; it diminishes when soils rich in organic matter are cultivated for a period of arable cropping. As W. F. Raymond has written, great stress was laid in the 1930s, particularly by Sir George Stapledon, on the value of ley farming. It was claimed that, where a period under herbage crop was followed by a period under arable crops, the system would improve fertility by accumulating soil organic matter and that a rotation of arable crops grown after the leys would produce more than similar crop sequences taken continuously. The important benefits from leys in building up extra nitrogen in soil, and their effect as a "break" to check soil-borne pests and diseases, were often ignored. Where successful organic farming systems have been examined they seem to depend on purchased feedingstuffs to supply extra nutrients to enrich manure made by livestock, on good clover leys that are grazed, and often on soils with good reserves of potassium. The best known test of organic farming, at Haughley in Suffolk, has been described by Lady Eve Balfour (1973).

The first of a series of experiments to compare ley and arable rotations began on sandy soil at Woburn in 1938; two others on clay loam soils at Rothamsted began in 1946. They compared rotations including 3 years of herbage crops against all-arable rotations. Similar experiments were made on NAAS Experimental Husbandry Farms. The practical importance of the changes in soil organic matter caused by different farming systems was tested by measuring the yields of the same arable test crops grown in all rotations. In the early years at Rothamsted the largest differences in yields were from differences in (1) amounts of N residues left by leys and (2) soluble P and K in soils under contrasted rotations where the management of crops removed different amounts. At Woburn the incidence of soil-borne pests varied according to the frequency with which certain crops were grown. Later the schemes were modified so that the test crops were grown under standardised conditions, at the same levels of P and K, and free from pests and diseases. Results from the later years of all these experiments provide no evidence that leys affected crop yields through their effect on soil organic matter. When the rotations avoided build-up of soil-borne pests and diseases, and the nutrients removed by crops were replaced, the value of leys was only to save part of the fertilizer-N needed in all-arable rotations.

Experiments done during the last 40 years show that most British farmers need take no special action to add extra organic matter to their soils if, by doing so, profitability of the system is lessened. If adequate fertilizers are used, organic matter will be maintained at sufficiently high levels in most soils by crop residues; the crops that are most profitable may be grown if weeds, pests and diseases are controlled. In many other countries where soil deterioration under arable cropping may be a serious cause of loss there is, unfortunately, no evidence on these questions.

## Cultivations

Until the 1930s the guidance that cultivation practices received from tradition and practical experience was not seriously challenged by scientists. In 1937 B. A. Keen and E. W. Russell showed that at Rothamsted ploughing soil was not essential for producing successful arable crops. The optimum cultivation was that needed to create a seedbed and destroy weeds; working the soil more was likely to lessen rather than to increase crop growth. Later field experiments on many kinds of soil showed that deeper ploughing was often no better than shallow and then all that was *essential* was surface tilling to control weeds and create an adequate tilth for sowing seeds. (Where heavy machines created ruts on the surface and compressed the subsoil, then ploughing was necessary.)

The next challenge to the traditional wisdom of cultivating was in the early 1960s when the bipyridyl herbicides were introduced. These chemicals, and later introductions with similar properties, kill all green plants and leave no active residue in soil; seeds can be sown directly in a slit, or narrow stirred ribbon of soil, in the undisturbed land surface. Farmers saw that "no-till" direct drilling, and minimum cultivations systems, saved tractor fuel and, even more important, time needed for autumn sowing. As machines improved, and experience was gained, direct drilling increased and in 1979 325,200 hectares of crops were established in this way in Britain. Experiments made by Letcombe Laboratory, Weed Research Organisation and the National Institute for Agricultural Engineering, and by University Departments sponsored by ARC, showed that direct drilled crops yielded as well as those grown after traditional cultivations. Soil structure improved under direct drilling and earthworm populations were larger than after ploughing. Plate 4 shows the better structure of soil under direct-drilling in an experiment done by Letcombe Laboratory.

These developments have provided a new concept for soil management and for fertility studies. Loss of soil organic matter, and damage to organisms living in the soil, both caused by cultivations, are no longer inevitable. It is not necessary to accept that

*Plate 4* Profiles 0.8m deep in clay loam soil (Evesham series) photographed in July 1975 to show the contrasted effects of cultivation on depth of cracking and profile development.
*Left* Continuous cracks extended more than 1m from the surface in soil on which cereals had been direct-drilled for 3 years.
*Right* In soil ploughed each year continuous cracks did not penetrate so deeply.

physical improvements to soil architecture created by an annual crop will be destroyed at the end of the season by ploughing or that its residues, which could increase the soil organic matter, will be decomposed and lost. Neither is it necessary to tolerate a sharp interface between the cultivated horizon and the subsoil beneath, the whole profile can be managed.

## The Future

Fifty years ago it was possible for one man to comprehend and integrate the research being done in most branches of soil science, as Sir John Russell did in his famous book. The period since has been marked by great advances in specialist knowledge, made possible by new techniques and instruments, and by large increases in numbers of workers in many countries. It is now difficult indeed for one person to be fully aware of the relevance of all the work being done and even more difficult to integrate chemical, physical, and biological information on soils and crops into systems for controlling soil productivity. Yet this must be done if work on soil science and crop nutrition is to be justified by practical application. ARC has established as one of its high priority topics — "The wider use of experiments aimed at maximising crop yields and elucidating those soil factors which limit yield." This initiative has resulted in strengthening work in fields and laboratories of the ARS, special emphasis being given to the vital region where roots meet soil. On these sites biologists, chemists and physicists will work to a common purpose. Full exploitation of their efforts will require multidisciplinary modelling to integrate the processes that affect the growth and performance of roots in soil.

In another essay in this volume L. Fowden has written that the task of soil scientists is to define the ideally structured soil matrix where root systems of crops develop unimpeded obtaining water and all nutrients in sufficient amounts to sustain the full photosynthetic capacity of the plant; they must then recommend how this situation may be achieved in farming practice. When we understand fully the conditions and processes in the rooting zone of soil it will be possible to plan for fertility management practices that realise the full potential of a crop. Our purpose must be to have the ability reliably to do the same thing twice; competent soil management will avoid the surprises now so commonly caused by failure to achieve potential yield. This may seem an academic exercise, but it is not. In an age when we have the ability to fly to the moon, through engineering skills and a full knowledge of the properties of the materials and processes that are involved, we must develop a fuller knowledge of the properties of our soils, and the transport processes which supply nutrients and water to roots. The purpose of this research is to have the power, through understanding, to assess and control soil productivity; it does not have the unrealistic objective of raising farmers' yields irrespective of input costs.

Sir Humphrey Davy's advice in the 1821 Edition of his book is still relevant. He discussed the need to substitute sound and rational principles for "vague, popular prejudices ... Nothing is more wanting in agriculture than experiments in which all the circumstances are minutely and scientifically detailed. The results of truly philosophical experiments in agricultural chemistry would be of more value in enlightening and benefiting the farmer than the greatest possible accumulation of imperfect trials conducted merely in the empirical spirit".

## Further Reading

Avery, B. W. (1973). Soil classification in the Soil Survey of England and Wales. *Journal of Soil Science*, **24**, 324–338.

Balfour, E. B. (Lady) (1975). *The living soil and the Haughley experiment*. London: Faber and Faber.

Bibby, J. S. and Mackney, D. (1977). *Land use capability classification*. Technical Monograph No. 1. The Soil Survey, Rothamsted Experimental Station.

Bunting, A. H. (1963). Experiments on organic manures, 1942–49. *Journal of Agricultural Science, Cambridge*, **60**, 121–140.

Childs, E. C. (1969). *An introduction to the physical basis of soil water phenomena*. London: Wiley.

Crowther, E. M. (1951). Experimental agriculture. *The Advancement of Science*, No. 30, Sept. 1951, pp. 1–13.

Crowther, E. M. (1937). The technique of modern field experiments. *Journal of the Royal Agricultural Society of England*, **97**, 51–81.

Crowther, E. M. and Yates, F. (1941). Fertiliser policy in war-time. *Empire Journal of Experimental Agriculture*, **9**, 76–97.

Greenland, D. J. and Hayes, M. H. B. (1978). *The chemistry of soil constituents*. Chichester: Wiley.

Jacks, G. V. (1963). The biological nature of soil productivity. *Soils and Fertilizers*, **26**, 147–150.

Ministry of Agriculture, Fisheries and Food (1970). *Modern farming and the soil*. Report of the Agricultural Advisory Council on soil structure and soil fertility. London: HMSO.

Mitchell, R. L. (1963). Soil aspects of trace element problems in plants and animals. *Journal of the Royal Agricultural Society of England*, **124**, 75–86.

Mitchell, R. L. and Burridge, J. C. (1979). Trace elements in soils and crops. *Philosophical Transactions of the Royal Society of London. B.* **288**, 15–24.

Nye, P. H. and Tinker, P. B. (1977). *Solute movement in the soil-root system*. Oxford: Blackwell.

Pereira, H. C. and others (1975). Agricultural science and the traditions of tillage. *Outlook on Agriculture*, **8**, Special Number, pp. 211–259.

Russell, E. J. (1932). *Soil conditions and plant growth*. 6th Edition. London: Longmans, Green & Co.

Russell, E. W. (1973). *Soil conditions and plant growth.* 10th Edition. London: Longmans.

Russell, R. Scott (1977). *Plant root systems.* London: McGraw Hill Book Company.

Shaw, K. (1979). *Fertiliser recommendations.* Ministry of Agriculture, Fisheries and Food. GF1. London: HMSO.

Soil Survey Staff (1975). *Soil taxonomy: A basic system of soil classification for making and interpreting soil surveys.* Agricultural Handbook No. 436 USDA. US Government Printing Office, Washington D.C.

Soil Science Society of America (1977). Bicentennial papers. *Soil Science Society of America Journal,* **41,** 221–265.

# Research in Agricultural Engineering, 1931–1981

## R. L. BELL and J. C. HAWKINS

National Institute of Agricultural Engineering, Wrest Park, Silsoe, Bedford

Since 1931 some 344 000 tractors have replaced 667 000 horses on the farms in England and Wales. During this same period the total number of workers on the land has fallen from 717 000 to 318 000. Yet agricultural production has more than doubled.

These dramatic changes derive from a number of important contributions to the development of modern agricultural technology, but among them the widespread adoption of mechanisation has been prominent. At first the agricultural engineer produced machines which performed operations closely similar to those previously carried out by hand or with the aid of horses. More recently attempts to further increase agricultural productivity have often involved a radical reconsideration of a whole farming system. For example, rather than trying to develop a machine which selects mature vegetables and leaves the others to develop, as hand workers do, it was better for the agricultural engineer to team up with agronomists and plant breeders to change the crop and/or the way in which it was grown so that it matured evenly. It could then be harvested in a once-over operation by a much simpler machine with less risk of damage.

There is another important distinction between the early research on mechanisation and that carried out today. At first there was a great deal to be gained simply from applying to agricultural situations all that the mechanical engineer had learned about power and machinery. Indeed there is still scope for applying in the agricultural context what has been gained in other branches of engineering. For example, the cheap, rugged and reliable solid-state electronic instrumentation that was developed for aero-space technology is poised to make its impact in agriculture. But agricultural engineering has also established its own disciplines and it is proving profitable to undertake basic research on the elementary processes carried out by machinery on soils, crops and agricultural materials. The fundamental knowledge gained from these studies will provide the springboard for the next generation of machines and structures. At the same time, the results of recent research in animal and crop husbandry, plant breeding, and pest and weed control will have profound effects on the opportunities facing the agricultural engineer and on the progress of mechanisation.

## Farm Power

### Tractor power

As can be seen in Plate 1, the typical agricultural tractor of 50 years ago looks very different from its modern counterpart, yet its main components and their layout are much the same. Fifty years of research and development have tended to add to the basic tractor rather than to change it. There is one subtle but important exception and this concerns the wheels. In the early thirties, every wheeled tractor had steel wheels with lugs or strakes; today all have pneumatic tyres. The importance of this innovation is that it has changed the tractor from a field traction vehicle to one which is useful for transport too, and this finally eliminated the horse from British farms.

Early research on pneumatic tyres soon established that they were more efficient than steel wheels, because they had a lower rolling resistance. Under some soil conditions there were limitations of grip at low speed and high pulls but subsequent work has shown how larger diameters, lower pressures and increased weight can improve traction. The advantages of exerting the drive through all four wheels of the tractor were recognised in the thirties, but the advent of pneumatic tyres has improved the performance of 4-wheel drive machines to a level about midway between that of 2-wheel drive tractors and track layers, although at high speeds a 4-wheel drive vehicle can be even more efficient than a tracked one.

*Plate 1* A 20.8 hp (15.5 kW) Forsdon Tractor, 1930.
A 77.6 kW (104 hp) 4 wd Ford Tractor, 1980

Of the additions to the early tractors, the rear linkage and power lift were probably the most important. In 1931 mounted equipment was largely restricted to mid- or rear-mounted toolbars which had to be lifted mechanically or by hand. It was not until 1936 when Harry Ferguson produced a tractor with 3-point rear linkage and built-in hydraulic lift that it became possible to replace difficult-to-manoeuvre trailed implements with a wide range of equipment that could be mounted on the tractor. He also introduced a draught control mechanism which removed the necessity for depth wheels and so allowed any available downward force from the implement to be transferred to the rear of the tractor to improve traction.

The addition to the early tractors which changed their appearance most was the cab. In the beginning it was introduced simply as weather protection for the driver, especially in exposed districts like the north and east of Britain. Following experience in Sweden which showed how a safety frame or cab could save lives in overturning accidents, they were made compulsory on all new tractors there. Similar regulations followed in Britain in 1967. These regulations governing safety cabs were extended in 1973 to include a maximum permissible level of noise at the driver's ear, so that he is now enclosed in a cab which protects him from the weather, from crushing in an accident and from excessive noise. Ironically, this last feature has produced a degree of isolation which limits what he can see, hear, and operate from his seat, and is now giving rise to calls for "signalling" equipment to help him control the implements attached to the tractor.

Although the layout of tractors in general use has changed little, there have been many experimental attempts to find a different arrangement of their main components that would make the driver's job easier or the tractor a more efficient and versatile source of power. Of the numerous unorthodox designs studied, four types have been produced commercially and used in significant numbers. These comprise tool carriers, modified cross-country vehicles, reversible tractors and, more recently, modified industrial mechanical handling vehicles. Research on reversible tractors has shown that they have few advantages over tool-carriers and that rear wheel steering with the fixed driven wheels in front is not satisfactory at high drawbar pulls and on side slopes greater than 1 in 10. On the other hand, modified industrial handling vehicles, such as rough terrain fork lifts, are being used in increasing numbers particularly on the larger livestock farms.

The declining labour force in agriculture has meant that it was necessary to increase the output of those workers remaining by increasing the power and therefore the output of the tractors that they were driving; hence the steady increase in the power of tractors over the last 50 years. The alternative of dispensing with the driver altogether by developing an automatic tractor has occupied inventors for almost as long as the tractor has existed. Only the system which uses a leader cable has been sold commercially and that for but a short time. An important consequence of the trend towards higher output per man has been greater attention to driver comfort and efficiency. Consideration has been given to the layout of controls, to the ill-effects of vibration on drivers and their performance, and to the use of hydraulics. They have been used both to reduce the effort required for steering and to facilitate the control of both mounted and trailed implements.

No account of hydraulics on tractors or tractor design would be complete without reference to hydrostatic transmissions with their ability to provide a steplessly variable ground speed. There has been considerable research on the subject but it has led to few commercial designs, probably because of the reduced power efficiency associated with hydrostatic transmission and because of the introduction of tractor gearboxes with a large number of gears which could be changed on the move. On the other hand the ability to supply hydraulic power to a wheel down a pipe has not been fully exploited. Almost any layout of tractor or self-propelled machine becomes possible: the power unit consisting of engine and hydraulic pump could even be towed behind. Such freedom in design may be of value in the future as the trend is clearly towards more specialised vehicles on farms. Starting with self-propelled combine harvesters it has spread to other self-propelled harvesters including those for forage, potatoes and sugar beet, whilst special transport, handling, and spraying vehicles have been developed from industrial or cross-country vehicles. It is quite possible to envisage a mixed farm of the future with no conventional tractors.

## Stationary sources of power

In 1938 only about 7% of farms in Great Britain were connected to the public electricity supply, so most of them relied on small stationary engines as sources of power for fixed machinery. With the spread of rural electrification all these engines were replaced by electric motors. This had a profound effect on many operations carried out in and around farm buildings. An early example of this was the change made in the method of grinding grain on farms. Before electrification it was usual to have a large mill driven by a tractor or stationary engine under constant supervision and running only during working hours. With electricity the same weekly output could be achieved more cheaply by a much smaller mill, driven by a 2 kW or 3 kW motor and controlled automatically so that it could run unattended day and night if necessary. The coming of electricity made possible the mechanisation and automation of many operations which had previously been done by hand.

However, the most profound effects of electrification have been on the way that animals are kept. The transformation from free range to cages and broiler houses and from pig sties to pig houses (discussed later) could not have gone so fast or so far without electricity. The intensive housing of birds and animals depends on electrically-powered mechanical ventilation systems, and good husbandry demands that this be closely controlled: neither would have been possible without an electricity supply.

## Crop Production

### Cultivations

Two developments have completely changed attitudes to cultivations in the last 50 years — tractors and herbicides. When the power available on farms was limited to what a team of horses or even an 18 kW tractor could provide, efficient soil cultivation was mostly a matter of starting something to be finished by the weather or of finishing something started by the weather. With more power and higher rates of work there was often more time for extra cultivations. The use of more powerful tractors also led to work on applying power directly to tillage implements through the power take-off and on operating at higher speeds to avoid the inefficiency and damage to soil structure associated with high drawbar pulls and heavy tractors.

Far bigger changes in cultivations, have, however, resulted from the developments in herbicides. Up to then cultivations had been essential to kill weeds; it now became important to find out what else cultivations did. There was already a good deal of evidence that they had very little effect on crop growth and could even be harmful. Over the years, the conclusion is emerging that, once weeds have been controlled, cultivations on soils with a stable structure are needed only to counter the ill-effects of tractors and traffic which are likely to appear as reductions in permeability to air and water and increases in resistance to root penetration. The problems remain of how to measure these properties in the field and to establish practical limits for them, so that it becomes possible to say when cultivations are needed and to define what should be done. In the meantime, farmers have increasingly substituted tine cultivation for mouldboard ploughing (Plate 2) reducing the depth and amount of their cultivations or avoided cultivation altogether by using direct drilling, for which a range of special equipment has been developed.

*Plate 2* Ploughing, the first of several cultivations for cereals in 1930.
Tines going through stubble, this one-pass operation is often the only cultivation for cereals in 1980.

Parallel to such work on cultivations, research by agricultural engineers on tillage tools has only just begun to explain their action on the soil and the origin and nature of the forces acting on them. It has been established, for example, that even vertical straight tines always bring some soil to the surface from the level at which their points are running. It has also defined the effects on draught of such variables as tine depth, width, rake angle and speed and has related these to the mechanical properties of soil. Research on the wear of metal by soil has shown that most of the wear is caused by stones, and that although it can be reduced by suitable hard facings, the future probably lies with new materials for points and edges such as ceramics, which can reduce wear rate by a factor of between 5 and 10.

## Planting

The seed side of grain drills has changed little in 50 years but most are now of the combine type because it was shown that crop yields were often higher when fertilizer was precisely placed during drilling. It is in the mechanisation of the planting of spaced row-crops and of sugar beet in particular, where the most significant advances in seeding have been made. The starting point was mechanical cross-blocking or hoeing across the rows to reduce the work of the hoemen. Natural multigerm seed was then processed by breaking or abrading it to produce a high proportion of single-germ units, which were planted with spacing drills. Mechanical thinning and the development of natural monogerm seed came along to reduce hand labour to 5% of what it had been originally. Finally, with improved herbicides and better monogerm seed, sugar beet seed is now largely space drilled to a stand, as are many other row crops, and hand work eliminated altogether.

The alternative of transplanting to establish spaced rowcrops has also received attention from agricultural engineers as rising labour costs have made them look for a fully mechanised system. The approach has been to develop a stationary machine which manufacturers and then seeds soil blocks which are strung together so that they can be handled mechanically. When the seedlings are ready for transplanting the strings of blocks are loaded on to a field machine which automatically separates and plants them at the required spacing.

## Spraying

When it is remembered that in 1931/32 only 120 ha of land in the UK were sprayed mechanically by less than half-a-dozen horse-drawn field sprayers, whilst today the figures are in the region of 10 million hectares and about 90 000 tractor-mounted sprayers, it is clear that spraying for pest, weed and disease control has become a basic agricultural operation. Probably the most dramatic changes have been made in orchard sprayers, Plate 3. In the thirties trees and bushes were sprayed with about 3000 l ha$^{-1}$ by men using hand lances supplied from sprayers towed round the orchard; by the fifties these had been replaced by machines applying less than 500 l ha$^{-1}$ and using powerful fans to blow the spray into the trees as they were drawn down the rows. Such a change, without a reduction in the effectiveness of pesticides, was achieved by research into nozzle design and studies of how spray droplets are carried by air jets and distributed over foliage and branches.

Parallel studies have led to improvements in field sprayers although there have been additional problems to be solved with them. These have been in marking, to make sure that successive runs across the field are accurately joined, and in improved boom design to ensure even coverage of the crop on each bout. The latter is particularly important with wide sprayers where uneven distribution results from errant boom movements unless special mountings are introduced to isolate the boom from the rolling and yawing motion of the tractor. Perhaps the most important problem with field sprayers is that of finding ways of reducing the drop size and hence the quantity of liquid which has to be applied without causing pollution by spray drift. Adequate coverage at the lowest possible application rate calls for a size of droplet which is just big enough to avoid it being carried away by ambient air movement. Much work has been done on conventional fan and cone nozzles and on alternative ways of producing a controlled smaller range

*Plate 3* Spraying fruit trees with hand lances, 1930.
Air blast sprayer for top fruit, 1980

of droplet sizes, such as by rotary atomisers. It seems likely, however, that any solution to the problem of minimal application rates must include some way of urging the droplets on to the crop. To this end the charging of spray droplets to make use of electrostatic forces is being studied. Additionally or alternatively it may be possible to make use of currents of air to guide the spray droplets on to the crop, not unlike the principle used with orchard sprayers.

## Harvesting and Storage

### Forage

Fifty years ago the main objectives of research on forage conservation were, as now, to reduce losses and to shorten the time that cut crops were exposed in the field. The latter is particularly important for haymaking. Tedding and various swath treatments designed to increase the rate of moisture loss were first investigated in the thirties.

Extensive research on methods and mechanisms has continued ever since. The advent of the pick-up baler in 1933 suggested that the time in the field could be reduced by baling earlier and completing the drying process under cover. More recently, the application of preservatives like propionic acid to hay during baling is being investigated as an alternative way of reducing the field drying period, while avoiding mould growth and so allowing conservation of wetter hay.

*Plate 4* Mowing 1930.
Mowing and conditioning 1980.

The individual machines required for haymaking have been the subject of continuing development, illustrated by the two photographs separated by 50 years in Plate 4. Cutterbar mowers have given way to rotary mowers which are capable of more than double the forward speed and rate of work. Wire tying by hand on pick-up balers has been replaced by automatic twine tying, and many ways of grouping or packaging the resulting 20 kg rectangular bales for mechanical handling have been produced. Perhaps the most spectacular change has been the development of machines to make 300–450 kg bales which can be economically handled as single units by a tractor or fork lift. Of the two types of big bale the "round" bale has not proved so suitable for hay, which has to be dried to a lower than normal moisture content in the swath to prevent moulds developing subsequently. Round bales cannot easily be dried artificially, unlike the large rectangular ones which can be dried when stacked in the form of a tunnel with closed ends and ventilated from the inside.

Many of the problems of conserving forage by making hay are solved by making silage. The increasing popularity of silage has been aided by the development of machinery like forage harvesters which make silage-making quicker, cheaper and easier. There has also been a substantial effort put into the design of silos. Studies of the origin and nature of the forces concerned has shown that pressures on silo walls are reduced significantly if the walls are allowed to deflect under load and this has led to a new form of silo with flexible walls.

*Plate 5* Towed engine-driven combine harvester, 1930
Self-propelled rotary combine harvester, 1980

## Cereals

The first combine harvester reached England from North America in 1927 and the performance of the ten at work by 1931 in "the wettest harvest for 50 years" confirmed the combine's place in British agriculture. In spite of a great deal of research into the design, setting and use of the rasp bar drum and concave threshing mechanisms of the combine the only major change in its design up to the seventies concerned the propulsion unit. Instead of a towed machine, driven either by its own engine or from the tractor power take-off, the most popular combine became the self-propelled one. Plate 5 shows two typical harvesting scenes separated by about 50 years. The change to the self-propelled combine led to the development of automatic controls for cutting height and sensors to monitor grain losses. It seems likely that, with the present trend to higher rates of work, even more of the adjustments on the combine will become automatic.

In the meantime, because of the British climate, the main research effort in cereal harvesting has been directed towards solving the problems of drying, handling and storing of grain on the farm. From the very beginning the need for some way of drying grain was recognised and industrial high temperature driers were adapted for the purpose. Safe drying temperatures were soon established but it was many years before maltsters, millers and merchants would accept dried grain as readily as undried. Because of this, and of the need to reduce the cost of on-farm drying and storage, research into the drying process has led to various forms of medium temperature bulk drier as alternatives to the high temperature grain drying. The first was "in-bin drying", in which bulk bins were ventilated through a perforated floor with warm air. This led to the construction of the first of many ventilated grain stores on farms. In-sack drying was developed for the small farms but, as the handling of grain in bulk became universal, this was replaced by on-floor drying for all sizes of farm. In the future, bulk drying is likely to continue to be the most widely used method and will probably be controlled automatically as high temperature driers are now.

## Potatoes

It is now about 50 years since attempts were first made to replace digging and hand-picking by a complete harvester for potatoes, yet a solution which is as universally effective as the combine for cereals has still to be produced. The main problem is the separation, without damage, of about 30 tonnes of potatoes from some 830 tonnes of soil for each hectare harvested. The problem has been ameliorated by a combination of suitable cultivations before planting and herbicides in place of inter-row cultivations to control weeds afterwards. There has also been a great deal of research into the design of complete potato harvesters, including web design, and particularly into the automatic separation of potatoes from clods and stones. The most successful separator makes use of X-rays to identify the potatoes and is used commercially both in mobile harvesters and in stationary separators at potato stores.

## Sugar beet

Single-row harvesters with the basic components of modern sugar beet machines, namely topper, lifting shares and cleaning mechanisms, existed in 1931 although they have been changed very much by developments since then. Research has concentrated on achieving as high or higher standards of performance at the increased forward speeds which are available with modern pneumatic-tyred tractors. Work on self-steering the shares or the harvester has raised possible speeds to as high as 2.7 ms$^{-1}$ and on toppers to 2.2 ms$^{-1}$ by reducing weight and finding the optimum form of damping. Better cleaning of the roots on heavy soils and under wet conditions has been achieved by the development of new cleaning mechanisms.

## Vegetables

Large complete harvesters have been developed for peas and beans for freezing, and sugar beet and potato harvesters have been adapted for root vegetables, but the average British grower for the fresh market would like a "vegetable combine" which could harvest a range of his crops. Attempts have been made to produce such a machine but further progress depends a good deal on the production of crops which mature evenly so that they can be harvested in a "once-over" operation.

Mechanised harvesting can have profound effects on the handling and preparation of produce for sale. In particular, with crops maturing evenly and higher rates of harvesting, the need to hold fresh vegetables in good condition for longer periods, becomes important. Research in this area has led to an improved cool store, based on air conditioning by an ice-bank cooler to remove the "field heat" of vegetables.

## Fruit

The mechanisation of fruit harvesting poses many of the problems of vegetable harvesting. For example, strawberry harvesting by mowing off the crop requires varieties whose fruits hang well clear of the ground and all ripen at the same time. For other soft fruit, research has led to the development and commercial production of a blackcurrant harvester which uses vibration of the bushes to shake off the fruit on to conveyors below. This principle is also being tried for other soft fruit including raspberries and gooseberries, and is the only one at present used to any extent for top fruit. It can be satisfactory for these crops when they are used for processing, but the damage caused by fruit striking branches or other fruit on the way down makes it unsuitable for dessert fruit.

## Glasshouses

Fifty years ago glasshouses were timber structures, glazed with glass held by putty, and painted. Modern houses are constructed of extruded aluminium sections which are much stronger and therefore slimmer than the equivalent timber members. Light losses have been reduced from 50% to below 25% and unsupported spans can be increased to 20 m or more across. The design of these glasshouses so that they would just carry the load of a good crop plus normal snow and wind loads was not easy because data for wind loading were limited. This deficiency has been remedied by extensive measurements of wind pressures at a number of sites in Britain and the results now form part of the Code of Practice for the design of farm buildings. Glasshouses are intended to provide optimum conditions for growth, so work has been done on heating, on ventilation systems for temperature and humidity control, and on the addition of carbon dioxide to the internal atmosphere. As the optimum levels for these are interrelated and dependent on the incoming light intensity, they cannot be manually controlled conveniently and so suitable automatic controllers have been developed. Some of these take the intensity of the incoming light into account. Recently the soilless culture of crops under glass, which had been known for many years, has been developed into the Nutrient Film Technique described in the essay by D. Rudd-Jones. For this it is necessary to control the properties of the nutrient solutions in which the crops grow, to within close limits. Again this presents an opportunity for automatic electronic control which is being made both cheap and reliable by solid state circuitry.

The future of glasshouses in Britain depends a good deal, however, on the cost and supply of energy. This was realised as far back as the thirties when workers were looking, as they are today, for alternatives to burning fossil fuels in boilers on site. It seems likely that glasshouses will have to be re-sited one day so that they can be heated by reject heat from power stations and industrial plants. In the meantime, it has been shown that as much as 35% of the annual heating cost of glasshouses can be saved if heat-retaining blinds or thermal screens are fitted under the roof and drawn across during darkness.

## Livestock

### Housing

Fifty years ago most livestock were kept in small groups needing individual attention. Rising labour costs put an end to such extensive systems of husbandry: as illustrated in Plate 6, pigs and poultry left the land and all stock were housed more intensively in much larger groups, usually in specialised factory-made buildings. At the same time the links between health and environment and the savings in feed that are possible when pigs and poultry are kept in the right environment were established, and so the control of environments inside buildings became of economic importance and the subjects of research, yielding results like the record of temperature and air movement patterns, inset in Plate 6. For ruminants, when the effects of convection were understood it became possible to design buildings with adequate natural ventilation at all times. With pigs and poultry, so many animals could be housed in one building that natural ventilation was neither adequate nor gave the required degree of temperature control. This led to automatically controlled mechanical ventilation to maintain the required house temperature.

### Feeding

It has been estimated that over 38 million tons of forage, concentrates and bedding are used by livestock annually in England and Wales. Much of this is handled more than once, both as inputs and as wastes, and so accounts for the major labour input in livestock production. For this reason modern livestock buildings are designed to minimise the amount of handling, as with self-feed silos for example, or to accommodate mechanised methods of feeding. All poultry and an increasing number of pigs are fed mechanically from the bulk feed hoppers and research on conveying pellets pneumatically down plastic pipes has led to an automatic dry feeding system for pigs.

Mechanical systems for feeding of forage to cattle from tower silos have been in use on a few farms for some time and some of these are capable of delivering automatically rations blended from controlled amounts of different ingredients.

### Milking

The way that cows are milked has probably changed more than any other single task in animal husbandry. Fifty years ago most of them were milked by hand and the few that were milked by machine were tied up in cowsheds and milked with bucket plants, although one or two pioneers were milking in bails like the one in Plate 7. Milking in parlours has been the standard practice for many years already and now the modern dairy parlour, like that in Plate 7, is in the vanguard where the new "silicon chip" revolution is making its impact on agriculture. It is possible to fit every cow in the herd with a device which will identify her as she enters the parlour. From then on her predetermined ration of concentrates can be weighed out automatically, the milker informed of any important information about the cow such as service or calving dates,

*Plate 6* Tethered sow and litter, 1930
Modern fattening piggery 1980 – inset, diagram showing isotherms and pattern of air movement
in half of the building

her milk yield recorded, and she can be weighed as she leaves the parlour. In the future
it should be possible to develop sensors that will allow oestrus and mastitis to be
detected as well. All this information can be recorded and analysed by a small computer
in the parlour office, or transmitted to a computer in the farm office which will not only
provide all the information needed to manage the herd efficiently but will cope with all
the business operations of the farm, too.

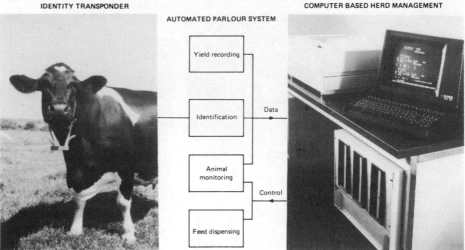

IDENTITY TRANSPONDER

AUTOMATED PARLOUR SYSTEM

COMPUTER BASED HERD MANAGEMENT

Yield recording

Identification

Data

Animal monitoring

Control

Feed dispensing

*Plate 7*  Milking bail, 1930
Diagram of computer controlled parlour, 1980

## Wastes

Dealing with livestock waste involves an even larger handling job than feeding, requiring in England and Wales alone the movement of some 50 million tons of manure annually. This has led to handling manure as slurry, which has brought problems of storage, handling, disease transmission, smell and water pollution. In Britain attention has been paid to mechanical slurry separation to provide a solid fraction which will compost rapidly into an easily handled, odourless material, and a liquid fraction which can be pumped and spread on the land as easily as water. This process simplifies storage and handling and can reduce odour nuisance, pollution risks and the chances of pathogen survival; but further treatment is often needed when aerial or water pollution problems are severe. Research in the EEC has suggested that aeration is the most practical method of reducing odour. In Britain research has been done on both aerobic and anaerobic treatment, the latter both to control odour and reduce pollution potential and to produce methane as a fuel. Where the land area is inadequate to receive the output of slurry without severe water pollution risks, some form of complete treatment is needed. Research has aimed at finding ways of converting as much of the slurry as possible to an odourless solid, so that it can be easily stored, transported and applied to land elsewhere. This has included work on composting with straw and on the complete aerobic treatment involving separation, aeration in a high-rate filter and sludge de-watering.

## The Role and Contribution of the ARC

Sir William Henderson in his history of British agricultural research (pp 32-33) has touched on some of the opportunities and problems that have faced the Ministry of Agriculture since tractors and other mechanical devices began to push or pull their way into the farming scene. On the one hand, there has been the possibility of conducting research and development to produce new and better implements; on the other, there has been the need to advise the Ministry and farmers at large on how best to make use of "new-fangled mechanical and electrical contraptions".

The most dramatic period was, of course, that heralded by the onset of war in 1939 when the requirement for the country to grow more of its own food using even less manpower than it had used previously became a top-priority item of strategic policy.

The Ministry took over the little Institute for Research in Agricultural Engineering, which it had set up in Oxford, transported it to Askham Bryan, renamed it the National Institute of Agricultural Engineering (NIAE), provided it with substantially increased resources and charged it with the tasks firstly of advising government on the allocation of labour and materials to the agricultural engineering industry, and secondly of setting up training and advisory programmes to assist in the rapid adoption of new machinery systems by British farmers.

The pace of agricultural mechanization continued to grow at the cessation of hostilities and the burden of direct advisory work grew with it until in 1946 this responsibility passed from the NIAE to the newly-formed National Agricultural Advisory Service.

This left the Institute and its new-born Scottish daughter station (SIAE) to concentrate on the original functions of research and testing. The two Institutes between them endeavoured to research most aspects of agricultural engineering as applied to the arable, livestock and horticultural sectors in UK farming with certain specialist inputs being made by the biological institutes (e.g. the National Institute for Research in Dairying). The foregoing sections of this essay are full of examples of the kind of work and achievements that the Institutes have made. Here it is appropriate to pick up the point made by Sir William concerning the dilemma which faces the engineering institutes when trying to transfer their know-how into machinery and systems available to farmers. If the institutes publish their findings in the technical literature or take out patents and then make no further effort to exploit them, the chances are that very little will happen. In order to ensure that agricultural engineering manufacturers adopt NIAE/SIAE developments the institutes need to develop close working relationships with them. Recent years have seen valuable new initiatives to improve collaboration with industry — both at the large multi-national end of the spectrum as well as at the small local level.

## The Next Fifty Years

The accuracy with which one can extrapolate from the past to suggest what agricultural engineering might achieve in the future is limited more by the uncertainties of social and political forces than by predictions of what science and technology might make possible. In the present microelectronic age there is already a wealth of measurement and control technique that could be developed to meet the specific needs of agriculture and horticulture. Until recently, however, it has been difficult to envisage that the price of the "hardware" could be brought within the reach of the farmer. With the advent of the ubiquitous silicon chip this began to look possible and the introduction of microprocessor-based control gear and minicomputers into the farming scene is already occurring. This trend will gather momentum to the point where many of the individual farm processes such as feed preparation, livestock feeding, crop drying and grading, irrigation and waste treatment, are automatically monitored and controlled. It is certainly possible to envisage the complete automation of cultivations and other field processes too; but whether this will occur will depend on the supply of energy, labour, and social attitudes to work. Practically all animals will be housed the whole year round to obtain maximum production from grass. Thus if many field operations go on day and night without an operator, as well they might if the most effective use of expensive automatic machines were to be obtained, the countryside would become even emptier than it is today. It could also take on a more rectilinear look, because automated field operations call for fields of regular shape and straight sides. Whether such an empty, mechanically efficient countryside would be accepted by the majority of people, who live there and use it for recreation, will not be decided by agricultural engineers.

## Further Reading

*Books*
Culpin, C. (1976). *Farm Machinery*. 1st Edition 1938–9th Edition 1976. London, Crosby Lockwood Staples.
Gibb, J. A. C. (editor) (1967). *Proceedings of Agricultural Engineering Symposium*. Silsoe, Institution of Agricultural Engineers.
Hawkins, J. C. (editor) (1979). *Engineering problems with effluents from livestock*. Luxembourg, EUR 6249 EN, EEC.
Wymer, N. (1961). *Harry Ferguson*. London, Phoenix House.

British Standards Institution (1978). BS 5502: 1978. Code of practice for the design of buildings and structures for agriculture. London, HMSO.

*Journals*
Agricultural Engineering Record (1945–1949). Vol 1, 1945–47—Vol 2—1947–49. Silsoe, National Institute of Agricultural Engineering.
Agricultural Engineering (1930–1957). Vol 1, 1930—Vol 38, 1957. American Society of Agricultural Engineers, St. Joseph, Michigan.
Farm Implement and Machinery Review (1930–1968). Vol 56, 1930–31—Vol 94, 1968. London, Morgan Bros (Publ) Ltd.
Farm Mechanisation and Buildings (1946–1968). Vol 1, 1946–47—Vol 20, 1968. London, Farm Journals Ltd.
Journal of the Royal Agricultural Society of England (1933–1971). The farmer's guide to agricultural research. Farm implements and machinery. Vol 94, 1933—Vol 132, 1971. London, Royal Agricultural Society of England.
Journal of Agricultural Engineering Research (1956). Vol 1. London, Academic Press.
Power Farming (1941). Vol 1. Sutton, Agricultural Press Ltd.
Transactions of the American Society of Agricultural Engineers (1958). Vol 1. American Society of Agricultural Engineers, St. Joseph, Michigan.

# Statistics and Computing in Agricultural Research

D. J. FINNEY

The ARC Unit of Statistics, Edinburgh

and

F. YATES

Rothamsted Experimental Station

Any review of the development of statistical methods in agricultural research over the last 50 years must emphasize the foundations laid by R. A. Fisher (Plate 1) during his 14 years at Rothamsted. At the end of World War I, the director, Sir John Russell, considered that re-examination by "modern statistical methods" of the accumulated data from the long-term Rothamsted field trials (one dating from 1843) might be scientifically valuable. To this end, he offered Fisher a temporary appointment "while funds lasted". Fortunately for agricultural research, Fisher accepted this post in preference to one at the Galton Laboratory. Although the modern methods that Russell had in mind were primarily those of the Galton-Pearson school, the Galton Laboratory had never much concerned itself with the problems of interpreting results of experiments that faced research workers.

Rothamsted, then a small station with an exceptionally free atmosphere for research, brought Fisher into close contact with biological and agricultural research workers of very varied disciplines and attainments. His appreciation of, and readiness to discuss, the practical needs and difficulties of field and laboratory workers, and his own liking for numerical work coupled with his great mathematical and logical ability, soon began to bear fruit. At Rothamsted he recast the whole basis of mathematical statistics, laid the foundations of the modern techniques for the design and analysis of experiments, and devised many highly original methods for the varied problems with which research workers at Rothamsted and elsewhere confronted him. *Statistical Methods for Research Workers*, first published in 1925 and essentially a practical handbook, made the new methods generally available to biologists, who were quick to take advantage of them. Almost all of what is today the philosophy and the practice of biometry and applied statistics derives from ideas originated by Fisher. So successful has been the collaboration between statisticians and agricultural scientists thus engendered that, in his 1953 address to Section A of the British Association, H. Jeffreys could say ". . . the standard of presentation of results in agriculture is better than in any of the so-called exact sciences; and this is a state of affairs that physicists should cease to tolerate."

In 1933 Fisher was appointed to the Galton Chair at University College, London, in succession to Karl Pearson, but he continued his interest in agricultural problems and from his home in Harpenden kept in close contact with Rothamsted. From the outbreak of war, he was accommodated at the Station until he moved to Cambridge in 1943.

*Plate 1* Sir Ronald Fisher, FRS
(Photograph: Godfrey Argent Studios)

## Experimental Design and Analysis

The foundations of the modern theory of experimental design and analysis are one of Fisher's greatest contributions to the improvement of research techniques, not only in agriculture but also in many other sciences involving highly variable material.

Agricultural field trials were of course no novelty. Lawes and Gilbert had made good use of them in their investigation of the plant nutrients needed by different field crops. These were mostly unreplicated long-term trials on large plots, but plant breeders and others had later developed techniques for experiments on small plots with replication of the varieties or other treatments. Analysis, however, seldom went beyond simple averaging.

What was lacking when Fisher came to Rothamsted was any coherent theory of how to estimate, from the yields of the individual plots of an experiment, the likely errors of the observed differences between the treatments. The possibility of calculating the standard error of a mean from the values constituting it was well known, but it was realized that a standard error based on a few values is very inaccurately determined:

the currently received wisdom was that 50 or so observations were required for a trustworthy standard error. Moreover, both in order to control variability and for practical convenience, experiments are often arranged in blocks, where each block is a set of plots including one replicate of every treatment. Differences between blocks will not affect the comparisons between treatments but will increase the crude standard errors calculated from all the replicates of a treatment. Such increases can be substantial if the blocks differ greatly in fertility.

In 1908, W..S. Gosset (writing under the pseudonym of "Student"), who was not a professed mathematician but a chemist at Guinness's brewery in Dublin, suggested an appropriate allowance for the inaccuracy of a standard error based on only a few values. He proposed to refer to what is now known as the "t" distribution instead of to the normal distribution, and he obtained the correct mathematical form by approximate methods. This suffices for experiments contrasting two treatments in matched pairs (equivalent to blocks of two units); the mean treatment difference is equal to the mean of the differences within pairs, and therefore the standard error calculated from these differences is free of the component of variation between pairs.

In blocked experiments containing more than two treatments, the standard error for the difference of the means of any chosen pair of treatments can be similarly estimated from differences within blocks. As Gosset perceived, all treatment comparisons are likely to have similar accuracy, and the separate estimates of error may therefore be combined to give a single substantially more precise estimate. Such calculations, however, were too laborious for routine use and Gosset sought Fisher's advice on how they might be simplified. In reply, Fisher showed how such a combined estimate can be simply obtained from the block and treatment totals and arranged the arithmetic in the now well known form of the analysis of variance.

When fully developed the technique soon showed its basic simplicity, logical power, and elegance in presentation. Table 1 shows the form of analysis for 4 replicates of 6 treatments. The total sum of squares of deviations from the general mean is thereby partitioned into a part attributable to differences between block totals, a part to differences between treatment totals, and a remainder. Division by the corresponding degrees of freedom gives the mean squares. That for the remainder, E, is the combined estimate of error variance (square of the standard error per plot) that Gosset sought. Moreover the ratio $T/E$ provides the basis for a test of significance on whether the observed differences between treatment means can be attributed wholly to experimental error. Fisher later obtained the mathematical form of the distribution of this ratio; he provided tables for the test, which is now familiar as the "z" or "F" test and which includes both the "t" and the "$\chi^2$" test as special case.

Table 1

Analysis of variance for 4 blocks of 6 treatments

|  | Degrees of freedom | Sums of squares | Mean squares |
|---|---|---|---|
| Blocks | 3 | From block totals | B |
| Treatments | 5 | From treatment totals | V |
| Error | 15 | By subtraction | E |
| Total | 23 | From individual plots | |

An important feature of the analysis of variance is that it exhibits the structural design of the experiment and is readily applicable to more complicated forms of layout and systems of treatments. Thus for a Latin square design (i.e. a square pattern of $p^2$

plots in which each row and each column contains one replicate of each of p treatments), items for rows and for columns replace that for blocks. Similarly in a combined variety and manurial trial, designed to test differences between varieties and also to see whether they respond differently to nitrogenous fertilizer, with 4 replicates, 6 varieties and 3 levels of N for each variety, the contrasts among the 18 variety-treatment combinations can be split; Table 2 illustrates how the basic analysis for 18 treatments, analogous to Table 1, extends so as to examine each component separately. A mean square for V×N that is similar to that for error indicates that the varieties are all responding similarly to nitrogen, i.e. there is no interaction between V and N.

Table 2

Analysis of variance for a combined variety and manuring trial

|  | | Degrees of freedom |
| --- | --- | --- |
| Blocks | | 3 |
| Average varietal differences (V) | 5 ⎫ | |
| Average responses to nitrogen (N) | 2 ⎬ | 17 |
| Differential responses (V × N) | 10 ⎭ | |
| Error | | 51 |
| | | — |
| Total | | 71 |

If, to simplify the agricultural operations, the varieties are sown on large plots each of which is split into three sub-plots for the nitrogen treatments, there will be two relevant plot errors, one for comparisons involving contrasts between whole plots and the other involving contrasts between sub-plots within the same whole plot. The analysis of variance then divides into two parts, that for the whole plots relating to the average varietal differences, and that for the sub-plots relating to the nitrogen treatments and their interactions with varieties.

Analysis of variance has proved valuable in many other contexts: its close relation to the logical structure of the data has given it a central role in a great part of statistical practice. It provides a unifying principle for regression analysis and many multivariate techniques, and its interpretation aids progress towards improved data collection and experimental design.


# Randomization

The use of standard errors and significance tests based upon an analysis of variance assumes that the errors of the observed experimental values are normally and independently distributed. Moderate departures from true normality matter little. That individual errors in a field experiment are independent of one another is patently untrue: neighbouring plots are likely to be more alike than those widely separated. Consequently if, for example, varieties in a trial are arranged in the same order in each block, comparisons between neighbouring varieties will be more accurate than will those between widely separated varieties; if also there is a fertility gradient across the blocks, some varieties will be favoured at the expense of others.

One of Fisher's most inspired contributions to experimental design was his recognition that assigning treatments at random to the plots (subject to design constraints such as blocks) would ensure that all treatments had an equal chance of being favoured by position, and that the estimate of error variance provided by the analysis of variance would be unbiased whatever the distribution of the actual errors. This ensures that tests of significance (using the F and t distributions) are satisfactory over a wide range of error distributions; in extreme cases, transformation of the experimental values before analysis may be desirable.

Initially the necessity for and effectiveness of randomization were hotly disputed, but, as understanding of experimental design grew, randomization within the constraints of a design became the norm for sound research. The merits are not restricted to field trials. Certainly in some types of investigation randomization is impracticable, but any scientist who does not randomize the allocation of experimental material to treatments needs to discuss carefully the likely consequences for validity of his inferences. The effects have spread far beyond agriculture: clinical medical research has improved immeasurably as a result of proper appreciation of randomization, as also has research in industrial technology. Plate 2 illustrates a modern field experiment.

## Development of More Complex Designs

A further important development in experimental techniques was a recognition of the advantages under many circumstances of factorial design, the inclusion of all combinations of several variants of two or more factors in the same experiment. Factorial experiments are clearly necessary to determine whether factors interact with one another; even when interactions are believed to be unimportant, the fact that in a factorial design each plot is used two or more times to give information on the average effects of the factors leads to considerable gains in efficiency and gives a wider inductive basis for inferences from the results. Factorial design was not a new idea: some of the Rothamsted classical experiments were basically factorial, and many of the fertilizer trials in this country and in Denmark and Germany in the early 1900s had good factorial structure. However, desire for simplicity and the aphorism that in scientific research we should ask only a few questions, or ideally one question at a time, led to failure to appreciate its advantages.

The main limitation to factorial design in field experiments is the large number of treatment combinations if many factors are included. Even with few replicates, therefore, many plots are required and the resulting large blocks will be relatively ineffective

*Plate 2* A modern field experiment on cereals at Rothamsted; rows of plots are arranged in blocks.

in removing the variability in the experimental material. Fisher early perceived that complete replicates could be split into smaller blocks in such a manner that the contrasts between the blocks corresponded to chosen experimental contrasts, usually components of unimportant high-order interactions. This device he termed confounding. In the 1930s, further development permitted use of only one replicate, by using a mean square from the unconfounded components of high-order interactions to approximate the experimental error. For example, the 27 plots of a single replicate of an experiment on three levels of each of three factors (a $3 \times 3 \times 3$ design) can be arranged in 3 blocks of 9 so that each block contains all 9 combinations of each pair of factors. This gives nine-fold replication for the mean effect of each factor and three-fold replication for each two-factor interaction. A further extension when there are many factors is to include only a balanced selection from all possible combinations. This is termed fractional replication.

In agricultural field trials there is no definite limit to the number of experimental units in a block; in other types of experimental material, natural limits occur, e.g. pairs of monozygotic twins, halves of a leaf in virus inoculation tests, litter sizes in many types of animal experiment. The traditional solution to the use of pairs to compare more than two treatments was to take one treatment as the "control" and to accept the lower precision of comparisons between non-control treatments. A surprising though easily deduced fact is that, with the same amount of experimental material but with all treatment pairs equally represented, every comparison has the same precision as that between the control and each remaining treatment in the traditional design. This led to the idea of designs for larger blocks with the number of treatments exceeding the block size. Maximum efficiency and numerical ease of analysis require that every pair of treatments occurs in the same block an equal number of times. Such designs are termed balanced incomplete blocks. Quasi-factorial designs were also devised for comparing large numbers of varieties by subdivision of the different replicates on the analogy of a factorial system.

These various types of design are useful in experiments in many sciences and industries. They give rise to interesting combinatorial problems. For example, much has been done on finding possible solutions for balanced incomplete blocks with given numbers of treatments and block sizes. Because such a fully balanced design may require many replicates, partially balanced designs have been developed; these give almost equal accuracy for the different treatment comparisons but are somewhat more tiresome to analyze.

Experiments on crop rotations, particularly those involving different crop sequences, present interesting but difficult design problems. Such an experiment takes a long time, with the consequence that changes in agricultural practice often limit the relevance of the results. One important advance that Fisher made was to include all phases of the rotation in the experiment, so acquiring information much more rapidly than did Lawes and Gilbert who, in an early experiment on the manuring of a four-course rotation, included only a single phase and so obtained information on any one crop only every fourth year. In long-term research on fruit crops, plants must be managed over many successive years; East Malling Research Station has been prominent in adapting biometric ideas and techniques to this very different range of problems.

## Coordinated Series of Experiments

The ability to do large and complex experiments of high and known accuracy had some unfortunate effects, such as the idea that complicated issues could be settled once and for all by a single experiment at one research institute. This is an illusion; any apparently exciting discovery from such an experiment has to be tested under a wide range of soil and meteorological conditions before it can safely form the basis of practical recommendations to farmers. The most effective procedure is a coordinated series of field trials, of similar or identical design, widely dispersed and extending over several years. Trials of new varieties, immediate effects of fertilizers, etc. each of which extends over a single season, can be quite effectively made on commercial farms, provided there are adequate teams of field workers to assist at critical times, such as sowing, application of fertilizers, and harvesting. Before the war, lack of such resources hindered the development of this type of experimentation. However, a small levy on the sugar beet crop for education and research enabled a good series of fertilizer trials to be started on this crop in 1934. Between 1934 and 1939, 156 trials used single replicates of the $3 \times 3 \times 3$ confounded factorial design mentioned above for all combinations of three levels of N, P and K. From 1940 to 1949, a two-replicate $2 \times 2 \times 2 \times 2$ design in blocks of 8 plots for N, P, K and salt was used in 204 experiments. From 1944, without any change in the basic design, borax was included as a fifth factor; this illustrates the potentialities of factorial design for including additional factors if need arises.

Lack of similar coordinated trials on other crops seriously hindered development of a rational policy for the use of scarce and varying supplies of phosphate and potash fertilizers during the war. To supplement the sparse and localized Rothamsted data, the results of some 5000 simple trials from 1900 onwards were assembled from reports of agricultural colleges, etc. Interesting statistical problems in the reduction of this heterogeneous mass of data to a common standard were successfully solved, and, with assistance from members of other Rothamsted departments, a coordinated summary was quickly achieved. The main conclusions were that much greater use could be made of nitrogenous fertilizer on substantially all arable crops and that phosphate and potash should be reserved for responsive crops, particularly potatoes and sugar beet. A further indication was that, if total supplies of a constituent changed, the levels of that constituent should be raised or lowered by the same (absolute, not proportional) amount for all crops. These conclusions served as a basis for a revised system of fertilizer rationing and for control of fertilizer imports in the light of changes in availability of shipping.

This work, initiated at Rothamsted, showed the important role of statisticians in extracting relevant information from heterogeneous sets of experiments. It also demonstrated the need for closer liaison between research scientists and administrative authorities. A similar investigation on the feeding of dairy cows, undertaken jointly with the Cambridge University School of Agriculture, and based mainly but not exclusively on a re-analysis of very detailed data provided by a coordinated set of Danish experiments on commercial farms, clarified the effects of variations in amount and protein content of food on milk production and live-weight changes.

Increased resources after the war enabled coordinated field trials to assume their rightful place in agricultural research; computers now facilitate more speedy and penetrating analyses. For example, a consequence of British accession to the EEC is that new crop varieties must be systematically tested and evaluated before commercial release. In cooperation with the National Institute of Agricultural Botany and the Department of Agriculture for Northern Ireland, the Unit of Statistics in Edinburgh has studied many relevant problems, including the choice of the number of experiments, design, variation in yields from place to place and from year to year, as well as the systematic handling of all records and analyses. The Unit has devised a new class of incomplete block designs that improves precision and a comprehensive computer program (now an integral part of British practice) that ensures efficient analysis despite a very tight time schedule. Problems of combining evidence from all trials on a crop still remain.

Long-term experiments are seldom practicable on commercial farms, but the Experimental Husbandry Farms and Horticulture Stations, established after the war by the Ministry of Agriculture, Fisheries and Food as part of the Advisory Service, provided opportunities for coordinated long term trials on important issues such as the value of ley farming and the disposal of straw, the results of which radically altered previously held views on these issues. One fruitful consequence of these activities is the close liaison that has developed between the research institutes and the advisory services.

The need for coordinated trials on farm animals is less than for crops, as animals react similarly to variations in nutrition, housing conditions, etc., wherever they are situated. Even with animals, however, coordinated trials on commercial farms can usefully supplement experiments at research institutes, and permit results established by short-term experiments to be tested over longer periods and under different managements. For example, iodinated casein was found to increase milk production when fed over a short period, but a coordinated trial on over 1000 cows, with a similar number of controls, on 37 farms and over three lactations, indicated that, taking all factors into account, its use should not be recommended.

## Sampling and Sample Surveys

Better understanding of the sources of error and their estimation, resulting from the development of experimental design and the analysis of variance, had important consequences in the improvement of sampling techniques. Two essentials are rigorous definition of the sampling units and a proper element of random selection of units for inclusion in the sample. These ensure freedom from bias and a basis for calculating the components of variation contributing to the sampling errors; the latter is especially relevant to multi-stage sampling, which involves more than one type of unit, e.g. farms and fields within a farm.

The basic principles have been applied to give rigorous yet convenient sampling methods for many purposes — studying individual plots for incidence of pests and diseases, examining the chemical composition of plants (both during growth and after harvest), estimating natural insect populations, and in laboratory work. During the war, assessment of crop danger from pests, particularly wireworm, by extensive sampling of many fields proved valuable to the advisory services. Techniques using recaptures of marked individuals, a complex and specialized topic, have been developed to a stage of practical utility.

Studies were made before the war of the feasibility of sampling commercial crops shortly before harvest so as to obtain more objective estimates of yield than were provided by the official estimates of the Ministry of Agriculture, and satisfactory methods were evolved. Through the initiative of Fisher, T. Eden, E. J. Maskell and A. R. Clapham, a scheme for studying the growth of the wheat crop by simple sampling observations from sowing to harvest was developed to provide more objective data for the Agricultural Meteorological Scheme of the Ministry of Agriculture and the Meteorological Office, which had been started in 1924. In their final form these observations ran for seven years at 10 stations. Though not revived after the war, as interest was then shifting to the study of micro-climates and to controlled experiments on water requirements, they provide an interesting example of monitoring the effects of natural variations in climatic conditions at several widely separated stations, and of using observations on the growth of crops to forecast future yields.

Surveys of agricultural practices and farming conditions have proved of great value both to research institutes and to the advisory services. For many surveys quite small samples are adequate, but relevant detailed technical information must be collected from the surveyed farms. The war-time survey of fertilizer practice is an early example. Because of doubts about pre-war practice, and to see whether farmers were using limited supplies of fertilizers effectively, a small rigorously-designed sample survey was proposed. After initial reluctance, in 1942 the Agricultural Research Council approved a start in three contrasting regions. Technical details were obtained of the fertilizers actually applied to one old-arable and one ploughed-out field of each crop on the sampled farms, and soil samples were taken on a sub-sample of fields. The survey yielded much useful and timely information; for example, it quickly revealed that much acid and phosphate-deficient ploughed-out grassland was not receiving lime or phosphate, with resultant crop failure. The Advisory Chemists were aware of these needs, but partly because of the belief in the "stored-up fertility" of old grassland the message had not got through to many farmers. One important consequence of this survey was that it showed the advisory services that only by properly designed but quite small random sample surveys could the true extent of problems existing in their districts be ascertained. After the war, the survey was gradually extended to the whole of England and Wales, latterly with the cooperation of the fertilizer industry, and a similar survey was started in Scotland. Within the same general framework flexibility has been maintained, thus preserving continuity and providing opportunities to obtain information on questions of current interest.

Surveys have since been used in many studies of agricultural practice, as well as into aspects of animal health and into pests and diseases of crops. Experience in the design of these varied surveys has contributed markedly to the practical development of survey methodology, and later to the effective use of computers for the analysis.

## Animal Experiments

The principles of design developed for field experimentation have been applied both to farm animals and to laboratory studies. With animals, the major differences in practice arise from interest in repeated observations on the same animal, either at regular intervals or at particular critical times. This is true for all studies of nutrient requirements, but especially in breeding animals for which there may be carry-over effects between pregnancy and lactation, and effects may be examined in the progeny or in maternal tissue over a number of reproductive cycles. By comparison with plants, there is greater emphasis on relations between measurements of different characters at one time and of one character at many times. Such relations will often be non-linear and of a complexity that was seldom handled before computers were available. Much research involves continuous monitoring of individuals and their environments, often with the aid of sensors and recording devices. Whether for body weight or for more sophisticated study of physiological variables, analysis of such records cannot ignore the correlation between successive times; developments in stochastic process methods begin to give help here, but the "non-stationarity" of the relevant processes creates major difficulties. Recent years have seen much interest in so-called "modelling", the representation of all major aspects of nutrition, growth, and productivity of an animal in terms of a system of interlocking equations, which can be solved by computers by iterative methods. Inevitably, on any one problem this has been restricted to very few animals. Early successes will need to be followed by proper studies of sources of error and the magnitude of variability between animals, and by comparison with the results of direct experiments under field conditions.

Today at many centres research on the nutrition, productivity, and health of animals takes full advantage of statistical science. Special types of experimental design, for example, have been devised to aid the comparison of different treatments on the same animal while allowing for residual effects of earlier treatments of an animal. A continuing difficulty is that animals may be at least as variable as field plots, and individually more expensive as experimental units, so that adequate replication is costly. This can be particularly true in research dependent upon a lengthy reproductive cycle.

## Genetics and Plant and Animal Breeding

Planned improvement of farm crops and animals requires quantitative evaluation of the probable consequences of any breeding programme. R. Riley (plants) and J. W. B. King (animals) have described practice and progress in other essays. For many purposes, primary interest lies in quantitative aspects of yield and quality that are governed by many genetic loci, the genes at each locus having only a very small influence. Identification of individual loci is impossible, but the total effect may be studied in terms of the statistical properties of a large number of small contributions and their interactions. Under the general heading of "Biometrical Genetics", techniques have been developed for dividing variability into components for the additive effects of genes, for dominance and gene interactions, and for environmental and random variation. Use of these techniques in order to distinguish contributions from different ancestral sources has become part of the standard technology for scientists engaged in plant and animal breeding. The highly specialized methods have put precision into breeding work through the testing of plant and animal genotypes for their potentialities. The structure of biometrical genetics owes much to the principles of analysis of variance. Experimental techniques, such as those commonly used for the evaluation of diallel crosses, are related to general practices in experimental design. Statisticians have examined how best a fixed amount of experimental effort can be used to estimate components of variation arising from different genetic and environmental sources; these estimates aid the devising of a sound policy for improvement under further breeding.

Problems of detecting and estimating the parameters of linkage between genetic factors commonly require special statistical analyses. These in turn aid the economy with which such important steps as transferring specific genes for disease resistance from one variety to another can be effected. Statistical techniques for estimating the sizes of natural populations are often important to genetical understanding.

The day-to-day management of a breeding programme, with proper emphasis on selection for continuing improvement of performance, involves extensive data. Under commercial rather than experimental conditions, such data will be far from any symmetric pattern, but computers now make possible their handling and analysis as well as numerical solution of estimation problems that are algebraically intractable. A pioneer effort was analysis of the way in which artificial insemination could best be used to raise milk yields in dairy cattle. Today, British cattle breeding involves management of data from hundreds of thousands of animals; selection indices for individuals must be regularly evaluated and updated, taking into account various confounding factors, a task that demands both statistical sophistication and effective computation. Computer simulation of breeding programmes is now proving valuable as guidance on alternative breeding strategies.

The approach and philosophy of statistics have given impetus to the quantitative application of genetical ideas for the benefit of agriculture. Confidence has developed that variation of all kinds can be measured, analyzed and interpreted meaningfully, and thence has come an incentive to get on with this job for the benefit of agricultural production.

## Statistics in the Laboratory

Modern agricultural research uses intensive laboratory studies essential to, though at times seeming only distantly related to, the growing of crops and the management of animals. Not only have these also demanded new statistical tools, but they have contributed to statistical practice in other sciences. For example, quantitative microbiology owes much to early work on estimating microflora in Rothamsted soil samples.

Research on insecticides produced data of quantal form: each insect tested could be classified only as dead or alive, and the proportions of deaths would increase with dose. General theory of statistical estimation led to analytical methods and computational techniques that proved of much wider use. Biological assay for estimating relative potencies of therapeutic drugs has gained in understanding from the participation of statisticians in insecticide research.

Especially valuable as a basis for analyzing new types of data has been Fisher's method of maximum likelihood. Provided that the origins of data can be fully described by a set of probabilities expressed as functions of specified parameters, maximizing the likelihood function leads to numerical estimates of parameters that have various optimal properties. Under very general conditions, the estimates utilize fully all information in the data. For all but the simplest problems, maximum likelihood used to require very heavy computations; today, widely available general computer programs make the method easily and rapidly applicable.

## Organization of Statistical Services

In the 1930s, agricultural research workers at many institutes (particularly those concerned with field experiments) realized that the new methods had much to offer. In 1927 East Malling Research Station, faced with major difficulties in designing experiments on perennial fruits, became the second institute to appoint its own statistician, T. N. Hoblyn, who had had a year of training under Fisher. Agricultural scientists with primary training in other disciplines, notably genetics, but also chemistry, botany and others, began to acquire good knowledge of the statistical needs of their own work. They were greatly helped by Fisher, who was always ready to advise on novel problems; scientists from home and abroad, especially North America and India, came to work with him for short or long periods at Rothamsted and later at the Galton Laboratory. Many British scientists working at Agricultural Research Institutes in the Commonwealth began to realize the benefits of consultation on statistical problems, particularly in the design of long-term experiments. F. Yates, who succeeded Fisher in 1933, extended the help that the Rothamsted Department gave in the design and analysis of experiments, and it became apparent that a computing service would be a great help to workers in tropical Africa.

As a result of the war, agriculture assumed much greater importance in the British economy. The need for research led to expansion of existing institutes and creation of many new ones, as Sir William Henderson describes in this volume. Not all could immediately have their own statistics sections, and indeed suitable young statisticians were not sufficiently plentiful. One proposal was that a single statistical research centre, possibly located at Rothamsted, should supplement the work of statisticians at separate institutes and undertake tasks that could not be done locally because of lack of adequate resources or expertise. Rothamsted, however, considered that no one institute would have enough background knowledge in the associated subject matter to give good service to all branches of agricultural research; also, that existence of more than one centre would encourage competition and a greater variety of approaches. Ultimately it was agreed in principle that there should be three centres, at Rothamsted, at Cambridge (which it was hoped would be attached to Fisher in the Department of Genetics), and in Scotland. In the event, the Rothamsted Statistics Department was given the added title of a Research Statistical Service and a small unit was attached to the School of Agriculture in Cambridge. In 1954, a Unit of Statistics (under D. J. Finney) was established in the Department of Statistics in the University of Aberdeen, and in 1966 this was moved to the University of Edinburgh.

In addition to advising on the planning of experimental programmes, and on the design of experiments and surveys, these centres initially had to provide a computing service to supplement the often inadequate resources of other research institutes. When computers became available, they were able to turn more to the development of general computer programs suitable for agricultural needs. Some centralization of this activity has been of great value, as uncoordinated work at different institutes could have resulted in much waste of effort and in scrappy and incompatible programs. The fact that the centres have only an advisory relation with statisticians and other scientists at the various research institutes has certainly proved to be the right policy. In some countries centralization has been carried so far that practically the whole of national statistical services for agricultural research are concentrated in one place, with the consequence that the statisticans lack direct knowledge of the agricultural contexts in which their advice is to be applied.

Throughout its existence, the Rothamsted Centre has given great help to the Ministry of Agriculture, Fisheries and Food's Advisory Services. Not only has it cooperated in planning experimental and observational work, but it has undertaken much of the associated statistical analysis of results. This and similar work by other institutes has greatly strengthened links between the advisory services and the research institutes. The work done for colonial agricultural scientists before the war has been continued, with the support of what is now the Overseas Development Administration; three statisticians who are available for overseas visits are attached to the Department at Rothamsted, and one with similar responsibilities is attached to East Malling.

The Unit of Statistics was established to help all agricultural research in Scotland, where the three Agricultural Colleges now have large research programmes in addition to those of the institutes. The type of help given closely parallels what has come from Rothamsted. Experience has shown that some disadvantages arise from not having the statisticians located within an agricultural research environment, but that the close association with a University Department of Statistics (with staff and with students) brings many compensations. It seems valuable to have this alternative pattern of organization.

## Development of Computer Applications

The immense development of statistical theory and methodology in the first half of the twentieth century would not have been achieved without parallel development in computing aids. The computation of sums of squares is at the root of all analysis of experiments. The introduction of desk calculators (Plate 3 shows an early model) made this one of the easiest of calculations, and scientists began to compute, by whatever method seemed appropriate, the standard errors of their experiments. This set Fisher and others thinking about the whole problem of estimating error and testing significance in experiments, and this in turn led to improvements in design. Analysis came first, the theory of design followed, as the history of the subject shows. Fisher's recognition of the value of computation in clarifying thought is shown by his comment on a junior who asked for a computing assistant: "Can she use an assistant? Most of *my* statistics has been learned on the machine."

With the mechanical aids available in the 1940s, the much heavier computations required for multivariate analysis (discriminant functions, principal components, etc.), remained a heavy burden. Consequently, although the basic theory had been established, its utility for the resolution of practical problems remained unexplored. Even multiple regression, the need for which is obvious in many contexts, was little used. The analysis of survey and other observational data on punched-card machines was also crude and time consuming.

The development of computers has changed all this. Even the early machines had obvious potentialities for speeding and widening the scope of work previously done on desk calculators and punched-card machines, and for making available procedures

*Plate 3* Dr. F. Yates using the Millionaire Calculator, Rothamsted's earliest aid to mechanical computing.

previously too laborious for routine use. Early exploration of these potentialities in agricultural research owes much to timely support from the Agricultural Research Council. In 1954, when commercially-built machines were still in an embryonic state, a small prototype machine, the Elliott-NRDC 401, was procured for Rothamsted. Here the Council acted on the advice of a Visiting Group, whose interesting recommendation read:

> "With an electronic computer of their own, both to use and 'play about with', we think that valuable advances may be made in the theory and method of handling this kind of data on electronic machines."

One of the most urgent tasks when the 401 was installed was to lighten the burden of desk calculation required for analysis of experiments submitted to the Statistics Department by other institutes at home and overseas. Because of machine limitations, the 401 programs dealt inadequately with covariance, and results were poorly presented; nevertheless, all programs provided for preliminary calculations on the data for the individual plots, for missing plots, and for the calculation of residuals. That the greatly improved service catered for a real need is shown by the rapid increase in numbers of experiments analyzed. In the early 1950s some 500 were analyzed on desk calculators each year; in 1964 the number had risen to 3 400, with substantially more variates per experiment.

The results provided by computer analysis of individual experiments can be stored on a computer file for retrieval later. This has many uses. In particular the results of coordinated series can be summarized, differences in responses attributable to districts, soil types, etc., can be sorted out, and the effectiveness of different methods of soil analysis for determining fertilizer requirements can be assessed. A pioneer study of this type (using paper tape for storage) was made on some 250 3 × 3 × 3 single-replicate fertilizer trials on rice in each of four crop seasons 1956–7 to 1959–60, covering the State of Bihar, India. The results for each season were critically analyzed as they became available, with a further combined summary of the whole series.

In spite of its limitations, the 401 also enabled far better provision to be made for the analysis of survey data. A general tabulation program was constructed which proved remarkably flexible and has served as a model for later Rothamsted programs. Crude tabulations can, however, be misleading in investigative surveys. An important adjunct to the tabulation program was a further program, based on least squares and maximum likelihood, for eliminating the distortions that occur in the marginal (overall) values of a multiway table of means or percentages owing to disproportionate numbers in the different cells of the table. This was found to be particularly useful for sorting out the effects of different factors on the incidence of animal diseases in veterinary surveys.

Table 3 shows some results on the incidence of milk fever (hypocalcaemia) obtained in a survey of 32 000 dairy cows. This serious disease mainly affects the older cows. The overall values, multiplied by the number of calvings in each season, correctly indicate the likely demands on the veterinary services. They are not a correct measure of the effect of season on incidence, owing to considerable seasonal differences in the distribution of calvings between the younger and older cows. This is apparent from the figures for the separate lactations (those for lactations 3 and 5 are shown in the Table). These show similar proportional differences to the likelihood estimates from the whole of the data, shown in the last column.

Table 3

Seasonal incidence (%) of milk fever

| | Overall values | Lactation 3 | 5 | Maximum likelihood estimates |
|---|---|---|---|---|
| Jan-April | 2.67 | 1.4 | 5.6 | 2.06 |
| May-July | 4.12 | 3.1 | 9.4 | 3.78 |
| Aug-Sept | 4.25 | 4.9 | 10.9 | 5.21 |
| Oct-Dec | 3.50 | 2.9 | 9.6 | 3.82 |

Some may object that, although the maximum likelihood solution is mathematically elegant, it merely gilds the lily as the true variation in seasonal incidence is apparent from inspection of the lactation × season table. The short answer is that (a) the least square or maximum likelihood estimates make full use of the data, which is important with sparse data; (b) they provide estimates of the associated errors; (c) if there are three or more factors, tabular inspection is much more complicated.

Quite apart from the range of extensive calculations that a computer can handle, an important feature is that, once programmed, a particular type of analysis can readily be repeated on different batches of similar data. Fisher's early investigation on the influence of rainfall on the yield of wheat on Broadbalk at Rothamsted involved very heavy computations, and he left it to others to make similar analyses on other long-term experiments at Rothamsted and Woburn. These dragged on for twenty years, and as the results accumulated contradictions emerged. Had all the results been immediately available to Fisher, he would doubtless have reached somewhat different conclusions.

The necessity of programming in machine code and other limitations effectively restricted use of the Elliott 401 to workers at Rothamsted. This situation changed when the 401 was replaced by the Ferranti ORION, a more powerful and, for its time, advanced machine with an early high-level language. Much more effective and more general programs could now be written, and for the first time statisticians at other institutes in the South of England were able to develop programs for their own special problems. The ORION was in its turn replaced by an ICL 4-70; this multi-access installation was linked in due course to an increasing number of research institutes in England and Wales by remote access terminals, and facilities were provided for fast data transmission and for printing results locally, thus providing computer services at other institutes equivalent to those at Rothamsted. To deal with the increasing load, an additional ICL 4-72 was installed in 1977 and the combined installation is now linked with over 20 institutes.

The Scottish institutes were less fortunate, but creation of the Computer Board for the Universities and Research Councils led to the development, from 1966 onwards, of a facility at the University of Edinburgh shared with the Research Councils and partly financed by the ARC. A succession of computers there has provided steadily improving computer resources for various agricultural research institutes and for the ARC Unit of Statistics, both in equipment ("hardware") and programs ("software").

At first, different language requirements of different computer systems restricted opportunities for shared software. This stimulated independent development, which was in many ways advantageous. Steady improvement in hardware, the general availability of the language FORTRAN (despite its flaws), and increasing facilities for communication from and to distant terminals has now given most Scottish agricultural research institutions access to powerful computer facilities with a wide range of programs. Many other small computers are now in some way linked into these systems, though one or two institutes still depend primarily on small self-contained computer systems.

Any computer that is to be efficiently used, not only by statisticians but also by other scientists wishing to do their own analyses, must have a set of general programs that cover common requirements, are statistically sound, and are easy to use. Moreover, although some diversity of programming is valuable as a basis for the evolution of still better software, excessive duplication of programming effort is a waste of time. The increasing demand for general packages is evident from the development of these (many of regrettably low quality statistically) in the USA and elsewhere, and the importation of some to university and other computer centres in the UK.

Rothamsted and Edinburgh have played an important part in making generally available to other centres programs covering many of the types of statistical analysis discussed in earlier sections. The most striking Rothamsted contribution is a large general statistical package, built on long programming experience; known as GENSTAT, this package handles a wide class of experimental designs, regression, analogous maximum likelihood procedures for quantal data, various types of multivariate analysis, and so on. Special precautions were taken to facilitate transfer to other machines. It is now (July 1980) available for 13 different types of computer, is in use at 59 British installations at universities and elsewhere, and at 66 installations overseas, and has become the standard general program for these types of work in the Australian Commonwealth Scientific and Industrial Research Organization. GENSTAT, however, is not well adapted to the analysis of survey data, particularly if hierarchical. The Rothamsted General Survey Program, RGSP, first written for ORION, was therefore enhanced for the 4-70 and is now easily transferrable to other computers. It is available at 14 installations in the UK and Australia.

A program that provides methods for handling regression and related maximum likelihood problems far more advanced than those available in any earlier package has proved of great value, especially for university and other specialized research purposes. This Generalised Linear Interactive Modelling Program, GLIM, can be used interactively, thus enabling the user to proceed step by step, requesting from his terminal further analyses in the light of the results already obtained. It was originally sponsored by the Royal Statistical Society, but much of the design and enhancement devolved on Rothamsted. It is now (July 1980) available at 124 installations in the UK and at 188 installations overseas.

General programs from the Unit in Edinburgh have been somewhat different. The Edinburgh Experiments Program, EDEX, was written before GENSTAT became available in order to handle a wide range of experimental designs; although it overlaps with GENSTAT, it continues to be important because it can handle a more general category of incomplete blocks. A program that produces experimental designs and field layouts from specifications chosen by the user, DSIGN, is especially helpful where a series of experiments to the same general specification must be designed, and is also extensively used at Rothamsted. Large general packages have many advantages for computer centres and for individuals who must handle a wide range of different problems. On the other hand, when a particular type of analysis, large or small, must be used very frequently a specially written program may justify its initial cost by having lower overhead costs in running, and by being designed with specialized input and output that facilitate regular use and that give results in a form suitable for wide distribution. The Coordinated Variety Trial package mentioned earlier is now a highly sophisticated system for handling all aspects of variety trials and is still being improved. The need for hierarchical analysis of variance and the production of variance components, especially in the analysis of quantitative genetical data, has led to a program known as HIERF. To meet early needs for general maximum likelihood and weighted least squares analyses, MAXLIKE and MINISQUARE were written; they continue to have advantages in respect of simplicity of use and quick adaptation to new problems. A derived program, BLISS, is possibly the only existing comprehensive program for handling from start to finish biological assays based on quantal responses.

Many major programming developments have taken place at various institutes, initially primarily for local use. Thus the Animal Breeding Research Organisation has done much on the manipulation of large files with reference to its own specialized needs for storage and retrieval of data. Some institutes, notably the National Institute of Agricultural Engineering and the Rowett Research Institute, have given much attention to data logging, that is to say the direct transfer of measurements from a recording apparatus of any kind to a computer store, in a form readily available for subsequent handling and analysis.

These developments have contributed greatly to the dissemination of sound statistical methods for the analysis of data. Computers have also made possible the use of novel methods, such as simulation and system synthesis, which were previously totally impracticable. Some applications are mentioned earlier. They have also contributed to the effective use of data provided by scientific instruments equipped with automatic recording. Such data are often very voluminous and require condensation, interpolation to deal with transient faults, and more complicated processes such as resolution of spectrographic observations. Mini-computers are a great aid to tasks of this kind. Indeed, the increasing power and low cost of very small computers is leading to greater decentralization of computer activities. Provision and dissemination of programs that are appropriate to such machines and are of high quality is now a challenge to statisticians concerned with computer activities for agricultural research.

## Conclusion

The development of better statistical methods has contributed greatly to the progress of agricultural research; the major impetus to this development, originating from the work of R. A. Fisher, has come from Britain. These statements can scarcely be questioned. In particular, the vastly improved techniques for the design and analysis of experiments soon came to be accepted by research workers; they have now been almost universally adopted, not only in agriculture but also in all subjects where highly variable material is investigated. The spectacular advances of the last 30 years in agricultural production in many parts of the world owe much to their consistent use. They have introduced a certainty of touch into well-designed experimental work that is the envy of statisticians faced with the interpretation of non-experimental data.

Although Fisherian methods were early appreciated by practical workers in the United States, and Fisher himself was highly regarded there, many theoretical mathematical statisticians at American universities failed to appreciate their merits and indeed never properly understood them. This led to much confusion. Even the analysis of variance was corrupted by promulgation of, and advocacy of different algebraic theory for, two separate "models", a distinction without a difference as the models are mathematically equivalent and rightly interpreted must lead to the same results. Regrettably, much theoretical argument divorced from statistical practice perpetuated the misunderstanding, and the two models became part of the accepted specification of the analysis of variance, expounded in textbooks and taught to all students. Little harm would have resulted in countries not wedded to this distinction were it not that emphasis on the models was embodied in statistical program packages emanating from the United States; in consequence, students (in Britain and elsewhere) are too often taught that this matter is important, and in their subsequent careers as practising statisticians waste time on it that could better be spent on more vital issues.

Other work by professional mathematical statisticians has served to confuse rather than enlighten. As Fisher remarked in a lecture he gave at Michigan State University four years before his death: "I am quite sure it is only personal contact with the business of the improvement of natural knowledge in the natural sciences that is capable to keep straight the thought of mathematically-minded people who have to grope their way through the complex entanglements of error, with which at present they are very much surrounded".

The moral is that, to contribute effectively to scientific research, statisticians must collaborate closely with other members of research teams. They must acquaint themselves with, and indeed be keenly interested in, both the relevant scientific background and the technical details of the problems under investigation. Equally, they should be partners of other research workers and not mere computing clerks or computer operators. Not all statisticians need be brilliant mathematicians, but they must be sufficiently at home with mathematics to be able to judge the true worth for the purposes in hand of the many alternative procedures that appear in statistical journals, and are even uncritically recommended in statistical textbooks; when they are not themselves competent to pass judgement on these, they must be prepared to consult more experienced statistical colleagues. Above all, they must have a well-developed critical sense, directed both to their own work and to the work of others.

When the Agricultural Research Council celebrates its Centenary, will it still be true that statistical thought is making vital contributions to the research programme, that statistical innovation in agriculture is a major source of development for the whole of statistical science, and that British statisticians are well to the fore in the sound practice and wise expansion of their subject? It is of the nature of research that the future can be only vaguely perceived, but certainly today one can see several likely lines of growth in agricultural statistics. Though the main features of experimental design are well understood, special requirements and constraints continue to pose new combinatorial problems of immediate practical relevance; we are perhaps only at the start of the use of computers for generating solutions. Much has yet to be done in making the analysis of large bodies of research data a dynamic process, in which the statistician at a computer terminal guides the detail of analytical techniques in the light of what has already emerged; the dangers of bias through seeing only what he wants to see, or through exaggerating the apparent importance of what is really a chance effect, are part of the challenge to be met. From the plethora of techniques of multivariate analysis to be found in journals and books, those particularly relevant to practical interpretation of experiments with many measurements recorded for each plot must be extracted and refined. Doubtless other needs and possibilities, as yet unsuspected, will emerge. At the same time, we must guard against the unnecessary and superficial analyses that are all too easy now that voluminous observations can readily be committed to the computer and that large collections of data, often from heterogeneous sources, are assembled into "databases".

Statistical science today has a far broader base than in 1931, so that the extent to which general advance stems from agriculture is likely to be less, but new developments for problems such as those mentioned above will find wider application in other sciences and technologies. The future role of British statistics depends in part on questions of politics and finance. No less important are continuance of independence of thought, determination to make valid theory serve the needs of practice, avoidance of the illusion that using a piece of sufficiently abstract mathematics is necessarily a contribution to a scientific problem, and refusal to compromise on basic requirements of the logic of statistical inference.

## Further Reading

Box, J. F. (1978) *R. A. Fisher: The Life of a Scientist*. Chichester, John Wiley & Sons.

Cochran, W. G. & Cox, G. M. (1955) *Experimental Designs* (2nd edition, 1966). New York, John Wiley & Sons.

Finney, D. J. (1947) *Probit Analysis* (3rd edition, 1971). Cambridge University Press.

Finney, D. J. (1952) *Statistical Method in Biological Assay* (3rd edition, 1978). London, Charles Griffin & Co.

Finney, D. J. (1960) *An Introduction to the Theory of Experimental Design*. Chicago University Press.

Fisher, R. A. (1925) *Statistical Methods for Research Workers* (14th edition, 1970). Edinburgh, Oliver & Boyd.

Fisher, R. A. (1935) *The Design of Experiments* (8th edition 1966). Edinburgh, Oliver & Boyd.

Fisher, R. A. & Yates, F. (1938) *Statistical Tables for Biological, Agricultural and Medical Research* (6th edition, 1963). Edinburgh, Oliver & Boyd: Longman.

Pearce, S. C. (1953) *Field Experimentation with Fruit Trees & Perennial Plants*. Technical Communication no. 23, Commonwealth Bureau of Horticulture and Plantation Crops.

Snedecor, G. W. (1937) *Statistical Methods* (6th edition with W. G. Cochran, 1967, 7th edition, 1980). Iowa State University Press.

Yates, F. (1937) *The Design and Analysis of Factorial Experiments*. Technical Communication no. 35, Commonwealth Bureau of Soils.

Yates, F. (1949) *Sampling Methods for Censuses and Surveys* (4th edition, 1981). London, Charles Griffin & Co.

Yates, F. (1970) *Experimental Design; Selected Papers*. London, Charles Griffin & Co.

# Animal Nutrition

## SIR KENNETH BLAXTER

Rowett Research Institute, Aberdeen

Judged by the extent of our present understanding, our knowledge of nutrition 50 years ago was incredibly meagre. The vitamins as a group were known at that time but their diversity was unrealized; while the importance of amino acids as determinants of protein quality had been shown by Hopkins many years previous, not all the amino acids now known to be essential for animals had been discovered, let alone shown to be necessary constituents of diet. Threonine ($\alpha$ amino $\beta$ hydroxybutyric acid), for example, which is the second limiting amino acid of cereal grains, was only discovered by Rose in 1935. The same dearth of knowledge was true of the mineral constituents of diet. The obligatory need for calcium, phosphorus, magnesium, sodium, potassium and chlorine — the major elements — was well established and so too was that for iron and iodine. The essential nature of copper was only discovered by Elvehjem in 1931, while experiments to find whether zinc and manganese were required in the diet for growth and well-being were, to say the least, contradictory at that time. In 1931 we did not know anything about the roles of vitamin K, riboflavin, niacin, vitamin $B_6$ (pyridoxine), pantothenic acid, biotin, para-aminobenzoic acid, folic acid, cobalamin (vitamin $B_{12}$), linoleic and arachidonic acids, selenium, fluorine or cobalt in terms of their nutritional essentiality. Experiments had, however, been made which in some instances predicated their existence and some examples may be given. Egg white injury, which is specifically reversed by biotin, had been discovered by Osborne and Mendel in 1919; it had been established in 1929 that pernicious anaemia in man responded to therapeutic doses of liver, a finding that eventually led to Lester Smith's isolation at Newcastle of vitamin $B_{12}$ in the 1940s. Again, the signs of essential fatty acid deficiency — the Burr and Burr syndrome — had been recorded long before the need for the two fatty acids was uncovered and this latter discovery preceded by four decades the finding that arachidonic acid was the essential precursor of the physiologically-active prostaglandins.

The early years of the Agricultural Research Council thus coincided with a massive growth in knowledge about the essentiality of nutrients. It also coincided with the elucidation of the chemical structure of organic nutrients and with commercial availability of them for the supplementation of feeds and fortification of foods. Thus, the Isler synthesis of vitamin A in 1947 resulted in large-scale synthesis of the vitamin and similar chemical syntheses which, together with microbial processes, ensured that a ready and relatively cheap supply of many but not all nutrients would be available for the feed and food industries.

Parallel with this work on discovery of the indispensable dietary factors and their isolation and synthesis has been the growth of knowledge of biochemistry. Again, it is remarkable how recent this growth has been, and the paucity of knowledge 50 years ago. Sir Hans Krebs, for example, only postulated the citric acid cycle, thus revealing the cyclic and dynamic state of molecular processes in the body in 1937, and the great edifice of knowledge of intermediary metabolism is very recent. The impact of biochemistry on nutrition has been and is immense. The biochemical interpretation of the concept of essentiality of a nutrient has changed our understanding; we no longer think in terms of a nutrient being required for growth but rather in terms of its role as a prosthetic group of an enzyme or co-enzyme controlling synthetic processes in cells.

Furthermore, the techniques of biochemistry, particularly the separatory techniques, have revolutionized nutritional studies. Outstanding here were the chromatographic separation methods devised by Synge, for which he shared the Nobel Prize with Martin. New techniques of analysis have enabled better diagnosis of nutritional disorders in man and animal to be made and have led to better assessments of the adequacy of food and feed.

The larger part of this great growth of knowledge did not come about through an appreciation of the likelihood that new knowledge would enhance food production or improve the well-being of man; it arose from a simple desire to increase understanding. It is to the great credit of the Research Councils of the UK and the analogous funding agencies of other countries that freedom and funds were provided to support what has undoubtedly been one of the greatest intellectually-creative episodes in man's history. Even so, many of the advances did arise through perception of real agricultural or medical problems. A good example is that of the discovery of the essentiality of cobalt by Underwood and Marston in Australia. Investigations were made of two diseases of sheep in Australia, "coast disease" studied by Marston and "enzootic marasmus" studied by Underwood. These were analogous to "bush sickness" seen in New Zealand and "vinquish" or "pine" which occurred in Scotland. Underwood showed that a trace metal was involved and that this was either nickel or cobalt. Cobalt was effective in prevention, the work established that cobalt was an essential element and this was soon confirmed in many parts of the world where sheep failed to thrive in the midst of an apparent plenty. A medical example relates to the causation of pellagra and also illustrates approaches generated by a concern about disease. The nutritional origin of the disease had been established by Goldberger in experiments with prisoners in 1915 and the pellagra preventative factor identified as nicotinic acid by Elvehjem in 1937. Pellagra still occurred, however, in maize-eating peoples, as was shown by the work by Dame Harriet Chick and Sir Charles Martin at Cambridge; this led to the discovery of the conversion of tryptophan to nicotinic acid by Krehl in 1945 and to Kodicek's later work at Cambridge on the nicotinic acid binding factor niacytin in cereals.

In much of this basic work to elucidate causes of nutritional disturbance the rat was the experimental animal of choice although some investigators, such as Chick and Martin, employed pigs, and the baby chick was used by many. The extension of work with rats and chicks to other species was secondary, leading to remarkable findings related to species specificity of both clinical signs and metabolic adjustments.

The study of the nutrition of farm animals is not, however, simply a cataloguing and quantifying of the effects of dietary deficiencies. It involves all those aspects of animal production which are influenced by the quantity and composition of the diet. It is primarily concerned with the conversion of primary plant products to secondary ones — the meat, milk and eggs which man requires for his own sustenance. Such nutritional studies involve consideration of complex interactions between diet and the physical infective and microbial environments, between diet and the genotype of the animal concerned, and study not only of adequacies in terms of nutrients but also the effects of toxic and non-nutritive components. Disease or abnormality which is plainly associated with diet is not necessarily due to absence of an essential nutrient, for toxins abound. The so-called X disease of turkeys, for example, was shown to be due to a fungal toxin and its investigation led to the discovery of the aflatoxins by Blount at Stoke Mandeville in 1961. This was extensively investigated under the aegis of a joint ARC Committee which indeed was responsible for the term "aflatoxin" used to describe the family of compounds produced by the fungus. Involvement in the study of animal nutrition thus ranges from animal husbandry to most of the biological sciences, for nutrition is an integrating discipline.

I have been favoured in having worked continuously in the Agricultural Research Service for over 40 years, a considerable proportion of the 50 years it now celebrates. It is impossible to compress an account of what has been achieved into a few pages and

I have therefore selected some areas in which advances have been both immense and exciting, and have dealt with them in two parts. Aware that to many the spectacular aspects of nutrition relate to the demonstration that dietary deficiency or excess can cause disease and death or to major revolutions in our understanding, I deal in the first part with some examples of research which led to the discovery of nutrient deficiencies and toxicities in farm livestock in the UK, and with the discoveries in animal physiology that led to an understanding of ruminant nutrition. In the second part I deal with the systematization of nutritional knowledge through the development of feeding standards and the evolution of more positive approaches to animal production by manipulation of the nutritional environment.

## Some Achievements in Nutritional Science

### The copper problems

It has already been mentioned that the essentiality of copper for the rat had only been established in 1931 by Elvehjem in the United States. A claim was made by workers in Florida at that time that copper deficiency was the cause of the "salt sick" disease of cattle in that part of the USA, but this was not substantiated and cobalt deficiency was later shown to be the cause. Probably the first demonstration of naturally-occurring copper deficiency in livestock was by Sjollema in 1933 who found a disease, characterized by emaciation and diarrhoea, in cattle grazing reclaimed land on the polders of Holland. It was associated with very low amounts of copper in herbage and grain, was called "reclamation disease" or "lechtsucht" and responded to copper.

In Somerset, a disease of cattle also characterized by diarrhoea was known on the "Teart" pastures. Herbage from these pastures was analysed by Ling at Long Ashton Research Station and the only abnormality found was a very high content of molybdenum of 20–100 mg/kg dry matter. The work was taken up by Ferguson at the ICI Research Station at Jealott's Hill and fully confirmed. In view of Sjollema's work, copper dosage was tried and it was found in 1938 that a dose of 2 g of copper per cow resulted in prevention and cure of the disease and this dosage provided an effective means of using these pastures. The copper content of these pastures was, however, quite normal.

Somewhat earlier, attention was focused on a disease of sheep evidently long known to flock-masters and shepherds in the Borders and thought by them to be associated with particular areas and particular soils. This was "swayback" which was first shown to be a demyelinating disease of brain and spinal cord by Lyle Stewart at Newcastle. The same disease occurred in Western Australia where it was earlier known as "Gingin rickets", in New Zealand, Sweden, South Africa, and in Peru. Stewart's findings were confirmed and extended by Innes at Cambridge who, by exchange of pathological specimens, confirmed that the diseases in sheep in all these countries were the same. A large amount of investigation followed to identify their cause. Lead toxicity was at first incriminated and tested, but in 1937 Bennetts and Chapman of Western Australia showed that copper administration prevented the disease. Dunlop and Wells confirmed this finding in the following year by field trials in the Peak District of Derbyshire. There were, however, problems for in the UK swayback occurred on farms where pasture copper was normal, certainly above 7 mg kg$^{-1}$ and even as high as 20 mg kg$^{-1}$, while in Western Australia the copper content was only 1–2 mg kg$^{-1}$ and clearly the latter pastures were as deficient in copper as were those of the polders of Holland.

In cattle grazing on the Western Australian pastures Bennetts found a very different syndrome to that seen in sheep — a sudden death due to cardiac dysfunction. He called this disease "falling disease" and he found that it also responded to copper. In New Zealand, Cunningham described yet another copper-responsive disease in cattle which he termed "peat scours" and which was very similar to that noted by Sjollema in Holland 11 years before. Ruth Allcroft from the Veterinary Laboratory, Weybridge, working on the peat lands of Caithness, Scotland, and Jamieson and Flora Russell from the Rowett Institute working on reclaimed heather land in Aberdeenshire, discovered a further copper-responsive disease in cattle, now called "Caithness Pine". This, in terms of its clinical and pathological appearance, seemed to be the same as the lechtsucht of Holland and the peat scours of New Zealand, but there was one major difference. As with British and Australian swayback, the copper content of the diet of cattle with Caithness Pine was apparently normal while that of cattle with what seemed the same disease in Holland and in New Zealand was obviously deficient. The finding that the pastures growing on the peats of New Zealand had moderate levels of molybdenum, together with the evidence from the teart pastures of high molybdenum concentrations in herbage suggested that the metabolism of copper was linked to that of molybdenum and much investigational work followed, particularly in Australia and in the UK, to resolve the causal relationships and distinguish between copper deficiency and molybdenum toxicity. Dick in Australia showed additionally that the sulphate ion was involved; work by Mills at the Rowett Institute demonstrated the formation of insoluble copper sulphide in the ruminant gut, while Suttle and Field at the Animal Disease Research Association's Moredun Institute showed that the copper-molybdenum antagonism occurred even at very low levels of molybdenum in the diet. Molybdenum is, of course, an essential element for animals as well as a toxic one; xanthine oxidase and sulphite oxidase are molybdenum-containing enzymes. Emphasis in present research is on the role of the series of thiomolybdates and their copper salts in the aetiology of these induced copper deficiency syndromes and progress is rapid. Further complexities are, however, present since there is little doubt that interactions of copper with dietary zinc, cadmium and possibly manganese take place. Even more complexity is present for clear-cut evidence of genetic differences between breeds of sheep in their copper requirement and resistance to excesses of copper has been uncovered at the Animal Breeding Research Organisation. The precise delineation of a copper requirement or the assessment of the adequacy of a diet in terms of its copper content as an aid to diagnosis is thus difficult.

The one disease which is apparently incongruous in terms of its clinical signs is the myocardial degeneration of cattle, "falling disease". This appears to be a derangement of collagen and elastin synthesis. Partridge's elucidation of the cross linkages of elastin, desmosine and isodesmosine undertaken when he was working at the Low Temperature Research Station at Cambridge showed that four lysine residues were oxidized to form them, the oxidation being catalysed by lysyl oxidase which is a copper-containing enzyme. Copper deficiency results in a lowering of the activity of this enzyme. In this respect, much work has taken place to find the precise loci of action of copper — and indeed other metals and non-metals — to provide ways of diagnosing deficiency states. One of the earliest made use of the discovery by Keilin and Hartree at Cambridge that cytochrome C oxidase, the terminal respiratory enzyme, contains copper. It was shown that in swayback and in experimental copper deficiency the enzyme is depleted.

One of the most extraordinary aspects of copper metabolism stemmed from the observation that Braude made in the piggery newly erected at the end of the war at the National Institute for Research in Dairying at Shinfield. The pigs licked the copper pipes placed by the builders to prevent rusting of the iron tubular structure to such extent that they were always shiny and eventually were completely consumed. Braude showed that this curious "appetite" was specifically for metallic copper, that pigs preferred meal with copper sulphate added and that by all the then known biochemical criteria of adequacy and by the absence of a response to diets containing 25 mg copper per kg, there was no deficiency of the element in the diets used. Later Braude measured the growth responses to very large dietary supplements of copper to find that 250 mg of copper per kg of diet, equivalent to 0.1% of the diet as copper sulphate, enhanced growth by 8–10%. These results were soon confirmed in many countries and applied in the field, though even today there is no entirely adequate explanation of the mechanism of this growth promotion.

The successful application of Braude's discovery, however, resulted in problems. The pig appears to be curious in that it can tolerate accumulation of very considerable amounts of copper in its liver without untoward effects. This is not so of sheep and when sheep were given proprietary feed mixtures prepared for pigs, acute copper poisoning and death occurred. Furthermore, since a large proportion of the copper given to pigs was excreted in the faeces, toxicity also occurred in sheep and cattle given hay grown on land manured with pig slurry. Why the pig should be able to accumulate copper without showing icterus and other signs of toxicity remains unknown.

## Selenium

In the late 1940s, Wood and I at the Hannah Research Institute were attempting to make a diet for young calves based on purified ingredients so to be able to measure the amino acid needs of these animals. The diet, which we thought adequate, produced massive muscle degeneration, and since the syndrome seemed analogous to that produced in guinea-pigs in the USA by Goettsch, we tried prevention with vitamin E. Large doses were successful and we showed that tocopherol requirements were increased by the unsaturated fatty acids in the experimental diet. We made approaches to the field staffs of the Agricultural Colleges to see if the disease occurred naturally and found it associated with feeding unsaturated fat in the form of cod liver oil. Sharman, then acting Veterinary Investigation Officer in Inverness, discovered, however, several farms on which the same disease occurred but in the absence of unsaturated fat. The disease, enzootic muscular dystrophy or white muscle disease, is recognized throughout the world. Our experiments showed that the disease in calves in North-East Scotland could also be prevented by giving either the cows or the calves vitamin E but the amounts needed were far in excess of what we knew to be required in the absence of unsaturated fats. Some other factor was obviously required. Our search for this factor was fruitless. Possible concomitant shortages of copper, iron and cobalt as causal factors were all ruled out by experiment.

A similar disease occurred in sheep in New Zealand, and workers from there visited the Hannah Institute to learn the analytical techniques for the tocopherols that Brown had devised. In New Zealand, unlike North-East Scotland or Oregon, USA, tocopherol therapy was virtually ineffective in preventing the disease. The solution to the problem came in a very indirect way. Schwartz, a German scientist, had uncovered during the war a liver necrosis lesion in rats induced by diets containing Torula yeast, and he had shown that this disease could be prevented by adding to the diet vitamin E, methionine or an unknown essential he called "Factor 3". The same lesion was produced by Naftalin at the Rowett Institute and he found it could be prevented by supplementing the diet with dried skim milk from Northern Ireland but not with dried skim milk from New Zealand. Naftalin also showed that if he kept rats in the cold, muscle lesions developed. Schwartz moved to the USA at the end of the war and in 1957 announced with Foltz the identity of Factor 3 with an organic compound of selenium. This was an astounding and unexpected discovery, soon taken up by those puzzling over the muscular diseases of cattle and sheep. We immediately tried the effectiveness of selenium; it prevented the disease in the cattle of the North-East of Scotland. Similar work took place at this time in the USA, Canada and New Zealand with lambs and it was evident that Schwartz's work with rats had provided the solution to the considerable problems of muscular disease in cattle and sheep in all those countries. Naftalin's finding was undoubtedly related to the low selenium content of dried milk from New Zealand where the disease was rife.

In New Zealand it was soon found that there were growth responses to selenium dosages in lambs on farms on which there was evidence of Se deficiency. These findings led to large-scale trials financed by the Department of Agriculture and Fisheries for Scotland to reveal widespread incidence of sub-clinical selenium deficiency. Mitchell at the Macaulay Institute for Soil Research provided analytical and geochemical evidence to show that soils derived from the Old Red Sandstone and certain granites were likely to be deficient in selenium; so they proved to be from the field tests for responses of growth were found in the lambs grazing on farms with soils derived from these rocks.

Selenium was shown by workers in the USA to be a component of the enzyme glutathione peroxidase, and assay of this enzyme is currently proving extremely useful in estimating areas where there is a risk of deficiency. The daily requirement of selenium is incredibly small; less than 50 mg selenium in every tonne of feed suffices. The complex relationships between the tocopherols, other anti-oxidants, unsaturated fatty acids and selenium in maintaining membrane integrity and in preventing tissue damage through peroxidation is an area of considerable current activity.

## Hypomagnesaemic tetany

A disease of adult cattle and sheep, usually fatal, and known as "grass staggers", "grass tetany" or "Hereford disease", had been known for some while in the UK and was often confused with milk fever (hypocalcaemic parturient paresis). It was shown by Sjollema and Seekles in Holland in 1930 to be associated with a low concentration of magnesium in the blood serum. The disease did not appear to be due to dietary deficiency of magnesium since the magnesium content of soft tissues and bones was perfectly normal and it was classified in the late 1930s as "a metabolic disorder of endocrine or neurological origin invoked by environmental stress" — a description that hardly advanced knowledge very much. Although the incidence of the disease was less than that of milk fever, it caused considerable economic loss because affected cattle usually died. In the 1950s a considerable amount of work was undertaken at a number of centres in the UK to ascertain the cause and provide methods of prevention. Work at Shinfield showed that fertilization of pasture with potash increased the incidence of the disease and so did nitrogenous manuring. Potassic manuring was shown by joint trials at the Hannah and Macaulay Institutes to depress the magnesium and sodium contents of herbage and elevate herbage potassium. The resultant high dietary potassium concentration was shown in some instances to depress serum magnesium and it was postulated that the disease might be a hyperaldosteronism. This was not supported by experiments by Care at the Rowett Institute with adrenalectomized animals maintained with cortisol. An inhibition of parathyroid hormone excretion was also postulated but it was found that the parathyroid responses to tetany-prone pastures were, if anything, enhanced. Studies were made of sites of absorption of magnesium to show that these were in the rumen and the view arose that the disease was an absorptive defect characteristic of spring grass. Such a view accorded with the finding that serum magnesium could be maintained at normal levels by feeding magnesium oxide or by liming affected pastures with dolomitic limestone. The increased incidence when pastures were manured with nitrogenous fertilizers was attributed to the high ruminal ammonia production or possibly to enhanced growth of ruminal micro-organisms, the walls of many of which contain appreciable techoic acids rich in magnesium. The difference between the intake of magnesium and faecal output in cattle grazing spring pasture was certainly small, but this did not provide an explanation of the factors controlling absorption.

The work provided effective practical preventative methods for grass tetany even if they did not provide satisfying explanations of its genesis, and a number of unexplained observations remain. Thus, the best predictor of tetany-prone pasture seems, from surveys in East Scotland, to be their sodium content. Again, the events at the neuro-muscular junction where the tetany originates and those at the surface of the bone mineral where magnesium is held, are not understood. A resurgence of interest in these problems is, however, now beginning.

## Feed additives

The possibility of stimulation of appetite, growth or milk secretion by dietary admin-istration of small amounts of substances has always intrigued people and some of the nostrums used in the 18th and 19th centuries are examples. Folley and Kay at Shinfield had shown in the early 1930s that milk secretion in cows could be increased by feeding dried thyroid gland or by the injection of thyroxine. During the war a considerable programme of work was undertaken jointly by the Medical Research Council and the Agricultural Research Council which led to the large-scale synthesis of thyroxine by iodination of the tyrosine residues in casein or crude conarachin. Experiments at Shinfield showed that, given to milking cows, these iodinated proteins increased milk yield by about 20% and the Agricultural Research Council then organized field trials involving about 1000 cows on commercial farms which provided a massive confirmation. The development was not taken further since the induced hyperthyroidism led to excessive weight losses.

Also arising from some of Folley's work on the induction of lactation in goats, attempts were made during the war to induce lactation in heifers using the synthetic oestrogen diethylstilboestrol which had been discovered by Dodds in London. While lactation was induced, problems of pelvic bone fracture arising from coital mimicry in the heifers precluded further development.

The synthetic oestrogens, however, were soon shown to augment growth rate in both castrated cattle and lambs. Work at the Rowett Institute showed that these effects came about through changes in the proportional deposition of fat and protein in ways analogous to those associated with males and females of the species. At first the oestrogens were incorporated in feed but later subcutaneous implantations of the synthetic hormones were used. There was obviously an interest in extension of this work to poultry and to pigs. In poultry this led to "chemical caponization", but in pigs the first attempts were not particularly rewarding and it is only in recent years that with the advent of a series of synthetic androgens and oestrogens the precise adjustments to the endocrine system to augment growth have been successful. Here the major work has undoubtedly been undertaken by the commercial drug houses, but the essential monitoring of effects has rightly been undertaken within the Agricultural Research Service.

In the late 1940s a considerable interest arose in the USA in what was termed the "animal protein factor" which, present in a number of protein sources of animal origin, augmented growth of laboratory animals and simple-stomached farm species. There is little doubt in retrospect that animal protein factor (APF) was largely vitamin $B_{12}$, but the work led to some remarkable findings. Material tested included the felted mycelial residues from antibiotic manufacture and these had high activity in the test for APF. It was eventually shown that pure crystalline aureomycin present in the residues from aureomycin manufacture stimulated growth and the same proved true of streptomycin and chlortetracycline. This discovery was soon applied commercially throughout the world. The ARC organized collaborative trials which confirmed the American work and extended it to penicillin. The problem then became one of understanding how antibiotics worked. Studies at Shinfield showed that the response to them was less in clean, disinfected premises than in dirty ones — dirty that is in the microbiological sense — suggesting that the antibiotic combated some low-grade and unidentified infection. Yet in germ-free animals a growth response was still obtained. Such was the increase in the use of antibiotics in the animal industry that considerable concern arose regarding the public health implication. Work at the Public Health Laboratory, Colindale, showed that plasmid-transmitted resistance to antibiotics could be transferred from organisms in the digestive tract to potential human pathogens. Following an enquiry (the Swann Committee), the United Kingdom Government proscribed the use in feeds of certain antibiotics valuable in human therapy but allowed others — the feed antibiotics — to be used as animal feed additives. In taking this step, the UK was in advance of other countries and in the ensuing years many of those countries have accepted the British point of view.

## Nutritional toxicology

Richard Synge once remarked that animals and man do not ingest nutrients, they eat food! The diets of animals indeed contain many chemical constituents which have adverse effects on them. Much is now known of these toxic constituents or antinutritive factors, but there is much still to be learned. Bracken on the hills had long been known to be toxic to livestock. Bracken contains a potent thiaminase which studies by Evans at Bangor showed can account for toxicity in horses. In cattle, however, work at the Rowett Institute showed that a diet of bracken resulted in death and thiamin had no effect in prevention. These animals showed severe changes in the bone marrow and Evans continued work on this problem with support from the Agricultural Research Council to show that the bracken toxin was a radiomimetic one though full experimental confirmation of the nature of the toxin has yet to be accomplished.

The study of the pathological changes in dietary toxicological problems developed rapidly during the period and besides the demonstration of the bone marrow lesion in bracken poisoning, the demonstration at Weybridge of the characteristic liver lesion in poisoning by the Senecio alkaloids are good examples.

The brassica crops, turnips, swedes, kale, rape and cabbage, were the crops on which the agricultural revolution of the eighteenth century was founded. They contain a number of toxic constituents, including the glucosinolates and erucic acid of oilseed rape which were intensively investigated in Canada and Germany in the post-war period. Another toxin in the brassicas which has proved to be more limiting agriculturally is the haemolytic anaemia factor in leafy brassicas. If cattle, and to a lesser extent sheep, subsist on diets containing large amounts of leafy brassicas they develop severe haemolytic anaemia. Small laboratory herbivorous species and pigs do not do so. The factor was isolated by R. H. Smith at the Rowett Institute and shown to be S-methyl cysteine sulphoxide. Strangely the sulphoxide was not the primary toxin for it was not toxic to the germ-free animal but only acted after ruminal fermentation to the toxic dimethyl disulphide. Whether plant breeding programmes can eliminate or reduce this toxin is not known; at present its presence appears to limit the use of this very productive natural order of plants as feed for cattle.

Many other toxins and other antinutritive factors exist in plants. Some are under active consideration at present, notably the isohaemagglutinins being investigated at Shinfield and the Rowett Institute, and the curious compounds induced by Phytophthora infestation of potato tubers and once thought responsible for the incidence of spina bifida in babies. These were thoroughly investigated at the Food Research Institute.

## Ruminant digestion

The digestion of fibrous feeds by ruminant animals has intrigued investigators for a long while. Work in the 19th century had shown that the ruminal fermentation was associated with the presence in rumen fluid of the lower steam volatile acids, acetic, propionic and n-butyric acids, but these were at the time thought to be of no value to the animal other than as a source of heat. These ideas were reinforced by the findings of Kühn and Kellner in Germany at the turn of the century for Kellner found that starch and cellulose had the same nutritive value in terms of promoting fat deposition in the body of the ox. While admitting that some steam volatile fatty acids (SVAs) were produced in the fermentation, the general conclusion accepted in the early 1930s was that fermentation of cellulose somehow stopped at the stage of hydrolysis at which glucose or some other simple carbohydrate, such as cellobiose, was formed and that hexose was absorbed. Only in this way could an equality of nutritive value be accorded to the two carbohydrates for it was assumed that starch was digested as in a simple-stomached species. All attempts to find the postulated hexose intermediary failed and it was in the Agricultural Research Council's Unit of Animal Physiology at Cambridge that the problem was resolved. Sir Joseph Barcroft, its first director, Phillipson and Rachel MacAnally showed unequivocally that dietary carbohydrate was fermented to SVAs, the acids were absorbed and that acetic acid could be oxidized to provide energy to maintain the beating heart. This was in 1943 and the methods used were the classic ones of physiology. Later Barcroft visited the USA to carry out some of the first experiments with acetic acid labelled with $^{14}C$ to clinch the matter. A massive amount of work followed to provide additional quantitative information about rates of production of the acids and their role in metabolism, not only in Britain but throughout the world. Associations were found between the type of diet and the proportional make up of the mixture of fatty acids produced and it became apparent that Kellner's findings arose from the fact that all carbohydrate is fermented to steam volatile acids and negligible amounts of glucose are absorbed from the alimentary tract. The direct determinations of the utilization of the energy of the fatty acids which Armstrong and I made at the Hannah Institute showed that they were not as efficiently used as a source of energy as glucose and that utilization depended on the length of the fatty acid chain.

With the ready availability of isotopically-labelled SVAs, considerable work was then done to define the rates of their production by fermentation and from endogenous sources. Soon a coherent body of knowledge was built up showing the interrelations involved, the pathways of metabolism and the significance of propionic acid as a glucose precursor in the body. The changes in fermentation patterns were shown to have considerable implications, notably in bloat, in ketosis and in the low milk fat syndrome. It was later discovered at the Rowett Institute by Garton and Ørskov that excessive production of propionic acid in the sheep was associated with the production of abnormal body fats in which the long-chain fatty acids had methyl branches and this work is now leading to studies of their occurrence in cobalt deficiency which is in effect an induced deficiency of vitamin $B_{12}$. This vitamin is a component of the enzyme which catalyses the metabolism of propionic acid.

In all this work it was apparent that the ruminal microflora was of paramount importance and commencing with Elsden's work at the Cambridge Unit in the 1940s and continuing with Baker's descriptive microscopic studies at the Rowett Institute, much was done to derive identification procedures and indeed isolation ones for these very demanding anaerobes. As identification methods based on fermentative characteristics developed, so morphological study became less important to undergo a current revival with the advent of electron microscopic techniques. The expectation in the 1950s was probably that ways might be found to select micro-organisms with superior fermentative capacities or best suited for particular feed substrates so to enhance animal productivity. As Baker, the microscopist, had pointed out in the late 1940s, the flora was so incredibly complex that this seemed unlikely and so it has largely proved to be. The microflora and fauna of sheep and cattle in different parts of the world appear to be virtually the same provided their diets are similar and the only factors which modify the flora seem to be the chemical composition of the diet, the physical form of its constituents and the frequency of feeding of the animal. Exceptions have been found and no doubt there are others yet to be discovered. Thus, it was found at the Hannah Institute that the methane production of the ruminant could be reduced by certain additives and the proportion of propionic acid produced then increased. This approach, which had obvious practical possibilities, was pursued until it was shown that after a period of time the ruminal organisms developed an ability to metabolize the additives concerned. Another example still being explored was the American finding that a coccidiostat, monensin, apparently alters the ruminal fermentation in such manner that propionic acid production is increased and animal growth is enhanced.

What was true of carbohydrates, namely a massive fermentation, was soon shown also to be true of protein. Proteolysis in the rumen was extensive and fermentation of the constituent amino acids released led to the formation of ammonia which together with amino acids served as the source of nitrogen for the microbial growth. McDonald's work at Cambridge which demonstrated that casein and gelatin disappeared completely and rapidly from the rumen and that the ruminal outflow of nitrogen-containing compounds was virtually entirely of microbial origin, gave rise to the concept that the source of amino acids for the body proper of the ruminant was entirely from these microbes. J. A. B. Smith's studies at the Hannah Institute of the fermentation *in vitro* coupled with practical studies at Shinfield of the utilization of simple nitrogen-containing compounds such as urea which showed they could sustain growth and milk secretion in cattle, supported the contention. Furthermore, the absence of any wide range in the biological value of dietary proteins for ruminants suggested that the microbial and protozoal protein was the sole source of their absorbed amino acids. The estimates of the biological value of isolated ruminal micro-organisms were such that the idea seemed reasonable. There were, however, difficulties. McDonald showed that only about 40% of dietary zein, the insoluble protein of maize, was fermented in the rumen and zein passed through to the abomasum. Synge, with Margaret Chalmers at the Rowett Institute indeed showed wide differences between protein sources for ruminants in their "solubility" in the rumen and their ability to promote nitrogen retention and milk secretion in goats. The fact that many high-quality proteins — that is proteins of high biological value as judged by tests with simple-stomached species — were degraded to microbial protein of lower value led to ideas of the "protection" of protein and indeed of other dietary constituents from microbial attack by the use of formaldehyde and other substances which prevented microbial hydrolysis and fermentation and yet permitted enzymic digestion lower in the digestive tract. This work later led to the devising of better ways of meeting the ruminant's requirements of protein and defining the conditions under which nitrogenous substances of a non-protein nature could be used.

Lipids were also shown to be affected. Work at the Rowett Institute demonstrated rapid hydrolysis of lipids with subsequent fermentation of the glycerol. What was remarkable was that the dietary unsaturated fatty acids were subsequently hydrogenated such that the ruminal outflow contained virtually no unsaturated long-chain fatty acids. Protection of unsaturated lipids by coating them with protein which was subsequently treated with formaldehyde made it possible, however, to avoid the microbial hydrogenation and to produce milk fat and body fat high in polyunsaturated acid content. In the ruminant animal given a normal diet questions then arose relating to the mechanism it adopts to absorb these non-esterified fatty acids for unlike the simple-stomached species the ruminant has no monoglycerides in its intestinal lumen for the formation of micellar complexes for absorption. It forms similar water soluble complexes, however, using lysolecithin. The problem remains, however, of how the ruminant survives without a continuing supply of essential fatty acids and this has not yet been satisfactorily resolved.

Microbial growth was shown to be associated with such a considerable synthesis of B complex vitamins that it seemed almost inconceivable that any deficiency syndrome involving them could occur. This was not so. Synthesis of vitamin $B_{12}$ was obligatorily linked to a supply of cobalt and the elucidation of the microbial production of vitamin $B_{12}$ and its analogues owes much to the work of Kon and Porter at Shinfield. Additionally, it was shown by Edwin at Weybridge that cerebrocortical necrosis in sheep and cattle was a tissue thiamin deficiency reversed by administration of thiamin. It is still not certain how this apparent deficiency occurs. It could be due to the thiaminase activity of certain ruminal organisms; many bacteria have such activities but tests of possible culprits have not produced the disease. The alternative explanation that microbial formation of thiamin analogues which compete with thiamin for enzyme sites though suggested has not been fully explored.

During the period of nearly 30 years since Barcroft's unit at Cambridge showed the significance of the ruminal fermentation, the immense and world-wide investigation of the physiology and biochemistry of the ruminant digestion process has created a new wealth of knowledge about these remarkable animals. In the process, a whole series of new techniques for the study of digestion have been devised including methods for studying the dynamics of the process of digesta flow through the use of markers, new surgical procedures of increasing complexity and new analytical techniques to differentiate components, both within the gut and after absorption. The knowledge has been put to great use for it has enabled diet formulation to be placed on a rational rather than an empirical basis and has made it possible for cognisance to be taken of the need to consider both the nutritional requirements of the tissues of the ruminant and those of its commensal and symbiotic microbes.

## The Application of Nutritional Knowledge

### Feeding standards

The concept of feeding standards, that is tabulations of animal needs for nutrients, was an early one with origins in German studies in the middle of the 19th century. It was the later forms of these German feeding standards which were adopted in the United Kingdom in the early 1920s and there is little doubt that in the hands of the advisory services considerable increases in animal output were achieved through their application. Feeding standards together with estimates of the nutrient content of feeds enabled animals to be given adequate diets, and more important perhaps rationalized the planning of feed resources on the farm. The feeds to be purchased to supplement home production could be assessed by calculation of the nutrients supplied by those produced on the farm and the numbers of stock to be carried. Even in the early 1930s there were simple systems which enabled farmers to purchase the cheapest source of the two major nutrients "energy" and protein. These were the forerunners of present least cost formulation methods based on the mathematical linear programming techniques which arose from the theory of games developed during the second world war.

There were, however, difficulties. Much of the information about animal requirements had been obtained under experimental conditions rather than those of the farm, and virtually all the early standards were qualified by remarks which indicated that their use did not preclude the exercise of the "art of the feeder". The farmer thus was expected to make adjustments if animal performance did not agree with theory. Additionally, "safety margins" designed to prevent under-nutrition were added to estimates of need; their implication in terms of an implicit waste due to unnecessary over-nutrition was hardly touched upon. The basic concept was simply that an animal at a particular productive level had a precise requirement for each nutrient and that the objective was to ensure that the diet provided this amount. The fact that some nutrients and particularly the energy supply are determinants of the productive level was given little emphasis.

By the middle 1950s there was an increasing concern about the reliability and applicability of feeding standards. Much of the information relating to the nutrient requirements of pigs and poultry was based on United States data, where different husbandry methods were in vogue. The starch equivalent system was applied to all classes of stock, including non-ruminants, despite the fact that the system had been devised for fattening adult cattle. This seemed logically inconsistent in view of the new findings related to the differences between ruminants and non-ruminants in their digestive physiology. It certainly appeared that feeding standards were by no means matters for the amateur. Charles Crowther indeed remarked "I have spent the first half of my life trying to make people use starch equivalents and the second half of my life attempting to stop them misusing them."

Largely at the instigation of Sir Richard Haddon, Chairman of Farmer and Stock-breeder Publications Ltd., a conference was called in 1958 at Brighton to examine the situation and to assess whether the then current standards based primarily on the German work at the turn of the century and added to in a somewhat arbitrary way were a satisfactory basis for meeting the needs of a modern animal industry. This conference uncovered a series of problems and confirmed the existence of a void between the known essentiality of several nutrients and quantitative information of practical value about requirements of them. The final recommendation of the conference was that the Agricultural Research Council should establish standing committees to review published information on nutrient requirements and "recommend to Agricultural Departments of the United Kingdom such alterations as appear necessary in the feeding standards as published in "Rations for Livestock" and other relevant publications". The Agricultural Research Council agreed to the proposal and technical groups were established to assess the nutrient needs of ruminants, pigs and poultry. The first series of their reports were published by the ARC in the period 1962–65. These were not simple reviews; they presented in many instances new approaches to animal nutrition altogether. One is worthy of comment. The ruminant technical committee proposed that the starch equivalent system should be abandoned and replaced by a new system, the metabolizable energy system which had been devised at the Hannah Institute. A similar formal break with the starch equivalent system was made by both the pig and poultry technical committees since they proposed using digested energy determined with pigs and metabolizable energy determined with poultry as the best criteria to use to assess the value of feeds as a source of energy. The Agricultural Departments undertook investigations of a more practical nature in the years that followed, showed that the new system for ruminants was more precise in terms of its predictive power than the starch equivalent system and in 1975, adopted the metabolizable energy system officially.

Currently the Agricultural Research Council is continuing the reviewing and interpreting of nutritional information and up-to-date reports on nutritional requirements for the three major classes of stock will be available shortly.

The feeding standard approach, however, is a peculiarly static one; while it states what an animal should receive each day given knowledge of its production level, it gives relatively little information about the consequences of adopting particular feeding practices in the longer term or the causal relationships between nutrient intake and attained production or the interaction between nutrients or the changes in nutrient need due to antecedent nutrition. Information of these latter types imparts a more dynamic dimension to the feeding of stock and in some respects is central to the decisions that the farmer makes in exercising "the art of the feeder". While much work had been undertaken to examine the consequences of departures from existing standards of need, pressure to do more undoubtedly stemmed from agricultural economists, particularly those who followed the approaches made by Heady in the United States.

The economists were less concerned with nutrient essentials than with the nature of the response to feed in different environmental circumstances. Given such input-output relationships in which inputs could be defined in terms of actual feeds rather than their attributes, then micro-economic theory could be applied to produce optimal economic operating conditions for different cost-price structures in the animal industry.

An interesting example of replacement of the rigidity of the feeding standard approach to practical feeding relates to the dairy cow. Yates and Boyd working at Rothamsted Experimental Station, early in the war, analysed all published work to show that milk yield responded continuously to increase in food supply, implying that optimal levels of feed were not fixed but depended on economic circumstances. It was at the instigation of R. A. Fisher that further experimental studies commenced at the Hannah Institute. Fisher argued that dairy cattle improvement could hardly be regarded as successful if in doubling milk yield feed requirements also doubled, and he pleaded for investigations concerned with a deepening of understanding of the relationships between feed intake and milk yield in individual cows. The work at the Hannah he had suggested led to the concept that the effect of nutrition on milk production has a very strong historical component, that antecedent nutrition contributes to current response and this concept further developed by Broster at Shinfield has resulted in a more sensible approach to the control of milk secretion by nutritional means.

Another example concerns the nutrition of the sow which is similar to that of the cow, for it illustrates the effects of pattern of nutrient provision on productivity. A series of experiments and notably those carried out on a collaborative basis by Elsley — the ARC co-ordinated trials with sows — reversed the whole of the practical thinking about the best ways of feeding breeding sows. Elsley's experiments were carried on for four or more parities and established the current practices of controlled feeding at low levels during pregnancy to take advantage of enhanced protein anabolism at that time with enhanced feeding during lactation. The feeding regimens Elsley suggested entailed a minimal accretion by the sow in successive parities amounting to about 10 kg and was soon accepted in farm practice. Some problems followed on a few farms. When the low levels of feeding were continued for three or more parities, precipitous losses of weight suddenly took place after weaning. This syndrome, the thin sow syndrome, occurred when gastro-intestinal parasitism or exposure to cold introduced an additional metabolic demand, a matter which emphasized the complex interrelations between the infective and physical environment and nutrition.

Further examples of more dynamic approaches to the nutrition of animals and of recognition of the importance of catering for cyclical changes associated with reproduction relate to sheep. At the Hill Farming Research Organisation a systematic study of the responses of breeding and lactating ewes to their feed supply was undertaken using as criteria of under-nutrition of the individual ewe the concentrations of non-esterified fatty acids and $\beta$ hydroxy butyrate in her blood. These results were related to the conditions of nutritional deprivation that occur on hill grazings where limitations on productivity were most acute. Before the work began the importance of under-nutrition in late pregnancy had long been recognized; the studies augmented these earlier ones considerably indicating the critical aspect of the availability of good summer grazing to maintain milk yield and influence fertility at mating time. The studies on nutritional status were confirmed by body analyses and, when combined with studies of herbage production on the hill, led to the formulation of hill sheep production systems, which when tested increased output from poor hill by a factor of two.

An analogous approach was made by Robinson at the Rowett Institute but with the objective of achieving increases in productivity in sheep kept more intensively. Breeding flocks were set up and by manipulation of the light and nutritional environment ewes were induced to breed continually at seven-month intervals to increase lamb output by a factor of over two. The nutritional implications were considerable and one of the most interesting ones was the control of lactational yield that could be exercised by control of the amount and quality of the protein supply. These aspects are currently being further explored.

## The utilization of feed resources

It was pointed out in the Introduction that animal nutrition is a wide subject which merges into animal production and husbandry. It is not only concerned with discerning what nutrients are required or what toxic effects are provoked by diet or with catering for cyclical and seasonal changes, but also with finding optimal ways of using feed staples. Possibly the best example of research undertaken in this latter sense relates to the utilization of the United Kingdom's major arable feed crop, barley. Bell's work at the Plant Breeding Institute at Cambridge in producing Proctor barley and the massive increases in yield that have followed have only been fully realized through parallel research on how to use the crop as feed for livestock.

Barley is conventionally the energy-providing feed for non-ruminant stock, but the story of the improvement of its use for pigs and poultry begins with studies made with milk. Kon and Kathleen Henry at Shinfield, studying the nutritive value of skim milk powders, found that powders with a high (7%) moisture content were of poor nutritive value for the rat. A collaborative investigation followed involving the Low Temperature Research Station, the Hannah and Shinfield which showed the reduction in nutritive value was due to the unavailability of lysine and possibly of histidine. This arose from the reaction discovered by Maillard in 1912, namely a condensation of the $\epsilon$ amino group of lysine with the aldehydic group of a reducing sugar. Additionally, dry heat also resulted in a fall in availability. This finding showed that the chemical determination of lysine and possibly of other amino acids was no guide to the nutritive value of a protein for any bound lysine would be released following chemical hydrolysis. Microbiological assay of lysine following enzymic hydrolysis gave values in broad agreement with biological appraisal of the available lysine, but the method was tedious. Carpenter and Gabrielle Ellinger at the Rowett Institute devised a method to assay available lysine based on the use of the end-group assay reagent dinitrofluorobenzene which Sanger had used to determine the amino acid sequence of insulin. This was used to assay many protein sources and also the cereals used for pigs and poultry. Much of the lysine of cereals was shown to be unavailable and the method provided a rational way of assessing the adequacy of cereal diets and the ideal supplementation. Other methods for assessing protein quality were studied and these studies were co-ordinated by a committee established by the Agricultural Research Council for the purpose and which involved both research workers and those in the feedingstuffs industry.

Cereals provide a major part of the protein required by pigs and poultry; the protein sources added to diets simply provide additional and supplementary amino acids. Studies showed that the protein content of barley varied with variety, as well as with season and manuring. Lysine content, however, did not increase in parallel with nitrogen content because the lysine-poor storage proteins augmented more than the lysine-rich ones. The discovery of lysine-rich mutants in barley led to ideas that the quality of barley proteins might be increased. This was not pursued very far since not only was high lysine content associated with low yield, but the advent of cheap supplements of lysine made this rather unnecessary. Indeed, recent work by Fuller at the Rowett Institute with pigs has shown that additions of lysine, threonine and histidine to a barley of normal to high nitrogen content results in growth fully equivalent to that obtained with barley supplemented with fish meal.

With large amounts of barley grain available and cheap calves from dairy herds, Preston at the Rowett devised what has been called the barley beef system. By lightly rolling the grain, supplementing it with protein and minerals and feeding it *ad libitum*, gains of over 1 kg per day were obtained and acceptable carcasses produced in 10–12 months. There were, however, problems. Vitamin A requirements were enhanced, the cattle developed rumenitis and a high incidence of liver abscesses was noted. The rumenitis was traced by Fell at the Rowett to a traumatic injury of the ruminal wall caused by ingested hair and by the small silica spikelets on the lodicule of the grain. The use of bicarbonate to increase ruminal pH and avoid the swelling of the lamina propria which seemed a prerequisite to the injury reduced the incidence and so too did inclusion of a small amount of roughage. More recently, the treatment of whole grain with alkali has been shown at the Rowett to avoid the necessity of rolling the grain and of adding roughage.

Similar developments took place to devise ways of using barley for fattening lambs. Initially similar problems of rumenitis arose and these in the smaller ruminant could be avoided by feeding the barley without any processing at all. A further development has been the addition of minerals and of urea to whole grain in liquid form to provide a cheap and effective diet for very rapid growth of weaned lambs.

This one example relates to an arable crop. Many other examples of the use of nutritional knowledge to devise ways of using primary crops and crop residues might be given. Thus, a series of technologies were devised to make better use of the grass crop as a source of winter feed. Woodman at Cambridge had pointed out that young grass after laboratory drying had a chemical composition similar to that of a medium protein cake made from oil seed residues and understandably considerable work was undertaken both before and after the war to devise methods of artificial dehydration to provide a high-quality home-grown feed based on grass. Raymond's work at the Grassland Research Institute at Hurley on the digestibility of grass and the effects of a variety of processing methods extended earlier studies and new commercial under-takings marketing artificially-dehydrated lucerne and grass developed. The action by the Organisation of Petroleum Exporting Countries in increasing the price of oil and indirectly of all energy sources has led to a reduction in activity in this area. Another approach by Pirie at Rothamsted was based on the separation of the protein from grass and other leafy crops. Pirie's idea was to produce an acceptable protein for human consumption directly from crops and some success has been achieved in this respect in the developing countries. Emphasis in the UK was different, namely to produce a high-protein feedingstuff for stock by mechanical means. Much work in the late 1970s at the Rowett Institute (Plate 1), at Hurley and at Shinfield and in New Zealand and North America, has indicated how far the Pirie process can be integrated into farming practice and work continues.

Other new feed technologies have arisen to make use of cereal straws, oilseed residues and a variety of new materials ranging from yeasts and bacteria grown on hydrocarbons to the residues from the paper-making industry. Each new product and each new process has created new problems which have posed not only husbandry problems but invariably nutritional ones as well.


## Conclusions

The immense improvement in the nutrition of man and animals that has taken place in the last 50 years has come about through a considerable international effort in research and in the application of research findings. In this international context the United Kingdom contribution has been impressive, and the transformation of our own animal production considerable. The almost anecdotal accounts given above can hardly do justice to what has been achieved and the greater part of the achievement has been the result of Government support of science as exemplified by its support of the Agricultural Research Council.

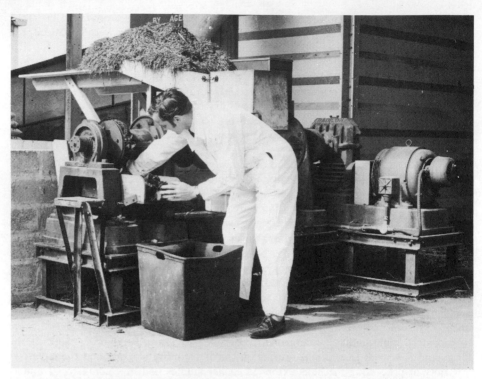

*Plate 1* The protein extraction plant at the Duthie Experimental Farm of the Rowett Research Institute.

It will, however, be apparent from the above accounts of some discoveries in nutritional science that there is no precise line of demarcation between research leading to primary discovery and investigations which lead to practical advance. The present day distinction between research and development is a very artificial one, or rather the boundaries between the two categories are, to say the least, hardly well defined. One can perhaps distinguish and separate the attempts made to systematize and exploit new information. That such attempts at exploitation uncovered new problems of considerable scientific dimension is fairly obvious and simply serves to show the importance in any field of agricultural endeavour of avoiding divorce of the applied from the theoretical and scientific.

Such has been the success in discovery in the nutritional field that some might think that in future progress will be slow. After all, we now have considerable knowledge of the essential nutrients and their mode of action and have grasped many of the problems about how to manipulate diet to improve animal production. To take such a view would be mistaken. It is true that it seems unlikely that there are more nutrient essentials to be discovered which will prove to be of major importance in maintaining animal health and productivity. The newly discovered essential elements, vanadium, chromium, silicon, nickel and arsenic, do not seem likely to have such large practical effects on animal production as have copper, selenium and zinc. There are, however, a series of hitherto unsuspected areas of animal physiology where diet is of importance and these are now to be explored. Nutritional effects on the immune system, nutritional aspects of behaviour, and what may be called the pharmacology of natural products are examples. Additionally, there are numerous problems in animal production, such as appetite regulation, seasonal effects on nutrient need, and genetic differences in metabolism that involve biochemical, nutritional and physiological study. Furthermore, no one can predict what is unknown and no doubt there will be many discoveries in nutritional science just as spectacular as, say, Schwartz's discovery of the essentiality of selenium. New studies leading to new discovery will be taxing, but no more so than that undertaken in the past. Effective research has always been difficult and is no more difficult today than it was 50 years ago. Provided that the Agricultural Research Council and other funding agencies exercise the same wise support of agricultural science that they have done in the past then there seems no reason to doubt that the achievements of the next 50 years will exceed those of the past.

## Further Reading

Much of the nutritional work undertaken within the Agricultural Research Service has been published in *The Journal of Agricultural Science, Animal Production* and the *British Journal of Nutrition*. The annual reports of the Institutes mentioned in the text include shorter accounts of work in progress and usually occasional reviews of particular facets when past results are collated and integrated. The list of books below is not comprehensive but presents a wider discussion of some of the aspects of nutritional science dealt with in this essay and an extension into fields which have, because of space limitation, been omitted.

ARC (1965). *The Nutrient Requirements of Farm Livestock. No. 2. Ruminants.* ARC: London.
ARC (1980). *The Nutrient Requirements of Farm Livestock. No. 2. Ruminants.* [2nd edition] CAB: Farnham Royal.
ARC (1967). *The Nutrient Requirements of Farm Livestock. No. 3. Pigs.* ARC: London.
ARC and MRC (1974). *Food and Nutrition Research.* London: HMSO.
Blaxter, K. L. (1969). *The Energy Metabolism of Ruminants.* [2nd edition] London: Hutchinson & Co. Ltd.
Hannah Research Institute (1978). *The Hannah Research Institute 1928–78.* [J. H. Moore and J. A. F. Rook, Ed.] Edinburgh: T. A. Constable.
Hill Farming Research Organisation (1979). *Science and Hill Farming.* Edinburgh: HFRO.
Preston, T. R. and Willis, M. B. (1974). *Intensive Beef Production.* London: Pergamon Press Ltd.
Underwood, E. J. (1977). *Trace Elements in Human and Animal Nutrition.* New York, London: Academic Press.

# Diseases of Farm Animals

EDITOR: K. N. BURNS

Agricultural Research Council, London

Most of the research on disease under the auspices of the Council is done at four Institutes. The editor has prepared the text mainly from material supplied by Dr. P. M. Biggs, Dr. W. B. Martin and Professor J. M. Payne, Directors respectively of the Houghton Poultry Research Station, Huntingdon, the Moredun Institute, Edinburgh, and the ARC Institute for Research on Animal Diseases, Compton, Berkshire. The section headed "Research on diseases exotic to Britain" has been prepared by Dr. J. B. Brooksby, Director of the Animal Virus Research Institute until his retirement in December 1979. Important work on disease is also done at certain other Institutes and this is indicated in the text; for example, there has been a large programme on the control of mastitis at the National Institute for Research in Dairying at Shinfield.

Research to control disease is a vital part of any programme to improve the productivity of farm animals and the Institutes concentrate on about sixty diseases which have the highest priority among the four hundred or so which affect British livestock. Some infectious diseases, like bluetongue or African swine fever, do not occur in Britain but, with international movements of animals, have now come close enough to be a threat in the near future and we must know how to handle them should they invade Britain. A further benefit of great importance from the research done on these overseas or "exotic" infections is in lessening the threat to Britain, because the results are applied world-wide and the general reservoir of infection is reduced; this applies particularly to foot-and-mouth disease.

Most of the diseases given priority are both widespread and economically important. The spectacular plagues such as rinderpest have been eradicated from Britain but there are still diseases which cause many deaths, for example, enteric diseases of young animals. Other diseases, such as mastitis, arc not usually fatal but they seriously reduce productivity. Priorities are also set by the need to safeguard public health, as with brucellosis and salmonellosis. More subtle considerations are the need to work on immuno-suppressive infections, such as toxoplasma or the viruses of infectious bursal disease and bovine virus diarrhoea, which render animals susceptible to other infections. Although we have long been aware of the importance of disease and have implemented control procedures which have successfully kept many infections out of the country, it is noteworthy that new infections still appear; the examples of the last ten years such as swine vesicular disease, bovine leucosis, maedi, streptococcal meningitis, and, in horses, contagious metritis, show that this happens with disconcerting frequency. In human medicine the appearance of a new infection, Legionnaire's disease, emphasises the need to be prepared. Much production is lost by nutritional disorders and ill-health from deficiencies and imbalances; we must have sound quantitative knowledge of the needs of fast-growing, high yielding animals to support modern intensive farming.

Much research is still being done on old topics. Sometimes this is because the problem, as in scrapie of sheep, has been very intractable. With other diseases control measures previously satisfactory are so no longer because husbandry methods have changed. Quite often different strains of an organism appear which behave differently or are not controlled by current vaccines. Sometimes a new technique developed in basic science provides the means to improve control measures; for example, applying genetic manipulation to produce diagnostic reagents and vaccines holds future promise.

We must recognise that research on animal diseases has been essential in backing up other improvements in animal production. Large intensive units, such as are now common, could not have been developed if measures to control infectious disease had not been devised.

In the following pages selected research programmes of the Institutes on a number of diseases are set out by species. Most diseases are mainly relevant to a particular species, but in a few diseases the research relates to several species.

## Cattle Diseases

Most research on cattle diseases by the ARC, other than on foot-and-mouth disease, is at the Institute for Research on Animal Diseases at Compton. Sir William Henderson has described how the Institute was founded in 1938. Its Isolation Compound is a unique facility for large-scale, long-term experiments on infectious diseases and its 800 hectares of farmland enable the Institute to breed its own animals for the research programme.

### Brucellosis

One of the most important uses for the Isolation Compound was the programme arranged by the ARC Committee on Brucellosis in the 1940s on vaccination against *Brucella abortus*, the organism causing the very serious "abortion storms" which had affected dairy herds for many years.

Two living vaccines, 45/20 and S19, were presumed to be avirulent strains of *Br. abortus*; the research was to decide which was the better and whether either could revert to virulence. Both were equally effective but the 45/20 vaccine became virulent after serial passage. Work then concentrated on S19 to determine whether it gave sufficient protection, the duration of protection, and the best age for vaccinating calves. By an experiment involving 534 cows in isolation conditions and lasting from 1949 to 1956, S19 vaccine was proved to be effective and long-lasting after only one dose administered to calves when 5 to 7 months old. The experiment gave information vital for establishing the Ministry of Agriculture, Fisheries and Food's vaccination policy which was a necessary preliminary to the present eradication scheme. The control of brucellosis as a whole is well described in the Ministry's "Animal Health — a Centenary 1865–1965".

Subsequently, a vaccine using killed 45/20 *Br. abortus* organisms was tested at Compton and found to be especially valuable when immunity from S19 needs reinforcing or where S19 cannot be used because it produces antibodies which interfere with the diagnostic method in the eradication scheme. The programme also provided important information on public health aspects of brucellosis because the frequency and persistence of infection in milk could be measured in animals under controlled conditions.

### Johne's disease and similar infections

An intractable and progressive diarrhoea resulting in emaciation and death, due to a bacterium related to the tubercule bacillus and known as Johne's bacillus, has been a subject of much research in many countries. Long-term work in the Compton Isolation Compound confirmed that resistance was strikingly age-related. The clinical disease which developed in adult cattle could not be produced unless they were infected while calves under six months old. The interest and expertise on Johne's disease led to work on related organisms within the group, the mycobacteria, which are widely distributed in nature, an example being the mycobacteria found in wood pigeons with avian tuberculosis. Several hundred strains were isolated from wild life and a system of classification devised in conjunction with the Public Health Laboratory Service and other medical laboratories. Many of the strains were "atypical mycobacteria"; like the Johne's organism, their growth required a factor known as mycobactin. These strains appeared to be intermediate in type between avian tuberculosis and Johne's disease mycobacteria.

## Respiratory diseases

These infections are a major difficulty for the industry and a complex problem for research workers. Many different micro-organisms, including a number of different viruses, mycoplasmas and bacteria are associated with them and environmental factors such as temperature, humidity, dust, and rate of air change, play a part. There is continuing controversy about the essential components of the "cause" but it is certainly multifactorial and very probably made up of different components in different outbreaks so that control by vaccination is unusually difficult and vaccines so far produced have had very limited success. It is essential to determine the most harmful organisms; the provision at Compton of gnotobiotic calves, that is, calves born and reared so as to be free of all micro-organisms and antibodies was a major advance since the effect of a particular organism, or of controlled mixtures, could be assessed and decisions made on the best components for a protective vaccine. The Institute developed monovalent vaccines containing killed antigenic material from each of four organisms, two mycoplasmas and two viruses. Laboratory trials are now proceeding with a polyvalent vaccine, which contains all four components, with the object of preventing colonisation of the respiratory tract by any of these pathogens. One of the components is of a novel kind, consisting of cultured cells carrying virus antigens. During the respiratory disease programme, Compton scientists made two important discoveries. They made the first isolations of *Mycoplasma bovis* in France and in Britain and they were the first to discover that there are viruses which infect mycoplasmas.

During a series of unusually severe outbreaks caused by infectious bovine rhinotracheitis virus in northern Britain in 1978, the Moredun Institute in Edinburgh examined strains of virus present in Britain before and after that year. As serological methods were not adequate, the relatively new technique of restriction enzyme analysis of viral DNA was used and showed that the recent outbreaks were due to strains not previously present in Britain and which had come from overseas. DNA analysis is also being applied to decide whether vaccinated animals can become latent carriers of field virus.

The Moredun and Rowett Institutes have investigated malignant catarrhal fever, a fatal disease of cattle and deer believed to be caused by a virus circulating in sheep, in which it causes no obvious disease. The infection in deer has recently been shown to be transmissible experimentally to rabbits; this should allow the precise nature of the virus to be determined and a study made of the epidemiology of this interesting disease.

## Diarrhoea in calves due to viruses

Diarrhoea or "scours", which causes much trouble to calf-rearers, is of several types, but "white scour" from some strains of *E. coli* is still the major problem. In the late 1960s, however, evidence accumulated that viruses are also important and could account for outbreaks in which bacteria could not be incriminated. Compton is in the forefront of this research and using gnotobiotic calves has shown that certain viruses are primary pathogens, damaging intestinal cells and reducing absorption of nutrients. These viruses include coronaviruses and rotaviruses, and a virus of the calicivirus group discovered by Compton workers and named the "Newbury agent". The success of this work was largely due to good electron microscopy and tissue culture, as well as to using gnotobiotic calves. The viruses were originally very difficult to grow in tissue culture but, nevertheless, the Institute workers succeeded in doing so. Current work on the immunology of these viruses shows the disease can be serious in single-suckled beef herds if calves exposed to the virus do not continuously receive an adequate amount of specific antibody in their milk. The efficacy of vaccinating the mothers during pregnancy to stimulate secretion of antibody into the milk is being examined in conjunction with workers at the Moredun Institute.

## Salmonella infections

Enteritis in calves caused by salmonellae is important and Compton research workers are working to produce a better vaccine than those now available. The experimental vaccine uses killed organisms administered intra-dermally; it is non-toxic and promises earlier protection. A better vaccine would reduce the need for antibiotics and alleviate the problem of transmissible antibiotic resistance in salmonellae. Cows which are carriers are important in the epidemiology of salmonellosis and Compton has shown that susceptibility to infection is greatly increased by liver fluke infestation; if such animals are exposed to salmonellae a high proportion become carriers and the mechanism of this and of other predisposing factors is being investigated. The Institute has shown that 11% of slurry samples from dairy herds and 23% of samples from pig units contained salmonellae. Subsequent work showed that slurry should be stored for at least one month before application to pasture and then another month allowed to elapse before grazing.

## Mastitis

One or other of the various forms of mastitis has always been a major problem for dairy farmers. Milking cows twice a day means that the ends of their teats are frequently contaminated by bacteria, which can cause mastitis on entering the udder. Machine milking and hand milking can both spread infection. Machines have the advantage that under good management they can be effectively disinfected, but mechanical problems, such as fluctuating vacuum, favour the entry of bacteria into the udder. Changes in farming methods result in different organisms becoming important and continual research is needed to keep mastitis at a tolerable level.

An early major advance was demonstrating the value of hygiene; Compton work contributed by drawing attention to infection spreading from cow to cow and the danger of carrier cows. At an early stage the possibilities for mastitis control by antibiotics were explored. Penicillin recovered from the urine of patients in Oxford was a successful treatment in experiments at Compton for mastitis caused by *Streptococcus agalactiae*, the predominant mastitis pathogen in the 1930s and 1940s. Collapsible tubes for injecting intramammary preparations were first developed in this work.

Research in the 1950s and 1960s concentrated on the form of staphylococcal mastitis which is not predominantly a clinical disease but which often produces subclinical inflammation with a raised white cell count and reduced milk yield in half the cows in a herd. The National Institute for Research in Dairying devised and proved a practical, economic control method through developing an understanding of the dynamics of infection levels in herds and by recognising that, of the available methods, the key to control was to reduce the exposure to pathogens and use antibiotic therapy more effectively. The practical methods developed reduced the sources of mastitis pathogens, the bacterial transfer from cow to cow, and the bacterial contamination of the teat skin. In large experiments on commercial farms these methods reduced the new infection rates by up to 65%, and post-milking teat disinfection provided the most important component. To reduce levels of infection within a year the duration of infections had to be reduced and this was achieved through antibiotic therapy given to all cows when drying off. In a major field experiment with the Ministry's Central Veterinary Laboratory at Weybridge the combined routine of hygiene and antibiotic therapy reduced levels of infection by 70%; this is now the recommended method of controlling mastitis in most dairying countries. Recent investigations are into the ways in which milking machines influence the transfer of pathogens during milking and induce bacterial penetration of the teat duct, pointing to modifications in the design of milking machines needed to reduce the new infection rate. These new machines have been promising in small scale trials and are now being tested in field experiments.

Problems due to "environmental organisms" such as coliforms have increased recently. Coliform mastitis, mainly affecting housed cows when there is much exposure of their teats to the faeces carrying the bacteria is an acute disease which can be fatal especially at calving. Compton work has shown that at this time parts of the defence mechanisms of the cow are weaker than at mid-lactation. Research at Shinfield has shown that sawdust bedding, inadequate housing and poor hygiene at milking, contribute to outbreaks; the relationships between exposure to coliform bacteria, hygiene, and the role of the milking machine are being investigated.

Other Compton work showed that anti-microbial factors are secreted into the milk and that a marked rise in concentration can be induced by injecting certain substances such as the lipopolysaccharide of *E. coli*. These anti-microbial factors may be related to genetic influences as the Institute has found, from examining stud data, that some bulls seem to transmit either susceptibility or resistance to mastitis to their daughters. Some years ago mice were infected with bovine mastitis organisms. The mouse model has proved useful for investigating the effect of treatments on infections; it has shown, for the first time, that mastitis pathogens can be present in milk-secreting cells as well as in white blood cells; this observation is important in understanding relapsing cases.

## Production diseases

This term was introduced by Compton workers to describe certain metabolic disorders which occur when the demands of production outstrip the supply of nutrients in the diet and the animal is unable to compensate by mobilizing body reserves. The usual result is that the level of one or more blood constituents becomes abnormal; beyond a certain point this indicates impending disease or loss of production. The outward manifestations vary considerably. Sometimes, notably in the acute grass staggers which occurs when blood magnesium falls sharply, cows go suddenly into tetany and convulsions and die within hours or even minutes; often finding one or more dead cows is the first sign of an outbreak. At the other extreme, as in some trace element deficiencies, the only outward sign is a check to weight gain. There is considerable overlap between the concepts of "disease" and "nutrition" and these paragraphs should be read in conjunction with the essay by Sir Kenneth Blaxter on Animal Nutrition.

Compton workers have done much to quantify the input/output relationships of certain body processes and they developed the Compton Metabolic Profile Test which has proved useful in herds with an ill-defined loss of production, not elucidated by the usual diagnostic approaches. Blood samples are analysed for a number of constituents and the results are printed as a histogram showing deviations from the mean values for the population. Interpreting this "profile" forms a basis for diagnosis and control. For example, the test often reveals an unexpected high incidence of low blood glucose and albumin concentrations. These may result from excessive accumulation of fat in the liver; cows with more than 30% of their liver occupied by fat frequently take more than 400 days between calvings.

Ketosis is a production disease on which Compton has made considerable practical contributions. In the 1960s, it was accepted that if the diet did not contain sufficient readily available carbohydrate to sustain milk yield in early lactation, the cow used its own body tissues, producing ketone bodies in the process. Compton work showed a high protein diet made matters worse and from existing knowledge, staff put forward a "10-point plan" for preventing ketosis which was taken up by the Advisory Services.

Sub-optimal growth in young cattle is sometimes due to a combined deficiency of copper and selenium; supplementation with these two elements markedly improved growth in Compton experiments. Obtaining sufficiently long-lasting supplementation is difficult, therefore water-soluble glasses which contain measured quantities of trace elements such as copper, selenium or iodine are being tested; pellets implanted beneath the skin slowly dissolve and release the elements over 3–4 months.

Hypomagnesaemia is an important nutritional disorder which is referred to in the essay on Animal Nutrition. The acute form of the disorder was a particular problem in the 1950s in dairy cows turned out from winter feed on to the rapidly-growing (and often heavily fertilized) spring grass grown to provide "early bite" to boost the milk yield of winter-calved cows. The concentration of magnesium in the spring grass was somewhat less than in the winter feed but the difference could not account for the characteristic very rapid and severe fall in blood magnesium. In the late 1950s scientists at the National Institute for Research in Dairying considerably advanced our understanding by producing experimental evidence showing that whilst the magnesium content of the herbage was not unusually low it was often linked with a low herbage dry matter intake and poor utilisation of the magnesium. These three factors in combination explained the rapid development of the low blood magnesium levels. Moredun Institute workers during 1958 and 1959 found that clinical grass tetany was most frequent on pastures where herbage was high in potassium and low in magnesium and sodium. This was consistent with Dutch results and is useful for predicting outbreaks of the disorder.

## Anabolic steroids

These substances have been used in human medicine either to improve protein metabolism of debilitated people or to improve muscular development in athletes; they have similar effects in animals. Compton experiments showed that calves given implants of anabolic steroids grew 20% faster than controls because protein was used more efficiently. There are important applications in beef production but using anabolic steroids to speed growth in dairy heifers is dangerous as they become masculinised, show delayed puberty, poor fertility, trouble at calving and poor milk yields. In addition, the public is concerned that anabolic steroids could be hazardous if residues remain in animal products; to aid in assessing risks Compton has developed new radioimmunassays, capable of detecting very low levels in meat and milk. These are now widely applied to monitor compliance with the different legislative requirements of several countries.

## Sheep Diseases

Most research on sheep diseases in the Agricultural Research Service is at the Moredun Institute of the Animal Diseases Research Association in Edinburgh. The programme started in 1922 with the appointments by the Association of Professor S. H. Gaiger

*Plate 1* A field laboratory of the Animal Diseases Research Association which toured Scotland studying sheep diseases in the 1930s.

and Mr. T. Dalling (later Sir Thomas Dalling); originally they had facilities at the Glasgow Veterinary School because there were no institute laboratories available. Gaiger and Dalling immediately started to work on two important and fatal diseases of sheep, braxy and lamb dysentery. Within a few years they had shown that braxy was caused by a member of the clostridia, the group to which the gas gangrene bacteria belong, and that it could be controlled by immunization. They then discovered that lamb dysentery was caused by a similar organism (*Clostridium welchii perfringens*); Dalling and co-workers subsequently developed preventive measures by inoculating lambs with antitoxic serum or by active immunisation of ewes with a formalised vaccine. Plate 1 shows the mobile laboratory used by the Moredun Institute in its early research.

## Vaccine production

Part of the early work of the institute was preparing vaccines and sera which were sold directly to farmers. This continued during the 1930s, even after the establishment of the Agricultural Research Council in 1931; and as late as 1950 braxy vaccine was being produced by the Moredun Institute. The sophisticated multi-component clostridial vaccines available today from the pharmaceutical companies owe much to the early achievements of the scientists within the Agricultural Research Service besides those of commercial organisations. Without these vaccines, many modern methods of sheep husbandry would not be practicable; clostridial organisms have not been eliminated and constant immunisation against them is essential. In special circumstances the Moredun Institute still has a part in making vaccines. A recent example has been production of the inactivated viral antigen developed at the Institute as the basis of an improved vaccine against louping ill.

## Respiratory diseases

As with cattle, respiratory diseases are important in sheep management, but the organisms are different. Research at Moredun during the last ten years showed that in lambs infection with a respiratory virus, parainfluenza type 3, followed several days later by infection with *Pasteurella haemolytica* results in severe, or fatal, pneumonia. This work, requiring specially-bred pathogen-free lambs, shows how the disease develops and provides facilities for checking the efficacy of vaccines against pasteurella organisms. The research has also led to a polyvalent vaccine (against several strains) for pasteurella pneumonia and the National Research Development Corporation has filed a patent; commercial development has now been taken up by a pharmaceutical firm and further improvement is being done jointly with the Moredun Institute. Other respiratory diseases being investigated by the Institute include jaagsiekte or pulmonary adenomatosis, a contagious tumour of the lungs of sheep. Two viruses play a part in the disease, one is primary while the other is probably a "trigger" factor.

## Enteritis

Enteric infections cause much illness and death in young animals. In diagnostic investigations into field outbreaks of enteritis in lambs the Moredun Institute found that viruses, subsequently named rotaviruses and astroviruses, were involved; this work is complementary to that in calves at Compton. The Moredun Institute has clarified the conditions under which the viruses cause disease in lambs and has developed diagnostic tests. An important advance was in showing that vaccinating ewes during pregnancy can result in sufficient antibody in the milk to protect the lambs. Another organism which causes enteritis, and which Moredun has reported for the first time in Britain, is cryptosporidium.

## Abortion

Abortion has always been a problem in sheep but serious outbreaks in the 1950s showed the need for control measures. Research initiated by Dr. J. T. Stamp when he was Veterinary Investigation Officer of Edinburgh and the East of Scotland, and continued after he became Director of the Moredun Institute, demonstrated that the organism responsible, a member of the chlamydia, causes enzootic abortion of ewes, known to farmers as "kebbing". The Moredun work led to a successful vaccine being produced; but some research continues because of variations in strain-type.

Other forms of abortion include border disease, vibrionic abortion and toxoplasmosis; their epidemiology and control are being investigated. Border disease is now known to be a virus infection which generally causes no illness in the ewe, but damages the developing foetus which may be aborted or may develop into a lamb with tremor or spasm and an abnormal birth coat. This virus is related to those causing mucosal disease in cattle and swine fever. The Moredun Institute has shown that affected lambs can carry the virus for long periods and may infect susceptible sheep or cattle that are in contact. During 1979 the Institute showed that border disease virus can be transmitted by semen. A vaccine for vibrionic abortion has been developed by the Institute and although the disease is not common enough in UK to encourage commercial development of the vaccine there is keen interest in New Zealand where the disease causes significant losses. Another serious cause of abortion and perinatal lamb loss is infection with the organism *Toxoplasma gondii*; its epidemiology and pathology are being investigated by Moredun in collaboration with the Edinburgh Veterinary Investigation

Centre. This organism is immunosupressive during the acute phase of the infection and lowers the resistance of the host sheep to other infections such as louping ill.

## Louping ill

Diseases of the nervous system of sheep are important and the Moredun Institute has investigated the particularly.troublesome problem of louping ill for many years. In 1931 transmission by ticks was demonstrated and it was shown that louping ill was a separate disease from tick-borne fever. Within a few years a vaccine prepared from the brains of infected sheep proved valuable in combatting the disease. Later modifications of this vaccine have been introduced; the one now available was developed by J. G. Brotherston and J. B. Boyce at the Moredun Institute. This is a much improved vaccine made by purifying and concentrating louping ill virus grown in tissue culture instead of in infected sheep brain.

## Parasites

One of the biggest problems of sheep rearing has always been parasitic infestations. Recently the anthelminthics available to control internal parasites have been much improved but sub-clinical parasitism is still a substantial problem. We need accurate information on the adverse effects of low levels of worm infestation and on the biochemical markers of the damage; Moredun work confirms and extends earlier research at the Grassland Research Institute and shows that even at levels too low to cause diarrhoea, or loss of body condition, there can be lost production. Indoor feeding experiments showed decreased voluntary intake of feed, reduced efficiency of feed conversion, and decreased absorption of phosphorus and amino acids, resulting in slower growth and poorly mineralised thin bones. Continued investigations with grazing lambs suggest there are similar problems on grassland.

## Copper deficiency

Swayback in sheep is referred to in the essay on Animal Nutrition. In spite of satisfactory control by copper supplements it was for a time doubtful whether the disorder was due to copper deficiency alone because the copper concentrations in pastures, and in the blood of pregnant ewes, were only poorly correlated with swayback in lambs. However, work at the Rowett Research Institute showed that swayback could be produced by feeding a copper antagonist, molybdenum, which occurs in many feedstuffs and which reduces the amount of copper absorbed by the ewe; Moredun work showed that a semi-purified diet of very low copper content produced the disease. Subsequently one key factor in the pathogenesis of swayback was found to be a low level of the copper-containing enzyme, cytochrome oxidase, in nerve cells; the roles of other enzyme systems depending on copper now merit investigation. The reason why swayback occurred in spite of normal pasture copper content was explained when the Moredun Institute showed that in autumn the absorbability of copper from herbage was poor and was lowered still further by small increases in molybdenum concentrations, such as those produced by liming or by soil contamination of the herbage grazed from sparse pastures.

Swayback is not the only manifestation of copper deficiency in sheep. The Hill Farming Research Organisation has shown that slow growth, poor fleeces and weak bones can occur in lambs on improved hill pastures where herbage contains too little copper. New methods of control are being investigated by this Institute and the

Moredun. Cupric oxide formed as rods or needles, and given by mouth, stays in the fourth stomach and slowly releases copper. A single dose is as effective as several copper injections.

## Scrapie

This disease, a fatal degeneration of the central nervous system of sheep and goats, has been a subject of great interest for many years to scientists throughout the world. Research on scrapie is done at three Institutes — Moredun, Compton and the Animal Breeding Research Organisation; some of the results from this work are summarised here.

Scrapie is caused by a transmissible agent with very unusual properties; because the disease has a very long incubation period it is included in the group of "slow virus" diseases. The agent is very small, does not stimulate an immune response by the host, and has great resistance to heat and to chemical disinfectants. Both the transmissibility of the agent and the genetic constitution of the host are important. Investigations involving both natural disease and experimental infections with specific strains have shown that it is usually acquired by transmission of the agent from ewe to lamb, but long-term breeding experiments with Herdwick, Swaledale and Cheviot sheep have produced lines of resistant sheep. This resistance is, however, unusual because it is due not to an ability of the host to prevent invasion by the agent but to prolonging the already long incubation period. Experiments show that the length of incubation is controlled by a single gene, the influence of which is sufficiently strong to make it appear that certain lines of sheep are genetically resistant. An important point is that while there may be prolonged incubation "resistance" to certain strains of scrapie agent, there may be the opposite effect with other strains. These results are consistent with continuing the recommended policy for minimising the spread of scrapie by rigorous culling of affected lineages, particularly the progeny of affected ewes.

In the 1960s a major advance was made when scrapie was transmitted to mice. For the first time it became possible to make accurate measurements of infectivity by quantitative assay in mice and most of our knowledge about the agent, and about the pathogenesis of the disease, dates from this time. In some combinations of agent strain, and inbred mouse, incubation period exceeds the life span of the mouse. This extreme slowness is intriguing because it occurs in the absence of an immune response; it seems to be due to the very small number of replication sites in the host. This may be a basis for control because we now know that different strains compete with one another; if a non-pathogenic strain of scrapie could be found it might be used to block the replication sites. Good use has been made of the genetic variation which both host and agent show. Using inbred mice as the fixed variable, the strain-types of the various scrapie agents can be determined by observing the effect on the host, particularly on the central nervous system.

Some of the "slow viruses" affect animals and others affect man. There is interest among medical scientists that scrapie may provide an insight into the way that some types of degeneration of the human nervous system develop and into the changes which occur in the body infected with slow viruses.

## Pig Diseases

While the Agricultural Research Service Institutes have been somewhat less involved with pig diseases than with diseases of other species, Compton has done important work on several topics where institute facilities have been useful. The Ministry of

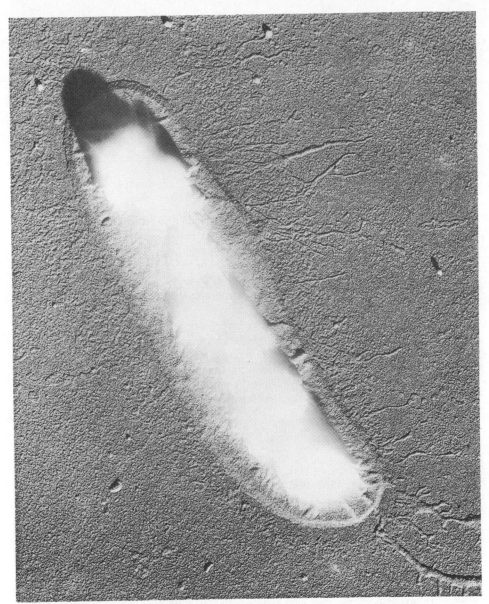

*Plate 2* The K88 antigen — a fibrillar structure on the surface of *Escherichia coli*, that is frequently associated with neonatal diarrhoea in piglets.

Agriculture's Laboratory at Weybridge has for many years had a strong department of pig pathology and the veterinary schools have also pursued several important topics, often with ARC grant-support.

## E. coli diarrhoea in piglets

This disease causes much loss in piglets. Certain strains of *E. coli* carry an adhesive factor known as K88 which enables the bacteria to adhere to the gut surface where they multiply and cause inflammation (Plate 2 is a relevant illustration). Compton workers produced a vaccine which, given to the sow, stimulates her to secrete in her colostrum and milk antibodies which specifically react with the K88 factor and so protect the piglets. Vaccines are now available commercially. During this programme the Institute developed a test, the brush border test, to show the presence of the adhesive factor and in carrying out this test became aware that in addition to the already-known absence of the K88 adhesive factor in some strains of *E. coli* there was also an absence of receptor sites to this factor in the intestinal cells of certain pigs. They then found that this was an inherited feature and in experiments with the Compton pig herd they showed that pigs can be bred which are homozygous resistant or homozygous susceptible. This work is now being extended into the field and promises to be a good example of the control of an animal disease by genetic means.

## Swine dysentery

This disease has recently become increasingly serious and widespread and is checked mainly by continuous medication of feed, which is expensive in the short-term and in the long-term carries the risk of the emergence of resistant strains and other problems. It has been known for some time that an organism of the spirochaete group is associated with field cases but that other organisms are also involved. Compton workers using gnotobiotic pigs confirmed that the spirochaete alone does not cause the disease but requires the presence of two other organisms.

To obtain better control of the disease one possibility is to eliminate the specific spirochaete from individual herds by high-level medication for a short time and then to prevent re-infection. For this a good diagnostic test is required and research into this is proceeding. Swine dysentery is a disease in which, unfortunately, immunity is weak and even pigs which have recovered from the naturally-occurring disease are easily re-infected; control by vaccination does not at present seem very promising.

## Transmissible gastroenteritis

Transmissible gastroenteritis (TGE) appeared suddenly in pigs in Britain and caused considerable losses in the 1960s and early 1970s. As the virus had never been adequately characterised, physicochemical work was started at Compton and this showed that the virus, having an outer lipid envelope with large petal-shaped surface projections, was a typical member of the Coronavirus family. The protein constituents of the virus were separated and it became clear that the only one necessary to induce immunity in pigs was the glycopolypeptide which makes up the petal-shaped projections. This polypeptide was an effective vaccine in young pigs but unfortunately, when inoculated into sows, it did not stimulate them to produce enough colostral or milk antibody to protect the piglets. It was also shown that cats can be infected with the TGE virus and may be involved in spreading the disease.

## Atrophic rhinitis

This infection has become increasingly important in the UK during the past 15 years. It causes changes in the facial bones and slow growth in young pigs, and economic losses to pig producers because of the effect on growth rates and also of the high cost of antibiotic treatment. Long-term medication carries the additional disadvantage that antibiotic-resistance sometimes develops in the bacteria. The precise cause of field outbreaks has still to be defined although most consider that the bacterium *Bordetella bronchiseptica* is principally involved. Compton workers have shown that *B. bronchiseptica* is present in most pig herds, including many without atrophic rhinitis. Experimental infections have shown that the rhinitis caused by *B. bronchiseptica* alone is relatively mild and transitory and that strains of the organism from herds which are affected with atrophic rhinitis do not cause lesions more severe than those caused by strains from herds which do not have the clinical disease. These results show that other factors are involved in the chronic, progressive field disease and work is continuing to define them and to devise control measures.

## Poultry Diseases

The Institute mainly concerned with poultry disease is the Houghton Poultry Research Station which was founded in 1948 by the Animal Health Trust; it became a State-aided institute in 1956, and since 1971 has been financed by ARC. The Station is well equipped and has high-quality isolation accommodation so that birds can be kept free from accidental infections.

### Marek's disease

Notable achievements by Houghton were to isolate and identify the agent of Marek's disease of poultry and to develop a vaccine. This disease causes tumours composed of white blood cells and was for long the main cause of loss to the poultry industries of many countries. The loss in the UK in the late 1960s was estimated at £10–15M annually; this was reduced by 80% through vaccination based on work at Houghton. In the USA a special laboratory was set up at East Lansing to study the avian leukosis complex, the group of diseases of which Marek's disease, under its original name of fowl paralysis, was thought to be one particular manifestation. In 1959 the ARC recognised that good isolation facilities were needed to speed up research on this intractable problem and established the Leukosis Experimental Unit at Houghton. Good progress was made, and the condition known as fowl paralysis was shown to be transmissible and a specific entity. It was named Marek's disease after the Hungarian who had originally described fowl paralysis. When "acute leukosis" appeared in Britain in 1965 Houghton workers showed it to be an acute form of Marek's disease, and in 1967 they grew the agent in tissue culture and showed it belonged to the herpesvirus group. They showed further that Marek's disease virus was itself the agent which produced the tumours and did not merely activate a latent RNA tumour virus. These were important results, not only to poultry keepers, but also because this was the first demonstration that tumours could be caused by a herpesvirus, a finding relevant to several tumours in man. The Houghton team grew the virus by repeated passages in cell culture until it was no longer pathogenic but was still able to produce immunity and so produced the first vaccine against a tumour-producing disease. This vaccine, and the related turkey herpesvirus vaccine from the USA, were used to vaccinate commercial flocks and reduced the disease so that it is no longer a problem to the poultry industry.

### Genetic resistance to tumour viruses

Houghton workers showed that it was practicable to select birds which are genetically resistant to lymphoid leukosis. Using inbred lines of birds maintained at the station they showed that the genetically determined resistance could be demonstrated in chick embryos and in embryonic cells in culture and that these techniques could be used to identify resistant birds. Similar techniques were shown to apply to another tumour virus of chickens, Rous sarcoma virus. These results are not only of commercial value but they make an important contribution to understanding genetic susceptibility and resistance to virus-induced tumours.

## Leukosis in turkeys

This problem has also been clarified by experiments at Houghton showing that there are two distinct transmissible diseases, now named lymphoproliferative disease or LPD, and lymphoid leukosis. Both are caused by viruses belonging to the family known as retroviradae. Little more is known about the causative virus of LPD, except that it is distinct from the causative virus of lymphoid leukosis, which is a member of the well-established reticuloendotheliosis virus group. The latter virus can be transmitted via eggs and by the semen of turkey stags during the phase of the disease when the virus is circulating in the bloodstream.

## Turkey syndrome '65 (TS'65)

This disease, causing poor growth and leg deformities in young turkeys, was recognised as an important problem in the UK in 1965 and was investigated by a working party chaired by the Director of Houghton. Blood samples from affected birds showed serum protein patterns which suggested that an infectious agent was involved and experiments showed that a condition indistinguishable from the TS'65 syndrome could be reproduced in young turkeys by infecting them with certain strains of mycoplasmae. The experimentally infected poults showed changes in the serum protein pattern similar to those observed in field outbreaks. This discovery gave added impetus to the mycoplasma eradication programme which, besides eliminating diseases such as TS'65, has resulted in a general improvement in health and productivity.

## Salmonellae in poultry

In contrast to the situation in cattle which are affected by clinical disease, the present-day problem with poultry is that they are the most important source of the salmonellae which cause bacterial food poisoning in man, salmonella organisms in the intestinal tracts of the birds being transmitted via their carcasses to people. Feed additives have important effects on the intestinal bacteria during the life of the birds. As a result of the 1971 implementation of the Swann Report on the use of antibiotics in animal husbandry, antibiotics used in human and animal medicine were no longer permitted as growth promoters in animals and a new range of antibiotics was substituted. Houghton workers studied these and other additives employed in the poultry industry to see their effect on the faecal excretion of salmonella organisms by poultry. Probably because they suppress the multiplication of salmonella-antagonising organisms in the alimentary tract, some of the antibiotics were found to have the deleterious effect of greatly increasing the numbers of salmonella organisms excreted and the duration of their excretion.

## Coccidiosis

This disease has long been a major problem in poultry-keeping. The coccidia are protozoan parasites which enter intestinal cells and, if not controlled, may cause a severe enteritis which, with two species, results in haemorrhagic diarrhoea and can cause severe losses. Generally, intensive poultry keeping would be impossible without continuous medication but a disadvantage is the problem of drug-resistance; workers at Houghton have found that in laboratory experiments strains resistant to most of the drugs in common use can develop relatively easily. Investigating strains obtained from the field has revealed that resistance is very common, so a programme to control coccidiosis by immunisation is being pursued. Institute scientists have adapted, by repeated passage, three species of coccidia to grow in chick embryos and these modified strains no longer produce disease but still provoke an immune response. Administering these attenuated strains in conjunction with low doses of pathogenic strains is giving promising results and vaccination may prove commercially feasible for protecting laying, breeding and possibly broiler flocks.

Because several species of coccidia parasitise the chicken, useful information on the general subject of immunity to intestinal parasites is being obtained. It has recently been found that immunity is specific to the species and even the strain of the parasite, and to a particular stage in its life cycle, and that immunity protects by arresting the development of the invasive stage. The Houghton workers demonstrated that chickens secrete an immunoglobulin which seems to be the avian analogue of IgA, the locally produced antibody of mammals. This material was found to be present in egg white, suggesting that this kind of antibody is maternally transmitted by birds as well as by mammals.

Electrophoresis of the enzymes of coccidia has been developed into a technique that permits precise identification of different species. The enzyme patterns of each species are unique and, unlike most of the characters previously used for identification, are not influenced by the different environmental conditions to which the parasites may be exposed.

## Effects of rapeseed meal

Rapeseed (*Brassica napus*) is an important source of oil and protein for human and animal foods and production is increasing rapidly in Europe with encouragement from the EEC. Unfortunately rapeseed meal has undesirable effects when included in poultry diets to provide protein. Until the factors responsible have been identified and preventive measures are available the use of the meal for this purpose, and the economic advantage that can be gained, will be severely restricted. Laying hens suffer from thyroid hypertrophy and liver haemorrhage and the eggs from certain breeds and individuals have a "crabby" or "fishy" taint due to the presence of trimethylamine. Tainting is caused by a drastic reduction in the hen's capacity for metabolising trimethylamine due to the adverse effect of certain constituents of rapeseed meal on trimethylamine oxidase. One of the other constituents of rapeseed has been identified as 5-vinyl-2-oxazolidinethione which is a potent goitrogen. Susceptibility is inherited through trimethylamine oxidase and a biochemical technique has been developed for identifying the genotypes among young males and females so that the character can be bred out from commercial flocks.

## Fatty liver and kidney syndrome (FLKS)

In the early 1970s the UK broiler industry lost about £1M annually because of this newly-recognised disease. Birds died within a few hours of showing the first symptoms and their livers and kidneys contained abnormally large amounts of fat. Scientists at the Poultry Research Centre, Edinburgh, discovered that FLKS could be induced by the type of poultry diet which is high in wheat or barley and low in the vitamin, biotin. They then showed that unless a biotin supplement is given, carbohydrate and fat metabolism become disordered and fat is deposited in the liver and kidneys. The Poultry Research Centre's recommendation that diets for broilers up to four weeks of age should be supplemented with biotin has been taken up by the industry with the result that FLKS has been virtually eliminated.

# Plasmids in Bacteria

Plasmids are DNA molecules which are not integrated into the main genome. They can be transmitted from one bacterium to another by contact and recent work shows they are very important in certain bacteria of the gastrointestinal tract.

## Antibiotic-resistance plasmids

Houghton scientists observed that diets containing tetracyclines fed to pigs and chickens in the UK gave rise to enormous populations of *Escherichia coli* organisms possessing transmissible tetracycline resistance. A high incidence of transmissible resistance to several antibiotics was found in pathogenic *E. coli* and other entero-bacteria. Under certain conditions, antibiotic resistance could be transferred in epidemic form between bacteria in the alimentary tract of chickens and calves. By contrast, experiments on a human volunteer with the K12 strain of *E. coli*, the strain most commonly used in genetic manipulation research, showed that the rate of transfer of plasmids from K12 was very small. This observation, together with others involving this strain, has substantially contributed to the current view that *E. coli* K12 is, within reason, safe to use in genetic manipulation research. In other studies at Houghton chloramphenicol-resistance plasmids in *Salmonella typhi* transferred much more efficiently at temperatures below 37°C, the normal temperature of human beings; this suggests that these resistant strains had acquired their plasmids outside the human body, possibly from sewage organisms.

## Pathogenic plasmids

Fruitful research has also been done on the plasmids that confer pathogenic properties. Some strains of *E. coli* contain plasmids known as K88 (see page 265) and K99 which enable the bacteria to produce an adhesive substance by which they stick to the surface of the gut and resist being swept away in the gut contents. One of the other important plasmids is named Ent because it controls the production of enterotoxin, a diarrhoea-producing substance. Strains of *E. coli* that possess both an adhesive plasmid and the Ent plasmid adhere to the gut wall and cause the coliform diarrhoea which is a major source of loss of farm livestock. Bacteriologists at Houghton have played a leading part in discovering these plasmids, and also others, notably those which enable *E. coli* to resist more effectively the defence mechanisms of the host.

The studies of the plasmids important in farm animals have stimulated workers in the human field to examine the *E. coli* that cause diarrhoea in human beings. They also found plasmids that enable these organisms to proliferate in the small intestine and produce a diarrhoea-provoking substance.

# Research on Diseases Exotic to Britain

This group of infectious diseases, of which foot-and-mouth disease is the best example, occur at any particular time in several countries, but not normally in Britain. Because they are infectious, highly damaging to the animal economy, and difficult and expensive to eradicate if they become established, the Ministry of Agriculture, Fisheries and Food makes special efforts to keep them out of the UK by stringent regulations. Research using the viruses of these diseases is also subject to stringent regulations, and, except for rabies, all work on these diseases is done in the restricted area of the Animal Virus Research Institute at Pirbright, Surrey.

This Institute began as the research establishment of the Foot-and-Mouth Disease Committee of the Ministry of Agriculture in 1924 and nearly thirty years later became part of the Agricultural Research Service, as a grant-aided Institute of the ARC in 1956. During this time good virological research was established and expertise developed on containment of viruses, both in laboratories and in experimental animals. Rapid progress has been made in the last twenty-five years and the Institute has a world-wide reputation as a centre for fundamental virus research. Studying diseases which are a hazard to this country helps to protect the livestock industry against invasion by exotic viruses and, should an invasion occur, provides a sound basis for control.

Exotic viruses diseases have a remarkable capacity for spread, not only between herds but also between countries and continents. Many diseases originally confined to small areas are now recognised as having a much wider distribution; several have spread as epidemics in hitherto unaffected areas. This wider distribution is often due to agricultural improvement in developing countries, with associated movement of animals in introducing new breeds and increasing exports of animal products. These new problems are likely to be as difficult to solve as were, for example, the control and eradication of rinderpest and foot-and-mouth disease. Because of these world-wide changes, even in a country such as Britain research is needed on diseases which are a potential threat. Control authorities need information to establish a programme to prevent importation of disease and deal with outbreaks, should they arise. Costs of controlling newly-imported disease can be high. Swine vesicular disease was estimated to cost about £20 million between 1972 and 1976 and might have had even more serious effects had research not been in progress on the virus and its pathogenicity.

## Foot-and-mouth disease

The major outbreak of foot-and-mouth disease of 1922–23, which led to setting up the research establishment of the Foot-and-Mouth Disease Committee, showed that there was little sound information on such problems as dissemination of the virus, its transfer from farm to farm, and disinfecting premises after slaughter and destroying carcasses. The earliest research was therefore on these applied topics to support the control measures of the Ministry of Agriculture. The extraordinary capacity of the virus to survive on contaminated materials such as hay and straw, and on the surfaces of farm buildings, was established and linked to the risks from livestock transporters and from contaminated pens at markets. Disinfecting by alkaline solutions such as washing soda was shown to be much more effective than traditional farm disinfectants. Preliminary experiments on vaccination and chemotherapy were attempted, with discouraging results, but the foundations were laid for studies of the disease in cattle under experimental conditions and for the search for small animals to be used as model hosts. The various regulations introduced as a result of work at Pirbright undoubtedly contributed to limiting the practical effects of the disease in Britain.

Outbreaks of foot-and-mouth disease, however, continued and the repeated cases led to arguments on whether the disease was endemic. The efficiency of the slaughter and disinfection policy, and the patterns of new outbreaks, many of which did not spread from the initial focus of infection, indicated that the disease was being re-introduced more or less often from abroad. Two sources were implicated. Meat from South America, of which more than 400 000 tons were imported annually, came from an endemic area and in spite of supervision might from time to time bring virus. Work at Pirbright clearly showed that virus could survive in carcasses and offal. The disease was also prevalent in Europe and some periods of increased incidence in Britain could be linked to major epidemics there. We now realise from recent studies at Pirbright and elsewhere, that airborne infection from Europe could have been responsible, although at the time carriage by migrating birds seemed likely.

The scope of the programme broadened in the 1940s. The landmarks were 1) development of quantitative assays of virus by multiple inoculation of dilution series in the bovine tongue (the Henderson method); 2) development of better serological methods for determining strain differences; and 3) the discovery that unweaned mice were susceptible which made possible more accurate quantitative work and led to the development of modified living vaccines. Methods for estimating the potency of vaccines were established and are still used internationally. The studies of viruses in overseas territories led to four new types of virus, in addition to the classical types O, A and C, being described.

The complexity of the antigenic structure of the virus did not end with the type difference, for in 1947 strains of virus of type A from Mexico were shown to vary from the standard A strain used at Pirbright, and also from one another. This variation within a single type was sufficiently great to necessitate the preparation of specific vaccines against the new subtypes for satisfactory practical results to be obtained with vaccines. This finding is of prime importance for foot-and-mouth disease vaccination campaigns throughout the world; although minor differences can be overcome by using high-potency vaccines and giving repeated doses, serious problems do arise when a widely different new variant strain appears.

In the 1950s, as a result of the developments in tissue culture, the possibilities for more intensive investigation of foot-and-mouth disease virus rapidly expanded. Virologists no longer depended on harvesting virus from lesions in animals or on cultures in surviving tissue collected in slaughterhouses. Infecting cell sheets and, later, suspensions of cells in nutrient media, gave good yields of virus and the same cells could be used for plaque assay, by counting of individual foci of infection on cell sheets.

The biochemical study of virus was advanced by labelling both the protein and the nucleic acid of cultured virus and using labelled virus to probe the stages in virus multiplication, and determine the roles of the structural components of virus particles. These studies continue and a biochemical map of the virus ribonucleic acid is being developed which indicates the regions coding for the four main viral proteins. In turn, analysis of these proteins is being correlated with antigenic differences between strains which will open new avenues in research on vaccines. Investigating variation in virus by genetic methods was also greatly helped by developments in tissue culture. Foot-and-mouth disease virus and poliovirus were the first small RNA viruses in which recombination was demonstrated and, with other techniques, recombination has been used to produce a genetic map for foot-and-mouth virus. Correlating the genetic and biochemical maps of the viral genome will greatly advance understanding of viral function.

However, applying tissue culture has provided the most dramatic outcome of research at Pirbright. When the potential of baby hamster kidney cells for producing virus was realised in 1960, great efforts were made to develop cell cultivation on a scale large enough to satisfy commercial requirements. Initially, cells were grown in a thin layer attached to the surfaces in glass bottles; this method was developed commercially, notably in one very large unit in Italy. Later it proved possible to grow cells suspended in nutrient media in glass, and then stainless steel, vessels; once this process was established, commercial development of plants at 5 000 or 10 000-litre scale followed rapidly. Three hundred million doses or more of vaccine are produced yearly in some plants and vaccination campaigns which would have been impossible with older production methods are now operating. Progress in controlling foot-and-mouth disease is now practicable in areas where it was not possible twenty years ago. Some of the results are now becoming apparent; for example, in some South American countries the number of outbreaks decreases annually.

In the United Kingdom the foot-and-mouth disease position began to improve in the early 1960s. The major outbreak of 1967–68 was a serious setback which emphasised the new problems posed by increased density of livestock production and the hazard of wind-borne infection. The Animal Virus Research Institute was involved in much *ad hoc* research on this outbreak and in planning future action if the disease should again appear. Happily, the measures taken to restrict imports to boned meat, and the relative freedom from disease of countries of mainland Europe have kept the United Kingdom free of disease since June 1968.

## Other exotic diseases

As the foot-and-mouth disease situation improved more consideration was given to the risks from other virus diseases of livestock. The facilities at Pirbright are uniquely suitable in the United Kingdom for research on exotic virus diseases and, because of its experience and its multidisciplinary approach, the research team was well qualified to work on such exotic viruses and the Institute now devotes more than one-third of its time to diseases other than foot-and-mouth.

## Rabies

The spread of rabies in wildlife in Europe, and the resulting public concern over the risk to the United Kingdom, gave new impetus to research on better vaccines for both man and animals. Using experience with vesicular stomatitis, a virus which is in the same group as rabies, rapid progress was made in studying the chemistry of rabies virus and an experimental vaccine of high potency was produced. Other research has been on the testing of rabies vaccines, and on the rabies-related viruses which cause problems in several parts of the world.

## African swine fever

African swine fever became endemic in Portugal and Spain from 1958 onwards. Severe forms of the disease kill almost all affected pigs; the less severe form is almost as dangerous since it produces a disease very similar to classical swine fever and it is extremely difficult to eradicate without extensive slaughter of infected and apparently healthy contact pigs. Recently the disease has appeared in Italy, France, Cuba and Malta, from which it has been eradicated by the draconian measures referred to, but it is now present in Sardinia, the Dominican Republic, Haiti and Brazil. In Brazil the extent of the outbreak is unknown but the disease is undoubtedly a new and important problem for the highly-developed pig industry of that country. There is no vaccine and prospects for producing one are not good since it is doubtful whether animals recovered from the infection are immune. Present research plans to clarify immunological aspects of the disease and apply newer biochemical methods to analyse the antigens of the virus.

## Bluetongue

Bluetongue virus, which infects sheep and also cattle, is an insidious agent now known to be present in many countries of the world from the USA, through Africa, to some Asian countries. In Australia one strain has been detected in insects and two other strains have recently been isolated from cattle; antibodies to all three strains have been found in cattle. Further extension of this disease is possible and, because of the frequency of symptomless carriers, new foci will be difficult or impossible to eradicate.

Great efforts must therefore be made to avoid increasing the international range of the disease and to limit its activity where it does occur. Work at Pirbright has extended our knowledge of the distribution of the disease, and the factors responsible for its spread in areas not regularly involved, e.g. in Cyprus. A vaccine has been prepared but its usefulness is not yet clear as there are about twenty serological types, the inter-relationships of which are still obscure.

## Swine vesicular disease

This disease, which first appeared in the United Kingdom in 1972, illustrates well the approach of the Animal Virus Research Institute. The virus was first isolated from an outbreak in Italy in 1966, the disease being localised on two farms. Nevertheless, research was done at Pirbright, in collaboration with the Italian workers, and material was held which allowed the virus to be identified when it next appeared, in Hong Kong in 1970. In 1972, when samples of material from lesions suspected to have been caused by the virus of foot-and-mouth disease were received from Staffordshire, a rapid diagnosis was made using serological methods depending on the sera stored from the Italian study together with biochemical and electron microscopic examination. Advice based on the earlier work with the virus was given to the Ministry of Agriculture, Fisheries and Food and the Institute played an important part in controlling the disease. The insidious nature of swine vesicular disease has led to new outbreaks from time to time but the record of control is at least as good as that for foot-and-mouth disease when it was a regular problem in this country.

## Future

As farming methods change, the types of diseases which affect farm animals are also likely to change. Increased reliance on home-grown feeds for high-yielding animals is a potential cause of multiple mineral and trace element deficiencies and research on monitoring methods and preventive procedures must continue. New organisms, and new strains of the organisms at present causing infectious diseases, are likely to continue to emerge. Infections will continue to move from one part of the world to another, with the additional problem of the movement by aircraft of both infected animals and of insect vectors.

New concepts and technologies offer new prospects. An example is the use of monoclonal antibodies where mouse myeloma cells are fused with sensitized lympho-cytes. The resulting cells produce a population of identical cells all of which produce the antibody to the antigen which was originally used to sensitize the mouse lymphocytes. Very specific pure antibodies will be valuable in differentiating one strain of virus from another closely-related strain; the various enteritis viruses discovered in recent years illustrate this. Monoclonal antibody production is an example of a technique which reduces the use of live animals in scientific work. Although mice are needed to produce the sensitized lymphocytes for the first stage of the process, the antibodies are produced by cells and not by animals as at present.

New methods in biotechnology will use recombinant DNA technology to produce antigen for vaccines. The portion of the virus genome which codes for the immunising protein is identified. It is separated by using the appropriate restriction enzymes and the segment inserted into the DNA of a suitable plasmid which is then introduced into *E. coli*. These bacteria can then be cultured to produce large amounts of immunising protein which is both pure and non-infectious.

Modern techniques can sometimes isolate and concentrate the parts of an organism which produce the antibodies and these are used to produce sub-unit vaccines which are usually both better and safer than the counterpart from the whole organism. The Moredun Institute has developed such a method to make a potent vaccine against the strains of *Pasteurella haemolytica* which cause pneumonia in sheep.

Transmitting antibodies through colostrum is a natural process which often has a crucial role in protecting young animals. Current research indicates that this means of providing antibodies to the young should be developed further, both during and beyond the colostrum phase. Suitable vaccines given to the mother during pregnancy stimulate sufficient antibody in the milk to give young animals local passive immunity in the gut for several weeks. We have known for some time that the gut surface is protected by presenting antigens locally to activate cells of the immune system to produce antibody. With a greater knowledge of the behaviour of circulating lymphocytes it may become practicable to use oral vaccines to activate lymphocytes which will then migrate to the udder and produce antibodies against mastitis. The possibilities of vaccination against parasites are illustrated by the work on immunity against coccidiosis; this subject interests both medical and veterinary research workers and will give large rewards if some biological problems can be overcome.

A method of disease control which has obvious attractions is to breed resistant animals. Commercial poultry breeders are already using this approach with avian leukosis in which there is a genetically controlled resistance to infection and the work on the K88 antigen of *E. coli* showing that some pigs do not have receptor sites to K88 provides the opportunity to breed pigs which are not susceptible to *E. coli* diarrhoea. There is little doubt that animal breeding will afford further opportunities to utilise inherited resistance.

Pressure to prevent suffering in animals increases and disease is a major factor in suffering; public opinion is unlikely to accept ill-health or death of a proportion of our flocks and herds as a normal feature of intensive production.

The foregoing sections have outlined some of the activities of the Agricultural Research Service in controlling animal disease. Even this incomplete account indicates the range and complexity of diseases caused by the many viruses, bacteria, parasites, and nutritional hazards to which animals are subject in all but the most highly-controlled environments. Continuing high-quality control of disease, with its research support, is necessary for effective and humane livestock farming.

## Acknowledgements

I would like to thank those Directors named at the beginning of this essay, and other staff in Agricultural Research Service Institutes, for their contributions and help in preparing this account of our work on animal diseases.

## Further Reading

Anderson, J. C. (1976). Mechanisms of staphylococcal virulence in relation to bovine mastitis. *British Veterinary Journal*, **132**, 229.

Biggs, P. M. (1973). Marek's disease. Reprinted from: *The Herpesvirus*. New York and London: Academic Press Inc. pp. 558–594.

Biggs, P. M. (1975). Marek's disease – the disease and its prevention by vaccination. *British Journal of Cancer*, **31**, Suppl. II, 152.

British Council (1978). The management and diseases of sheep. Papers presented at a British Council Special Course, Edinburgh, March 1978. Published by The British Council and The Commonwealth Agricultural Bureaux.

Brooksby, J. B. (1958). The virus of foot-and-mouth disease. *Advances in Virus Research*, **5**, 1.

Henderson, W. M. (1960). Foot-and-mouth disease and related vesicular diseases. *Advances in Veterinary Science*, **6**, 19.

Jones, P. W. (1980). Health hazards associated with the handling of animal wastes. *Veterinary Record*, **106**, 4.

Ministry of Agriculture, Fisheries and Food (1965). *Animal health, a Centenary, 1865–1965*. London: HMSO.

Payne, J. M. (1977). *Metabolic diseases in farm animals*. London: Heinemann.

Rose, M. E. and Long, P. L. (1980). Vaccination against coccidiosis. In: *Vaccines against parasites*. Symposia of the British Society for Parasitology. Vol. 18. Edited by A. E. R. Taylor and R. Muller. Oxford: Blackwell Scientific Publications.

Sellers, R. F. (1980). Weather, host and vector – their interplay in the spread of insect-borne animal virus diseases. *Journal of Hygiene*, **85**, 65.

Smith, H. Williams. (1976). Neonatal *Escherichia coli* infections in domestic mammals: transmissibility of pathogenic characteristics. In: *Acute Diarrhoea in Childhood*, Ciba Foundation Symposium 42 (new series). Amsterdam: Elsevier; Excerpta Medica; North Holland. pp. 45–72.

Smith, H. Williams (1977). Antibiotic resistance in bacteria and associated problems in farm animals before and after the 1969 Swann Report. In: *Antibiotics and Antibiosis in Agriculture*. Editor: M. Woodbine. London: Butterworth. pp. 344–357.

Woode, G. N. and Bridger, J. C. (1975). Viral enteritis of calves. *Veterinary Record*, **96**, 85.

# Animal Breeding Research in Britain, 1931–1981

J. W. B. KING

Animal Breeding Research Organisation, Edinburgh

The re-discoverers of Mendelism at the beginning of the century were quick to attempt to apply their new science "genetics" to the practical ends of agriculture. In Britain, the enthusiastic disciples of Bateson examined variation in the different species of farm animals and found many good examples of Mendelian inheritance. When it came to dealing with continuous variation, however, their enthusiasm often led to attempts to identify major genes where none existed and many early recommendations to animal breeders must have caused disappointment if not disaster. So many characteristics of concern to farmers, such as milk yield, growth rate and fleece weight show continuous variation that until the methods of quantitative genetics were introduced only few, specialised, uses were found for the new-found science.

The theory of quantitative genetics derived largely from three intellectual giants of the time, Fisher, Haldane and Sewall Wright but it was the 1930s before their ideas began to influence animal breeding research. The beginning of this decade is therefore an appropriate starting point for a review of the subject in Britain.

## Pre-War Era

Animal breeding research in the period 1931–39 is largely the history of the Institute of Animal Genetics in Edinburgh and the Animal Research Station at Cambridge.

In Edinburgh the creation of an animal genetics research institute had been contemplated in 1911 as part of a general scheme for the development of agricultural research but no action had been taken until 1920 when a University department was started. The department was re-named the Institute of Animal Genetics in 1930 and the present building of that Institute was completed in that year. The endowment of such a large Institute, with an income for the year 1930–31 estimated at nearly £14 000, was a major achievement for Professor Crew. Unfortunately the research programme was severely hit by the economic depression and by the mid-thirties the income had been reduced to around £6 000 per annum and many staff dismissed. The work of the Institute of Animal Genetics had originally been intended to be concerned mainly with the genetics of farm animals but Crew's wide personal interests led to an expansion of work into investigations on the determination of sex, sex reversal, sex hormones, relationship between the gonads and other endocrine glands, and general biological problems such as fertility. In 1932 a visiting ARC Committee found a whole range of activities. Firstly, there was work in general genetics under Crew involving a range of species from Drosophila to poultry. Closely allied with this was work on the physiology of reproduction and on the endocrinology of the fowl, the latter carried out by Greenwood. The practical aspects were covered by work on livestock breeding led by Buchanan-Smith, by fleece studies carried out by Miller, and rabbit genetics carried out by Pickard with support from rabbit breeders. The Imperial (now Commonwealth) Bureau of Animal Genetics had been formed in 1930 and attached to the Institute so that from early days attention was paid to the information aspects of work in animal genetics. It is interesting to note that having heard an account of the statistical work that had been carried out on herd book information, the Visiting Committee emphasised the importance of experimentation with cattle despite the long time element and high cost that was already recognised in such experiments.

The other major centre of animal breeding research at this time was Cambridge. Nominally work on genetics was confined to the Small Animal Breeding Institute which was run by Professor Punnet. His own work was concerned with fecundity of poultry, with sex-linkage, and the inheritance of egg shell colouring. Great effort was put into the production of sex-linked strains of chickens and substantial numbers were used in the industry during the early 1930s. The poultry work was also supplemented by other work on inbreeding of poultry carried out at Reaseheath in Cheshire. Although Hammond worked at the Animal Nutrition Institute at Cambridge his many interests included genetic studies. Fertility was a topic of major concern and studies on the inheritance of fertility were instigated in rabbits.

In the early years pigs appeared to have received rather little scientific attention. Nevertheless, pilot litter recording and litter testing stations had been set up, the pioneering scheme being carried out by the Rowett Research Institute in Aberdeen. In 1937 the Council convened a conference to discuss the practical and scientific problems of pig breeding. In this Hammond's ideas came to the fore. From the Institute of Animal Genetics, Buchanan-Smith presented a comprehensive review of the existing literature on pig breeding, which is a model of its kind and still useful today. Some pioneer crossbreeding work in pigs, using the Large White and Saddleback breeds, was also carried out by Fishwick at Wye College in Kent.

It is interesting that Wye College clearly had an interest in crossbreeding not only pigs but also poultry. Attempts were being made, by crossbreeding a variety of breeds, to produce a small chicken which could be marketed for 2/6 (12½p). This particular programme did not however find favour with the Development Commissioners who insisted on birds being marketed at older ages. Could the broiler have appeared on the scene earlier and as a British rather than an American development? We will never know but it is clear that new ideas can so easily be stopped in their tracks by review committees conditioned to existing agricultural practices.

By the end of the pre-war era the centres carrying out animal breeding research had come under scrutiny again by review committees. The lines of work had become rather clearer although probably not radically different from those existing at the beginning of the period. In Edinburgh, Greenwood had developed lines of brown Leghorns selected for different characteristics which were clearly seen to be important in egg production. The need for statistical involvement in large animal experiments was now seen and was met, in part, by collaboration with the University. Large animal experiments received support, despite the increasing cost of the work. At Cambridge the sex-linkage work on poultry continued but the real developments seemed to have been in the Animal Nutrition Institute. This department had developed a herd of inbred pigs, then in their sixth generation, and embryonic mortality was examined in detail. Through his interest in the meat trade, Hammond was making big contributions to the study of growth and body composition for which he is now so well remembered. This department was also concerned with the development of artificial insemination. The potential of this technique seems to have been well recognised from the beginning, and as will be seen later, it was to play a key role in the genetic improvement of dairy cattle.

The end of the pre-war period is perhaps marked by the International Congress of Genetics, which should have been held in the USSR at an earlier date but, because of the political climate, had been postponed and was held in Edinburgh in September 1939. The proceedings of the Congress were interrupted by the outbreak of war and with it one phase of animal breeding research was ended.

## Origin and Early History of ABRO

Although during the war most research centres were on a care and maintenance basis, time was found for consideration of what might be needed in post-war years. As one of several such bodies, a joint committee of the Agricultural Research Council was set up in the summer of 1943 under the chairmanship of James Gray to consider the directions which research in animal genetics and breeding in Great Britain as a whole should take.

The members of the Group included R. T. Clark, Professor of Animal Husbandry at the University of Montana and associated with beef cattle research at Miles City, who was given the task of surveying the breeding industry in Great Britain and reporting on the foundations for research which had already been laid. The Group, reporting in 1944 and 1945, recommended that a national institute of animal breeding and genetics should be established and that it should be directly associated with the Agricultural Research Council. The Group did not attempt to define precisely any research programme but did draw attention to two particular matters; firstly, the extent to which high grade stock could be produced by a policy of relatively intense inbreeding suggesting that this problem should be explored although to do so might delay other lines of attack and, secondly, the need for the statistical analysis of records forthcoming from National Milk Records, AI Centres and Pig Testing Stations was recognised.

The Report was apparently accepted by the two Councils and as a result R. G. White, who was then Professor of Agriculture in Bangor, was offered the position of Director of the national Animal Breeding and Genetics Research Organisation (ABGRO). Professor White took up his appointment in September 1945 and, as he records, "sailed at once for New York". During the war the USA had become the main source of new ideas in animal breeding and a detailed study of activities in that country was called for.

Choosing a location for the first headquarters was a lengthy procedure with Edinburgh, Cambridge and Oxford as the contenders. Edinburgh was settled upon, the University offering some laboratories in the Institute building. Waddington was appointed Professor of Animal Genetics in succession to Crew and his post combined University teaching with direction of the research in animal genetics within ABGRO. As the Institute could not accommodate the whole Organisation, a temporary home (Glenbourne) was purchased for administrative staff and for those mainly concerned with the various field stations. At a later stage, ground was feued from the University and in 1964 a suitable permanent headquarters was erected on the King's Building campus.

The work of the Organisation was initially sub-divided into three sections:

(a) Fundamental research dealing with such matters as the theory of selection, general control of growth, polyploidy, gene action and sex control.
(b) Applied research which would study the inheritance of the important characters of various farm livestock with a view to discovering the system of breeding and selection best designed for the creation of superior stock.
(c) Operational research which would include the analysis of data from private breeders, breed societies, milk recording associations, AI centres and so on to serve as a basis for advisory work or future research.

A number of large out-stations had been envisaged at an early stage and the first years of the Organisation were much occupied by finding suitable sites and devising recording methods appropriate to the species.

When Professor White retired from the Directorship of ABRO in 1950 the Organisation was divided into two sections a) animal breeding and b) animal genetics, with

Dr. Donald and Professor Waddington as the respective heads, although under a common administration. In 1952 the two sections were separated completely, Dr. Donald becoming Director of ABRO and Professor Waddington the Director of the group of workers who in 1957 became the ARC Unit of Animal Genetics (see page 44).

Of the many early experiments a few can be picked out for special comment. Experiments with Drosophila and mice were used to validate quantitative genetic theory, they helped to fashion the thinking of many and stimulated many derived theoretical investigations. For example, such "model" experiments with mice by Falconer raised issues about maternal effects which are important in many areas of animal production.

Analysis of dairy records from the field, carried out by Rendel and Robertson sparked off what was, at that time, a new investigation into the theoretical basis of dairy cattle improvement. This work laid the foundations for the basic structure of progeny testing as currently practised in the majority of countries, and these developments will be described later.

The practical experimentation carried out with cattle was of two kinds. The first was a cyclical crossbreeding experiment with Friesian, Jersey and Ayrshire cows carried out at Cold Norton. Through the use of AI, extensive sampling of bulls was possible making it feasible to sample the breeds widely and to compare first crosses and later crosses with the parental purebreds. What was not fully envisaged at the beginning of this experiment was the long time period that was involved. The results suggest that, where appropriate parental breeds can be found, crossbreeding for milk production may well prove to be commercially desirable. For a variety of reasons this finding is not at present used by the dairy industry but with changing market circumstances could easily become relevant. The other major cattle experiment involved the comparison of twins of different kinds and of single born animals treated as twins. This material formed the basis for extensive studies on growth and development carried out by Taylor and has given us new insights into the growth process and the genetic opportunities for manipulating it to desired ends.

With sheep, inbreeding was not favoured in the initial experiments and the scene was set with long-term selection experiments in both Scottish Blackface and Welsh Mountain sheep. These experiments have fully vindicated the selection theory which at the time these experiments were started was still viewed with much scepticism (Plate 1). Moreover, correlated responses to selection have produced unexpected changes relevant to hill sheep production. Early sheep experiments included several on crossbreeding and, somewhat later, a major one in which the crossbreeding phase was followed by an experimental inbreeding phase.

With pigs the early work was much coloured by the American emphasis on inbreeding and crossing. The example of hybrid maize made the more fecund farm animals such as poultry and pigs, candidates for similar treatment. In the event inbreeding and crossing proved not to be a useful method for pig improvement for reasons which had not been anticipated. The production of inbred lines was feasible, but the process of inbreeding and crossing was so lengthy as to prove non-competitive with straightforward selection without inbreeding. As had been the case with dairy cattle, the combined analysis of pig testing records and related theoretical studies showed that improved breeding methods were feasible and that progeny testing of pigs which had long been practised by the Danes was, theoretically at least, not the best method. Some elaboration of the alternative is given in the next section.

Early investigation into blood groups, particularly in cattle and sheep, showed the presence of extensive variation. The introduction of electrophoretic methods showed there to be variation in many proteins and opened up many new studies. Unfortunately little of the new variation appeared to be associated with performance in traits of commercial importance. Despite the initial disappointment a very practical end for

*Plate 1* Blackface sheep of two lines selected from the same stock over 20 years for short and long cannon bone length. Cannon bone length is related to body and carcass shape, and to fertility and survival.

these studies was found with the use of these simply inherited variants for the control of parentage records. The Cattle Blood Typing Service, run by ABRO, was started in 1966 and now tests around 5,000 samples per annum as a means of checking on putative pedigree records and resolving parentage in cases where alternative parents are known. The widespread use of the service by Breed Societies, AI operators and private breeders testifies to its utility.

In the Unit of Animal Genetics there was continuing theoretical work with much direct relevance to animal breeding. Progress by Alan Robertson on the prediction of long-term responses to selection and ultimate selection limits led to many telling experiments with Drosophila and mice with important implications for animal breeding. Statistical investigations by Hill in the University Department of Genetics advanced thinking on genetic drift and many important aspects of experimental design were put on a sound basis.

The contribution of other Universities to animal breeding research was also appreciable. Merely by way of example a few developments may be noted. The large commitment of the University of Newcastle to pig breeding research was especially prominent with many experiments of an applied nature. This involvement was not, however, only practical — Bichard was responsible for far-reaching theoretical developments in "genetic lag", important for the dissemination of genetic improvement through populations. The University of Reading experimented with sheep and pigs carrying out genotype/environment experiments relating to the formulation of improved production systems. Owen, then at the University of Cambridge, used the method of screening large populations for high performing individuals to establish the Cambridge breed of sheep, noted for its high prolificacy. There were thus many contributors to animal breeding research and, while this review is concerned with British contributors, many ideas continued to flow from the USA and also, increasingly in later years, from research centres in Europe.

## Industry Developments in Animal Breeding

In the 1950s, the research ideas emanating from quantitative genetics began to have a major impact on the improvement of farm animals in Britain. It is appropriate to recall how this came about and to describe briefly the present status of improvement schemes. The account differs for the different species.

### Poultry

The first candidates for improvement were poultry — perhaps a natural choice in view of the high reproductive rate and the large size of flocks. The initial stimulus for this improvement work came from the USA and from the success story of the hybrid maize programme. Commercial attempts were made to emulate this progress with poultry both by inbreeding and crossing and with other breeding methods. In Britain there were many small-scale breeders and attempts were made by the Government to co-ordinate their efforts with a Poultry Improvement Plan and the erection of three progeny testing stations which came into operation in 1956. The testing method used was criticised at the time of its introduction as being already outmoded and the stations rapidly became redundant (closing in 1963) as large-scale breeding companies appeared on the scene. Much of the expertise of these companies was imported from the USA and it is commonly held that many American stocks came too (although officially imports were banned for health reasons). There was a large input of professional genetical advice into breeding programmes which certainly brought rapid initial progress but also engendered fierce commercial competition between companies which was eventually rationalised by takeovers. Poultry breeding rapidly became international and the number of companies still in business at the present time is small.

Programmes to improve egg production were remarkable for the variety of breeding methods employed, from simple strain crossing to complex methods of reciprocal recurrent selection for the combining ability of strains to be crossed. No one breeding method emerged as the most successful and many different systems are still represented and used by the surviving breeding companies.

The broiler industry was another import from the USA. Simple mass selection methods for growth rate produced remarkable changes not only in growth but also in efficiency of food conversion. These genetic changes were an essential part of a new large scale industry producing meat at prices which housewives found increasingly irresistible. It is a new and still growing industry despite complaints over the bland taste of the product and criticism from the welfare lobby of the large scale production methods.

### Pigs

Because of the development of large scale husbandry methods and a high reproductive rate the pig was logically the next candidate for innovative breeding methods. Although there had been a history of improvement by progeny testing in Denmark dating back to 1906, attempts to translate the same system into other countries had been slow and usually not successful. Britain was slow to imitate the Danish model and five testing stations built on the Danish pattern were not put into use until 1958. Analysis of the results by Smith in 1964 showed that there had been little improvement in performance and that this was not due to deficiencies in genetic predictions but resulted from the lack of selection on test results and absence of any coherent breeding plan. The breeding industry was not well structured for improvement, with insufficient testing accommodation for the many pedigree breeders. Furthermore it had been earlier shown by King at ABRO that the progeny testing methods hitherto adopted could give only a slow rate of improvement and that it would be more efficient to use so-called "performance testing" in which potential breeding animals themselves were measured. This development was accelerated by the introduction of methods for measuring fatness in the live animal and, of several methods tried for this purpose, the sophisticated ultrasonic method became standard. Such radical changes in breeding methods are not easily accomplished and a pilot scheme to introduce the method was set up in 1963 as a co-operative venture based on the University of Newcastle and involving several cooperating institutional herds. This scheme made good progress but before its full impact was felt the general message had been accepted and the necessary reduction in number of testing herds and changes in testing methods were introduced by the Pig Industry Development Authority in 1966.

These changes were accelerated by the appearance on the British scene of pig breeding companies, some modelled on the poultry example with a few financed from the same sources but with others deriving from other commercial interests. Experimental results showing that crossbred pigs and particularly crossbred sows had appreciable advantages for commercial production led to wide scale promotion of "hybrid gilts". Private breeding companies also exploited the advantages to be gained from the use of breeding stock of a high health status and, to maintain this status, developed their own testing facilities. There has been a decrease in central testing of boars and this seems likely to continue. To measure the performance of company pigs, the Meat and Livestock Commission set up "Commercial Product Evaluation" — the pig equivalent of a poultry random sample test — in 1972 and reports regularly on the products of different companies. This form of testing is spreading around the world as pig breeding companies become increasing international. The combined effects of private and public enterprise has been to produce a technically-based industry in Britain which is widely recognised as a world leader.


## Dairy Cattle

When compared with the 20 or so piglets per annum for each sow, the reproductive performance of the average cow would not seem to make it a prime candidate for an improvement programme. Add to this the complication that in dairy cattle the performance of interest, i.e. milk production, is expressed only in one sex and one has an unpromising situation for a useful breeding programme. While these features are a handicap, the opportunities for improvement in cattle have been transformed by the introduction of artificial insemination. The pioneering efforts of Hammond and Walton at Cambridge have produced a technological change in cattle breeding which has had a world wide impact, particularly in dairy cattle. The discovery of methods of deep freezing sperm by Rowson and Polge at the Unit of Reproductive Physiology and Biochemistry at Cambridge further extended the use of bulls both on a national and international level.

The use of AI was promoted in the early days by Hammond as a means of upgrading inferior stock to the levels of the highest pedigree herds. It was soon found that these high expectations were not realised and that most of the differences observed between herds were non-genetic. Analysis of early results made it possible to devise improved breeding methods which relied on AI to progeny test bulls, the daughters of these bulls being spread over a large number of herds. The original plans of Rendel and Alan Robertson were revolutionary to many cattle breeders of the time and a pilot improvement scheme was set up at the Cambridge AI Centre. This was started in 1953 and achieved useful improvements. As with the pig scheme, however, officials and breeders were soon converted to the new methods and in 1961 the Milk Marketing Board of England and Wales introduced what was for the times a revolutionary large scale scheme leading up to more than 100 young Friesian bulls being progeny tested through AI each year. An essential ingredient was the statistical method which came to be known as the "Contemporary Comparison" by which the fragmented data on progeny records from different herds could be aggregated into a single meaningful statistic. The two products of research, AI and the Contemporary Comparison, have revolutionised dairy cattle breeding all over the world.

As a footnote it is interesting to recall that the method of contemporary comparisons was originally devised as a simplified method of progeny assessment. The mathematics of a more complex method was worked out but its implementation had to await the arrival of large computers.

## Beef cattle

In beef cattle, AI for improvement purposes has not been readily acceptable to the majority of beef cattle breeders. As a consequence genetic change in beef cattle has not been as rapid as it might have been. The recording of performance on farms has however met with good success and following the pioneering efforts of the Beef Recording Association, started in 1963, the Meat and Livestock Commission now record about one-third of all pedigree beef cattle in Britain. What has proved the greatest stimulus to beef cattle improvement is, however, an unrelated phenomenon which came to be known as the "exotic boom".

For many years livestock imports into Britain had been prevented because of the widespread incidence of disease in Europe and particularly foot and mouth disease. In 1955, however, the Milk Marketing Board of England and Wales asked for permission to import Charolais semen into Britain for experimental trial. The move caused objections from the National Cattle Breeders Association but in 1960 the Terrington Committee, who looked at the arguments on both sides, recommended a controlled import. In due course 31 Charolais bulls were imported to Britain and a large scale evaluation experiment was started using resources in many different parts of the country. Before the results were available, however, pressures had built up to allow the establishment of the breed in Britain with the importation of breeding females. In 1970 two additional breeds, the Simmental and Limousin breeds were imported, again with the proviso that an experimental evaluation programme should be carried out. By this time, however, there was a growing demand from North America and Australasia for large-framed Continental cattle and the exotic boom had really begun. An import panel was set up to adjudicate on import applications and to allocate available spaces in quarantine stations. The issue of an import permit has been likened to a licence to print money and the race was on to find an, as yet, unexploited continental breed, to form a British Breed Society and mount pressure for an import. While this trade proved to be for some breeds nothing more than an ephemeral import-export business, the early comers have established themselves in Britain and in terms of leanness and growth rate provide strong competition for native breeds. The competition produced the stimulus for weight recording of pedigree beef cattle and good support for performance testing stations but the elaboration of these into effective improvement programmes has still to follow.

The exotic boom has benefited research in two ways. Firstly much comparative information about beef breeds has been acquired. In Britain this was limited to the Charolais, Simmental and Limousin breeds but other developed countries mounted larger and more informative trials. Secondly, the demand for breeding stock proved a great commercial incentive to the further development of ova transplantation. The research methodology being developed at Cambridge was accelerated by commercial exploitation and made remarkable progress in a short period of years. Now that the heady days of the exotic boom are over, the method still finds practical application.

Although the greatest theoretical benefits would appear to be in beef cattle breeding, dairy farmers have also adopted the technique. History was certainly created by the first public auction of embryos held at Reading in 1979.

## Sheep

The sheep is the species least affected by modern genetic thought on animal improvement. One immediate problem for those who seek to improve the national flock is that there are still some 50 breeds of sheep in Britain. Attempts to reduce this number by way of rationalisation and in order to improve the uniformity of slaughter lambs are not likely to meet with great success. Starting with hill breeds adapted to different areas there are a succession of different crosses used in a variety of different environments. Despite the difficulties of recording performance, appropriate schemes have been introduced by the Meat and Livestock Commission and a number of development flocks are being set up in which selection will be carried out both for practical ends and by way of demonstration.

Although imports of Continental breeds have been made, they have not produced quite the exotic boom experienced with beef cattle. Imports of the Finnish Landrace breed by ABRO in 1962 showed that this breed justified its reputation of high prolificacy with a lamb crop averaging 3 lambs born alive and that an advantage in prolificacy could be transmitted to Finnish Landrace cross ewes. Although these benefits were demonstrated in field trials, the Finnish Landrace has proved unacceptable to British sheep breeders. The reasons seem to be that the small size of the lambs at birth often requires special husbandry to avoid high mortality, that the crosses grow slowly and have poorer carcass quality by conventional standards. Experiments with various strains containing lesser proportions of Finnish Landrace genes are in progress and seem to offer commercial promise although handicapped by the disrepute in which the parent breed is now held. Breed comparisons have also been carried out among those breeds used to sire lambs for slaughter. Work at ABRO has amply confirmed results from the Republic of Ireland that the Texel breed has substantial advantages in leanness although its lambs are slightly slower growing than crosses from some British breeds. With the stimulus of a demand for lean lambs for export to Europe, the Texel has found widespread acceptance and the demand for purebred breeding stock has indeed reached boom proportions.

The organisational difficulties of sheep improvement are not insuperable. One development which has been imported from New Zealand is the concept of a group breeding scheme. In this a number of cooperating breeders record ewes in a simple manner and then send the best performing individuals to a nucleus flock. In this central flock, full scale recording is carried out and intense selection imposed with the object of sending improved rams back to the collaborating breeders. The first such group breeding scheme has been set up in Britain by ten Welsh Mountain breeders who maintain their central flock at ABRO's Rhydyglafes Farm in North Wales. Hopefully this idea will spread to other breeds of sheep and cattle and there are indeed signs that this is happening. The changes from the traditional pedigree scene are quite profound and there is no doubt that the long-term application of genetic ideas can produce just as useful changes in sheep as they have done in other species.

## Current Research

It would not be appropriate to catalogue all current research activities but the description of some will highlight areas of particular topical interest. A common theme in many is the measurement of the biological efficiency of animal production, so bypassing the

*Plate 2* Early weaned Ayrshire heifers on complete ruminant diet, using individually keyed electronic doors. Control of feed quality and of feed consumption allow measurement of the biological efficiency of milk and meat production in cattle.

vagaries of economic fluctuations in the market for animal products. In many agricultural systems the outputs alone tend to be emphasised and the measurement of inputs, even important and expensive ones like feed, tend to be neglected. The biological efficiency of different breeds is a recurring theme in many investigations. In cattle, a large multibreed experiment is measuring the extent of breed variation in efficiency and a variety of other characteristics (Plate 2). In sheep and pigs, comparisons are being made between specific breeds of potential value for different uses and this type of information finds immediate application in breed substitution.

Although the general form of breeding plans for the improvement of all the major species is well known, some of the details of how testing procedures are best carried out have still to be elucidated. Thus in sheep and beef cattle, experimentation directed at finding the most efficient form of performance test is under way. With pigs the basic form of the test is clear but details of the feeding methods that are best employed and the precise selection objectives still await experimental attack. Discussion of these difficulties has become multidisciplinary with nutritionists, geneticists and biometricians co-operating to formulate meaningful approaches to the problem.

Longer range work which could alter the basic form of breeding plans also forms an important growing point where physiology and genetics interact. Attempts to improve the productivity of ewes are slowed down by the fact that rams cannot be assessed except through a progeny test of daughters or through the performance of their close relatives. This sex limitation can hopefully be overcome by the realisation that there is a basic unity in the sex hormones of the two sexes so that there may be opportunities, pointed out by Land, of making hormone measurements on the male which can be used in the prediction of the productivity of his female descendants. The growth of the testes is being used as a potential integrated measure of hormone production which could be readily applied in practice. More sophisticated measures of actual hormone levels also seem to be feasible and are being put to experimental test. Sex limitation also complicates the improvement of dairy production in cattle and application of the same philosophy may result in alternative testing procedures. Ways of predicting the breeding merit of young dairy bulls by study of their hormone levels and their metabolic make-up, particularly under nutritional stress, are being investigated.

Disease is unfortunately a recurring problem in animal production systems and research is being carried out to investigate cases in which genetic remedies to this problem might be appropriate. One disease which has attracted a great deal of attention is scrapie in sheep. The infectious agent is a very small virus-like organism with many unusual properties including extreme resistance to most disinfectants and decontamination procedures. The study of scrapie has proved challenging both from the pathology and genetics that are involved. Methods for identifying and separating different strains of scrapie have been developed and work with mice has yielded several methods for increasing or decreasing susceptibility and for delaying the progress of the disease. The host as well as the pathogen show genetic variation and it has proved possible to breed sheep resistant to one strain of scrapie — the unanswered question is whether this resistance would extend to other scrapie strains. More general aspects of disease resistance are also studied and genetic variation in active and passive immunity has been investigated in both sheep and cattle. In these two species, systems have been developed for the typing of white cell antigens as potential markers of disease resistance. Investigations in humans and laboratory animals have shown strong associations between white cell antigens and the incidence of some diseases and if such correlations are also found in farm animals they would clearly be important.

## Concluding Remarks

From the descriptions of industry that have gone before it should be obvious that the science of genetics is only one part of the practice of animal breeding. The development of effective breeding plans depends very much on the rewards afforded to breeders for their endeavours and the extent to which these benefits are recognised by commercial producers. In some instances structural changes by way of increase in flock or herd size are desirable before large scale improvements can be hoped for. Growing realisation of these realities should help to make national improvement schemes increasingly effective. Past Government attempts at improvement through legislation by the imposition of laws requiring the licencing of bulls (1931) and boars (1949) were repealed in 1976 and 1975 respectively. No assessment has been made of the contribution of this legislation to improvement but its passing has not been lamented and there seems to be no noticeable decline in standards of performance or conformation demanded by breeders. Remnants of these legislative attempts remain in the regulations surrounding the use of bulls in AI and it is to be hoped that they too will be finally abandoned and Government assistance channelled into more appropriate education and advisory efforts. The number of specialist advisers in public employment in animal breeding in Britain is lamentably low (depending on how they are classified — only three altogether, one in Scotland and two for the whole of England and Wales) and much could be done by way of promotion of existing knowledge.

Animal breeding has already made substantial contributions to improving the performance of poultry, pigs and dairy cattle in Britain. For example, in pigs it has been estimated that the annual rate of improvement of lean meat food conversion amounts to 2.4% per annum. This is much greater than the annual improvements in the yield of wheat and barley attributable to the introduction of new varieties and so often held up as prime examples of genetic achievement. Improvements in milk yield are lower but perhaps, not dissimilar to increases in potato yields due to breeding. Economic studies emphasise the value of animal breeding as an investment for the future and a means of securing efficient animal production in the face of competing demands for some animal feeding stuffs.

For the future the promise of further radical new techniques is no less encouraging. Reproductive physiology plays a key role in animal improvement and ova transplantation shows every sign of augmenting the tremendous changes already achieved by artificial insemination. Although developments of reproductive techniques such as *in vitro* fertilisation, cloning and sexing of embryos are all techniques waiting in the wings, perhaps the most exciting prospect of all is genetic engineering. Here, my own opinion would be less optimistic than many that have been advanced. While it may be possible, in the not too distant future, to introduce to the mammalian genome certain structural genes, a great deal has yet to be learned about the control processes by which such genes could be turned on and off to produce the end product in desired quantities and without undesirable interactions with other performance traits. While genetic engineering seems a most legitimate area of enquiry its practical application is likely to lie well into the next 50 years.

## Further Reading

ABRO (1979) Group Breeding Schemes (mimeographed).

Bichard, M. (1975) Pig breeding — a British success story. Proceedings of the Ninth Annual Conference, Reading University Agriculture Club.

Edwards, J. (1959) Genetic considerations in breeding two million cattle to two hundred sires. (Printed privately).

Robertson, A. (1979) A review of AI and dairy cattle improvements. Proceedings of the 1979 Winter Conference of the British Cattle Breeders' Club.

# Animal Husbandry, 1931–1980

## W. HOLMES

Wye College (University of London)

Animal husbandry refers to the care and management of farm animals, and the provision of an environment, in the widest sense, which allows the genetic potential of the animal to be realised and an optimal level of production to be attained. It also implies a concern for the comfort and welfare of the animals.

In the period under review there have been enormous changes in animal husbandry. Advancing scientific and technical knowledge combined with the reduced availability and escalating cost of labour have resulted in profound changes in housing, breeding and feeding of farm animals.

Table 1

Animal production in the 1930s and in 1978 in the UK.

|  | 1930s | 1978 |
|---|---|---|
| Milk yield per cow–litres (1931) | 2100 | 4626 |
| Number of eggs per hen | 150 | 242 |
| Home produced–thousand tonnes |  |  |
| Beef and veal | 550 | 1048 |
| Mutton and lamb | 190 | 238 |
| Pork | 210 | 634 |
| Bacon | 160 | 214 |
| Poultry meat | 89 | 726 |
| Imported feeds–M tonnes | 8.4 | 14.9 |
| Total milk production–M litres | 4500 | 15093 |
| Agricultural workers (in 1931) | 829 000 | 367 000 |
| Total human population (millions) | 47 | 58 |
| Self sufficiency in human food supplies (%) |  |  |
| Energy | 30 | 45 |
| Protein | 45 | 66 |

Some measure of the magnitude of these changes is given in Table 1 which illustrates the increases in productivity per animal, per man and in overall animal production which have occurred in the UK. There have also been marked changes in breeds of farm livestock. This is most obvious in the increase in Friesian and the decline in numbers of Dairy Shorthorn cattle and in the introduction of European beef breeds such as the Charolais and Simmental in recent years. With sheep the diversity of breeds has remained and some new breeds, such as the Colbred, have been established. In pig and poultry production many of the former breeds have declined in number, and commercial production is based mainly on hybrids. Indeed the decline of many pure breeds of stock has stimulated the establishment of the Rare Breeds Survival Trust so that these breeds are preserved, both for aesthetic reasons and as a source of genetic material.

Of course the changes in productivity are not due entirely to the influence of agricultural research but they could not have been achieved without the application of the results of research conducted in the United Kingdom and elsewhere. The developing Agricultural Research Service, the Universities, commercial firms concerned with agriculture, the advisory services, and farmers themselves, have all contributed to these changes in productivity and animal efficiency.

Efficiency in animal production has many aspects. To the farmer it is measured as profit per animal or per hectare and return on capital. But since prices of input and products can vary widely, more basic measures of efficiency in biological terms, in use of feed supplies, fossil fuel energy and of labour are also important.

Biologically the efficiency of a farm animal population depends on its reproductive efficiency, in particular the mass of progeny per unit metabolic weight of breeding female and on its productive efficiency, in terms of production as growth, eggs or milk per unit metabolic weight. The nutritional efficiency of farm livestock has been estimated by many workers. Precise comparison of such estimates is difficult but the data of Leitch and Godden (1942) relating to the late 1930s and those of the author for the 1970s (Holmes 1977) indicate that substantial increases have occurred in biological efficiency, largely attributable to higher yields or rates of production per animal.

Table 2

The energy ratio, and quantity of fossil fuel energy required per unit protein, from animal production (*Leach, 1975*).

|  | Food energy in product / Food energy required | MJ of fuel energy per kg protein |
| --- | --- | --- |
| Milk | 0.37 | 208 |
| Lamb* | 0.37 | — |
| Broiler meat | 0.10 | 290 |
| Eggs | 0.14 | 353 |
| Dairy farm | 0.38 | 240 |
| Cattle and sheep farm | 0.59 | 185 |
| Sheep farm | 0.25 | 372 |
| Pig and poultry farms | 0.32 | 316 |
| Cereal production | 1.9 | 64 |

*Spedding and Hoxey (1975) in *Meat*. Ed. Cole and Lawrie; London: Butterworth.

The recent increase in fossil fuel costs stimulated an appraisal of the efficiency with which agriculture used these fuels. Table 2 shows that although crop production generally yields more food energy than the input of fossil fuel, modern animal production incurs heavy fuel energy inputs and the return is generally only a fraction of this energy. Economy in human labour has been achieved partly by the expenditure of fossil fuel energy and in part by handling animals in groups rather than individuals. As an example, milk costs show that the average labour per milk cow per year has been reduced from some 200 hours in the 1930s to about 40 hours, and there has been an overall increase in labour productivity in agriculture, part of which is attributable to animal production, from an index figure of 83 to 115 from 1969 to 1979.

The purpose of this essay is to outline and examine some of the scientific developments which, applied to animal husbandry, have contributed to those changes in productivity and efficiency. A section contributed by Dr. D. W. F. Shannon of the Poultry Research Centre, Edinburgh, describing changes in poultry production is at the end of this essay.

The first report of the Agricultural Research Council covering 1931–1933 included an interesting introduction on the economic circumstances affecting British agriculture. Economics and politics still have a profound influence on agricultural policy and technology and although in recent years the place of economics in agricultural research planning has been less obvious, it contributes implicitly to the priorities indicated by the Joint Consultative Organisation. The first ARC report made brief reference to many aspects of animal husbandry which have since been greatly developed. The developments in nutrition which are a feature of a separate essay stem from work at the Cambridge Institute of Animal Nutrition done by Wood, Woodman and Creighton and at the Rowett Research Institute by Boyd Orr and his colleagues. Much of the animal physiology basic to modern animal husbandry stems from the work of Marshall and Hammond, also at Cambridge. In dairy husbandry, calf rearing, the analysis of the lactation curve and machine milking were already aspects of the work of the National Institute for Research in Dairying at Shinfield, the potential productivity of grass had been shown by Woodman's work at Cambridge and exploitation of this potential with fertilizers had begun at Jealott's Hill, ICI's Research Station, and at the Hannah Research Institute where, to quote the first ARC report, "on the rich Scottish grassland, unmanured plots gave as good yields as Woodman's best manured plots (which received 106 kg N ha$^{-1}$ and yielded 6000 kg DM ha$^{-1}$) at Cambridge". This finding was in a sense confirmed by a recent co-ordinated grassland manuring trial which in fact reported the lowest yields in England and Wales from a site at Cambridge.

## Housing

Changes in animal housing have arisen from the increased cost of labour, the natural resistance of mankind to hard and unpleasant work, and the considerable increase in scale of animal enterprises. Many aspects of housing are for man's convenience rather than that of the animals but the results of physical, physiological, and indeed behavioural studies now enable the optimal environment to be described and provided.

Animal enterprises have increased in scale. Chickens 50 years ago were in colony houses in the fields, then in groups in deep litter houses, now in large "controlled environment" houses where one man with machinery attends to the needs of up to 50 000 birds. Similarly pigs, which roamed the orchards or lived in small groups in semi-covered sties, now often spend their whole lives under cover, sometimes (for sows) restrained in conditions which society will not tolerate for much longer. Many pig units now have over 100 sows and their progeny per attendant.

The average size of dairy cow herds has increased from about 12 in the 1930s to some 53 cows per herd. Cows introduced in the arable areas occupied beef cattle yards and were milked in a separate building, the milking parlour. "Comfort stalls" were used in USA in the 1940s and a somewhat similar development, the cow cubicle, was developed by several farmers in the 1950s with considerable assistance on design from Shinfield. Even sheep, the least intensively managed livestock of the farm, are now housed for part of the winter on many farms.

These trends towards aggregation of stock in much larger groups have aggravated and highlighted three problems, the importance of ventilation, the risk of respiratory disease, and the disposal of excreta.

Perhaps the widest variety of housing exists for cattle raised for meat. This can range from environmentally-controlled buildings for rapid growth of veal and beef cattle to airy covered yards, old fashioned semi-covered yards, open cubicles and open range. Scientific understanding of the housing environment has developed from *ad hoc* observations on the ventilation of cattle byres (often kept warm for the comfort of the cow-man and not the stock) to detailed studies of the physics and physiology of heat production and dissipation made at the Hannah and Rowett Institutes and the Institute of Animal Physiology at Babraham (Cambridgeshire). Findlay stressed the importance of outlet ventilation in cow byres. The development of automation led in the sixties to the provision of controlled environment houses (in which air flow, temperature and sometimes humidity and "day" length were adjusted according to predetermined programmes). But these resulted in many problems of operation and control. It may be a healthy sign that naturally-ventilated buildings such as the climatic calf house designed by the Scottish Farm Buildings Investigation Unit are now more popular, and close environmental control in British conditions is now regarded as necessary only for poultry and young pigs.

Part of the work on climate was funded by the former Colonial Office and provided for fundamental studies in specially designed climatic chambers on the mechanisms of temperature control of farm animals in tropical conditions, but the climatic environment also affects animals out-of-doors in temperate regions and much information has been accumulated on the requirements and adaptation of farm animals to the external environment (Monteith and Mount, 1974). The influence of natural cold environments was studied by Blaxter and Webster at the Hannah Institute and later at the Rowett Institute. This work based on physical measurements, the use of "artificial sheep", and live animals of different breeds, allowed accurate assessment of the effects of cold temperate environments on animal productivity. It has shown that the zone of thermoneutrality in the adult ruminant extends to $-20°C$ but has also emphasised the adverse effects of wind and rain on the insulative qualities of the coat and the thermal environment of the animal.

An unfortunate but unsurprising feature of the housing of large numbers of farm animals together is the accumulation of large volumes of faeces and urine, often more than the surrounding land can effectively absorb. The ARC has supported many investigations into the utilization or disposal of such material. That they have not provided all the answers indicates the complexity of the problem. It is still agreed that to utilise the P, K and, if possible, the N which slurry contains it should be spread where possible uniformly on arable land, or on grass to be conserved as silage or hay. Although the difficulties of storage and of distribution at the optimum time and in a uniform manner are considerable, the economic incentive for better utilization of slurry increases with increasing fertilizer cost. Increased fossil fuel costs make the application of anaerobic digestion to animal residues, investigated at the Rowett Institute, of economic interest in addition to its contribution to amenity by the reduction of odour.

Injuries are responsible for considerable loss in farm livestock. The survey and description of housing arrangements which minimise injury to animals is important. Such unspectacular applications of research can be most valuable. Because of the difficulties in conducting and interpreting surveys, and the high cost of *ad hoc* investigation of animal housing, the Agricultural Research Service (ARS) has contributed only to specialised aspects such as environmental control and the development of specialised equipment, as in the mechanised dairy unit at Shinfield.


## Feeding

In terms of husbandry the major changes have been the increased use of barley and silage in ruminant feeding. Understanding of nutritional principles has been transformed in the period under review. This is the subject of a separate essay (by Sir Kenneth Blaxter) but the considerable implications for practical animal husbandry deserve attention.

A major contribution was the publication in the 1960s of the ARC reviews on the Nutrient Requirements of Farm Livestock which summarised available information for poultry, pigs and ruminants, stimulated interest and discussion world-wide and led in the United Kingdom to a total revision and improvement of nutritional advice and of advisory publications from official and commercial bodies. The reviews are now being revised to incorporate the additional information resulting from the stimulus of the earlier publications.

The maintenance of groups of animals with little control over individual allocations of feed, has increased the importance of research on the factors which affect voluntary feed intake. The animal to an extent defines its appetite depending on its size, its physiological state and its productive potential. The non-ruminant animal normally receives a diet of high nutrient concentration and appetite is regulated chemostatically. The conflict between the animal's innate demand and the economic optimum is then achieved either by control of the energy concentration of the diet or by control of the quantity offered.

The ruminant can utilize a wide range of feeds which at 1980 prices range in cost from 0.2 to over 1p per MJ of metabolizable energy and the attainment of the optimal combination of feeds within the animal's appetite has a great influence on costs of production. Whether the ruminant can satisfy its needs then depends on the quality of the feed available and on the opportunities in terms of access, ease of prehension and freedom from competition which the management system provides. The ARC report on the Nutrient Requirements of Ruminants (1965) indicated upper limits to appetite. The importance of the subject and the additional stimulus from the recent interest in "complete" feeds for ruminants has encouraged further work.

Studies on young mammals have been stimulated by the economic advantages of replacing saleable milk by a cheaper substitute and of reducing the reproductive interval (in pigs) by earlier weaning of piglets. Detailed studies on the nutrient requirements of young animals have now resulted in the provision of milk substitutes for baby pigs, calves and lambs and in the availability of well-balanced creep feeds for baby pigs. These now take account of the importance of colostrum, and the peculiarities of the young animal, in particular its inability to utilize carbohydrates other than glucose and lactose.

The observation that liquid feeds maximise intake and growth has been exploited in feeding veal calves on high fat milk substitutes which can result in growth rates of 1 kg per day. However, the provision of liquid milk substitutes demands high standards of hygiene difficult to maintain in practice and this has encouraged the development of dry early weaning feeds. These reduce labour costs and achieve adequate if not maximal growth from young animals. In this field an important example of the applicability of research work to husbandry is the publication by Roy of successive editions of his book "The Calf"; the fourth edition (1980) is a major source of information on this important subject.

The high growth potential of the calf when nutrition and environmental conditions are non-limiting was also exploited in the development of intensive cereal beef production, notably by Preston at the Rowett Institute in the 1960s; he showed that with high cereal diets correctly prepared, lifetime daily growth rates in bull calves of 1 kg could be attained, and beef carcasses of 220–240 kg produced in 12 months at an economic cost.

Preston's work was important in demonstrating the growth potential of cattle when nutrition was non-limiting and was also one application of the growing understanding of the nature of the fermentations which take place in the rumen and of the influence of the relative proportions of the volatile fatty acids produced on animal production, a subject which had been under investigation at several research institutes and was outlined by Blaxter (1962).

The importance of the microbial flora of the rumen and their contribution to the energy and protein metabolism of ruminants has been elucidated. Some of the earliest work on non-protein nitrogen was conducted by Smith and his colleagues at the Hannah Institute while the fermentation of carbohydrates to volatile fatty acids in the rumen had been established by Barcroft and Phillipson at Cambridge and the relative importance of the various fatty acids was elucidated by Blaxter and Armstrong at the Hannah Institute and by Rook at Shinfield.

An important aspect of this work was the emphasis which it gave to a principle of good husbandry that, particularly in feeding ruminants, changes in diet should be made gradually. This had long been recognised. It was now realised that time had to be allowed for gradual change in the microbial population to take place. As a result of these studies the unique properties of the ruminant in utilizing fibrous feeds and non-protein nitrogenous materials has been placed on a sound scientific basis.

Dairy farming is a major enterprise in British agriculture. Milk yield per cow has been raised nearly threefold in 50 years. The genetic capacity exists, partly as a result of breed changes, particularly from Dairy Shorthorns to Friesians, and use of improved animal breeding techniques, but an environment, including nutrition, conducive to high milk yield is essential for the genetic potential to be realised. The nutrition of the dairy cow has been studied at Shinfield and the Hannah and Rowett Institutes. The experiments and reviews of Broster have considerably influenced dairy husbandry. The relevance of the dry period, the beneficial influence of improved body condition in late pregnancy, and the combined effect of feeding in late pregnancy and early lactation on total milk production have now been described quantitatively, and indeed are incorporated in current advisory material (MAFF, 1975). It is now possible to define reasonably precisely the energy requirements of dairy cows at all stages of lactation. In the 1930s Morris, Wright and Fowler drew attention to the differences in biological value of protein for milk production. The discoveries of microbial synthesis of protein in the 1940s overshadowed this but recent work included in the revised edition of ARC Nutrient Requirements of Ruminants suggests that a synthesis of old and new ideas may apply and that for very high yielding cows, and rapidly growing calves, some protein of high biological value and of low degradability may be necessary.

The importance of fat stores as energy reserves in early lactation is now well recognised. Some uncertainty exists however on the magnitude and lability of protein reserves; high protein concentrations in the diets of high yielding cows in early lactation may be beneficial.

Reserves of body fat are exploited in dairy cows. Similarly work with sows, breeding ewes, and suckler cows, has emphasised the economic advantage of a build-up of reserve tissues when the physiology of the animal and the nutritional environment permit this to occur. The work of the Hill Farming Research Organisation in identifying the reasons for the normal low level of productivity in hill ewes and in showing the positive relation of body condition at mating to conception rate, and of good nutrition at lambing time to the survival and development of the lamb, is an excellent example.

Research at the Rowett Institute on the role of body reserves in the sow, and the dangers of under-nutrition resulting in the thin-sow syndrome, have also contributed to improved husbandry and efficient use of feed.

## The Productivity of Grass

The work in the 1920s of Woodman, Martin Jones, Stapledon and Fagan formed the basis for the great expansion in knowledge of the grass crop in the past 50 years. Some aspects are of considerable relevance to animal husbandry. Since efficient harvesting of grass is important, systems of grazing management were studied at several ARS Institutes, at Wye College and at some of the Experimental Husbandry Farms of the Ministry of Agriculture, Fisheries and Food (MAFF). The electric fence greatly facilitated subdivision of pastures, and enabled many alternative management systems to be investigated. These studies emphasised the important influence on herbage intake of herbage allowance, herbage digestibility and sward density. They have also shown that while the precise grazing system chosen may have considerable advantages from the point of view of management, and may vary considerably in cost, the dominant factor affecting productivity per hectare is the demand placed on the pasture by the stocking rate imposed. The harvesting efficiency of grazed pasture over the season as a whole may range from 40–95% and at the lower level considerable increases in production per hectare with negligible effects on production per animal are attainable merely by increasing stock numbers.

The relation of grazing management to parasitism was fully investigated. Although the complexity and resilience of parasite life cycles preclude complete control and elimination of worm parasites from normal pastures (Michel, 1976), creep grazing systems for ewes with lambs, leader and follower systems for young cattle, and clean grazing systems were developed to reduce the incidence of worm parasites.

Improved agricultural systems can be adopted only when the benefits are readily demonstrable and the additional cost and effort is fairly easily provided. A treatment by a single injection or spray is more likely to be adopted than one depending on regular daily or weekly attention. For this reason while the advantages of rotational methods of pasture management are demonstrable and quantifiable at 5 to 10% increase over continuous stocking methods, the ease and lower costs of the latter methods have resulted in recent years in their widespread adoption or readoption. But they are now practised at stocking rates two or three times higher than those adopted in the 1930s and research has enabled the effects of the different grazing methods to be defined and distinguished.

In recent years the Hill Farming Research Organisation has developed better management methods for hill grazing. These depend on early work on hill pasture improvement by the Welsh Plant Breeding Station, the concept of complementary grazing developed by Gregor at the Scottish Society for Research in Plant Breeding, and the analyses of the nutrient requirements of hill ewes. As a result of the application of these principles production on some hill farms has been doubled at costs far below the returns received (HFRO, 1979).

With current knowledge and a high level of technology recent work at the Grassland Research Institute at Hurley has shown that milk yields of 5000–6000 kg per cow are attainable from diets based mainly or exclusively on forage. The potential productivity from grass has also been demonstrated for beef and lamb production by work at Hurley. The widely practised 18-month beef system, stimulated partly by the challenge from intensive cereal-beef, was developed at Hurley (Baker et al., 1967) and can produce over 1000 kg ha$^{-1}$ liveweight gain while the "Grasslambs" system, the intensive management of ewes with lambs, can also achieve gains of about 1000 kg ha$^{-1}$ of lamb in the grazing season.

## Applied Physiology

Following the initiatives of Marshall and of Hammond in Cambridge many studies based on anatomy and physiology of farm animals have contributed to understanding and control of growth and development of farm animals, of reproduction and of milk production.

### The control of growth

Hammond's book "Growth and the development of mutton qualities of the sheep" (Oliver and Boyd, Edinburgh (1932)) stimulated studies by McMeekan on pigs and by Palsson and Verges on sheep at Cambridge, by Wilson on poultry at Wye and on goats at Makerere (Uganda), followed by further work and re-analysis at the Rowett Institute and the Meat Research Institute and by dissection of cattle of several beef crosses by the Meat and Livestock Commission.

Hammond and his colleagues described in detail the changes in the weights and proportions of the major tissues, bone, muscle and fat in the body as it developed and examined the influence of sex and nutritional plane on these developments. They suggested that plane of nutrition could influence considerably the relative proportions of the tissues. However both Wallace and Wilson pointed out that the variable proportion of fat (the reserve tissue) in the carcass distorted these conclusions and Elsley, McDonald and Fowler (1964) in a re-analysis of earlier data showed that when proportions of tissues were expressed relative to the fat-free body mass (or the mass of bone plus muscle) the differences within a breed type attributable to variations in the plane of nutrition were small. However, their review confirmed that of the major tissues, bone was the earliest maturing and fat the latest, and agreed with the observation of many stockmen that the head and neck increased relative to the body mass, when feed was restricted. This later work, supported by the anatomical dissections of cattle by Butterfield and Berg in Australia, indicated that the relative proportion of the muscles in the carcass was but little changed by plane of nutrition or breed. The recent comparisons conducted by the Meat and Livestock Commission on a wide range of cattle breeds have confirmed that when fed on a similar diet and slaughtered at similar proportions of mature weight the differences between breeds are small. Some exceptional breeds, e.g. Limousin cattle and Soay sheep show a higher muscle : bone ratio at a standard proportion of mature body size than the majority of breeds in the species, and may deserve particular attention.

The early and later work has confirmed that as the animal develops, the proportion of fat in the carcass increases, and except in pigs, females generally mature in this sense before castrated males, which in turn mature before entire male animals. Moreover the rate of development is influenced by plane of nutrition, so that inherent growth capacity may be modified by feeding practice.

A clear application of this knowledge is the widespread adoption of relatively high quality diets for breeds such as Friesians or Holsteins which naturally mature late and conversely the preference for early maturing types of cattle such as Aberdeen Angus or Hereford when the nutritional conditions are poor.

McMeekan and Palsson varied growth rate by controlling nutritional plane over the lifetime of the animal. In practice, nutrition at some periods of life may be inadequate to sustain growth. The consequences of such treatments have been examined. Tissues are then utilised in reverse order to that in which they are laid down, fat being catabolised first. This need not permanently affect the animal provided at a later date it receives sufficient feed to compensate for its deprivation. An exception may occur when the animal is very young when cell division may be impaired in tissues which may then not recover fully. The phenomenon of compensatory growth is of practical importance for animals with a longer life span, since some retardation while feed is expensive can be recouped when feed is cheap and plentiful as on pasture.

Changes in growth rate and body composition are under the control of the hormones secreted by the endocrine glands, themselves a reflection of the genotype of the animal. The possibility that exogenous hormones might be administered to modify growth has been examined. The administration of stilboestrol or of its synthetic analogue hexoestrol was found in the 1950s to delay maturation and allow sheep and cattle to develop a higher proportion of lean at an acceptable carcass weight and, since fat is more costly to deposit, some economy in feed was demonstrated. The use of entire male animals for meat production in preference to castrated males was found to have a similar effect.

However these procedures have been regarded as hazardous because exogenous hormone residues might remain in the meat and endogenous hormones might lead to undesirable flavours in the meat (e.g. boar taint). They may also be dangerous since young bulls may be aggressive. The search continues for non-hormonal growth promoters and several are now being investigated.

In investigations on the efficiency with which feed is used for body tissue formation several serial slaughter trials have been made with farm animals and the changes in carcass composition with time have been related to feed consumed. These generally show that as the proportion of fat deposited increases so does the quantity and cost of feed per unit gain. Indeed, in most of our meat animals the final development of "finish" is attained at an uneconomic cost.

Calorimetric investigations of the economy of lean and fat deposition have shown that while the energy cost of fat deposition per unit weight is much higher than for lean tissue, the energetic efficiency of the transformation is similar. Moreover, partly because of the greater insulative property of fat the maintenance requirement of the fat animal is relatively less than the lean animal (Webster, 1977).

In considering the growth and development of meat animals reference should be made to body condition scoring. Stockmen have for long assessed bodily condition in a subjective manner. Recently this has been standardised, and the fat reserves on the spinous processes of the lumbar vertebrae, assessed by handling, are used as a guide to the condition of the animal for breeding, for milk production, and for slaughter. Such a method has considerable value since it is cheaper and probably as useful as weighing. In pigs of course similar measures have been used to assess carcass fatness, on the live animal by the use of ultrasonics, and on the carcass by use of a calibrated probe.

Intensity and duration of light affect reproductive behaviour in sheep and poultry. The control of light regimes is now commonly adopted in commercial poultry production, both to control development of pullets to point-of-lay and to maximise egg production. By these means the seasonality of egg production has been largely overcome.

## Carcass quality

Animal husbandry is concerned primarily with the production of animal products as far as "the farm gate". However meat quality is influenced to some extent by the treatment applied to the animals on the farm. In the 1940s Callow working at the Low Temperature Research Station in association with Hammond, organised detailed dissections and analyses of meat animals and showed that for beef, mutton and pig meat over a wide range of maturity, protein content and calorific value of the meat could be predicted accurately from the fat content of the boneless meat.

The work at the Low Temperature Research Station expanded when the Meat Research Institute was set up at Langford near Bristol in 1967. While much of the Institute's programme is concerned with the processing and hygiene of meat after slaughter it included a Production Division interested in the "factors in the breeding, selection, rearing and slaughter of animals that influence the composition of the carcass or the quality of the meat". The activities of this Division included production of animals under controlled conditions and collaboration with other organisations within and outwith the Agricultural Research Service. Recent topics of particular interest concern the use of entire male animals for meat production, the importance of pre-slaughter treatment on meat quality, the comparative merits of different breeds of meat animal and the development of systems of carcass classification.

Many growth studies have shown that the uncastrated boar, ram or bull grows more rapidly, matures later, provides a leaner carcass and requires rather less food per unit of lean meat than the castrate or the female. Abandoning castration would also reduce stress on young animals and reduce costs. Nevertheless there remains a widespread prejudice by butchers and consumers against boar meat and bull meat, and only in abnormal circumstances do farms raise entire ram lambs or bulls for meat production. Androstenone is responsible for boar taint, and its incidence varies between boars. It may be possible to select against this trait or to develop immunological methods of combating it. The taint develops with age and in the majority of boars no problem is encountered before 140 days. However the taint is identified to a greater extent by women than by men and many retailers are not prepared to accept the risk of rejection by their customers.

With bull beef a different problem arises. The animals tend to be excitable so that minimal disturbance and the maintenance of group homogeneity is important. Young bulls subjected to stress in transport to the abattoir, may yield carcasses with muscle pH in rigor as high as 6.5. This results in dark, firm, dry meat which impairs quality. Taste panel and other assessments of eating quality have all emphasised the importance of the last 24 hours of life and the first 24 hours after slaughter. Only if the stock can be adequately nourished and handled with minimum stress in the period before slaughter will the best quality of meat be provided. Another example of this, and a possible forewarning for other species, is found in the response of some breeds or types of pig after slaughter. Some carcasses develop acidity to pH 5.5–5.8 very rapidly and because of the denaturation of the muscle protein from the interaction of acidity and temperature the meat appears pale, soft in texture and exudes fluid from the cut surfaces. This pale, soft exudative (PSE) condition is frequently found when animals suffer stress before slaughter. It is widespread in the Pietrain breed of pig (Plate 1) and also appears to be increasing in rapidly-growing selections of other breeds. The susceptibility to stress has been found to be an inherited character, identifiable in young pigs by the halothane test and it may be possible to select against it.

Apart from the recognised incidence of PSE in the Pietrain there have been many studies to evaluate differences in meat quality between breeds of farm animal. Comparisons of breeds and breed crosses made by the Meat Research Institute on their own experiments, and on cattle carcasses provided from the beef breed evaluations conducted by the Meat and Livestock Commission, have recorded no major differences.

In both nutritional and economic terms the final stages of finishing in meat animals are costly. This, the reduced energy requirements of an increasingly sedentary consumer population, and the possible health hazards from the consumption of large quantities of fat, have encouraged a trend to leaner carcasses. Increased fatness reduces yield of saleable meat; the Meat Research Institute has co-operated with the Meat and Livestock Commission in devising standards for classifying carcasses, paying attention to fatness and conformation.

For cattle and sheep this classification is based on visual observation related to standardised scales, for pigs additional measures or probes of back fat thickness are

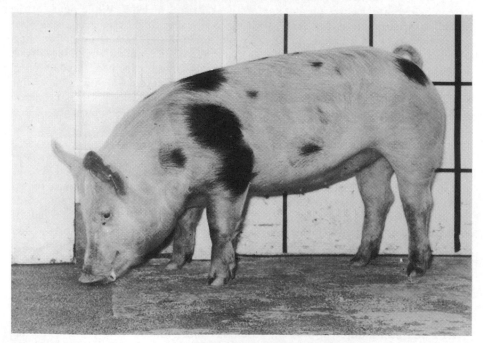

*Plate 1* The Pietrain. A breed of pig which is particularly susceptible to stress.

recorded. The object was not only to describe the type of carcass objectively so that buyers of meat could select the type which suited their business, but also to guide farmers in producing the leaner more economic carcass. It is unfortunate that trade prejudices have hampered acceptance of this development.

## Milk secretion

The physiology and biochemistry of milk secretion has received much attention at Shinfield and Babraham. The detailed anatomy and physiology of the mammary gland is now well described and the relevance of diet and of rumen fermentation in milk composition has been the subject of considerable research described by Dr. Rook in this volume.

Understanding of milk production was transformed when Ely and Petersen in Minnesota (1941) demonstrated the neurohormonal control of milk ejection. Application of the theory to the organisation of milking techniques is now standard. It is established that milk secretion is continuous at a rate which declines only slowly under normal conditions. Milk ejection occurs in response to natural or conditioned stimuli. The implication of prolactin, growth hormone, thyroid hormone, and adrenocortical hormones in milk secretion, and of oxytocin in milk ejection, has been demonstrated. Differences have been found in the hormone balance of milking and beef breeds of cattle but attempts to modify milk production by providing exogenous hormones, such as thyroxine, or oestrogens, have been shown to have little practical application.

The detailed studies of milk ejection following Ely and Petersen have a direct influence on husbandry. The stimulus of udder washing which substitutes in the cow for the nuzzling of the calf, elicits an almost immediate release of oxytocin from the posterior pituitary. This, transported in the blood stream, causes contraction of the myo-epithelial cells surrounding the secretory alveoli in the mammary gland and results in milk ejection when milking can be easily accomplished. The effect normally lasts for only 5–10 minutes. Delays in milking after stimulus, or the release of adrenalin, caused by fright or disturbance of cows impair milk ejection. These principles are now included in modern milking routines which emphasise the important of regularity of routine, providing adequate stimulus by washing or massaging the udder, and avoiding disturbance.

## Milking technology

Machine milking is now almost universal in advanced dairy farming countries and in Britain milking installations have increased from under 5000 in the early 1930s to over 50 000 in 1980. Machine milking has been the subject of much research, particularly at Shinfield in close collaboration with manufacturers of milking machines and related equipment. Basic studies on the mechanism of milking, the improvement of equipment, the organisation of the work routine, the epidemiology of mastitis and the maintenance of hygienic conditions have been conducted, and improved methods have been put into practice.

The mode of operation of the double-acting milking machine was not understood until cine-radiographic studies were reported in 1958. These and associated studies demonstrated the action of the milking machine liner throughout its cycle, recorded the variation in vacuum to which the teat was exposed, and measured the characteristics of teat cup liners as they opened and closed under the influence of the pulsation cycle. "Machine Milking" edited by Thiel and Dodd (1977 and 1979) summarises much of the work done at Shinfield.

The sampling procedures and sampling errors in milk recording have been examined at Shinfield and the Hannah Institute and form the basis of current National Milk Recording practices. Analyses of such data have increased knowledge of the factors influencing milk yield and the components of the lactation curve.

Lactation yield is closely associated with the size of the cow and with her dairy merit; it normally increases with age. The nutritional environment affected directly by feeding, and indirectly by season of calving, has an appreciable influence on yield and the physiological state of the cow with respect to pregnancy and length of calving interval is also important. In order to compare the inherent merit of cows of different ages, and seasons of calving, correction factors have been calculated. The principles were outlined by Dodd (1957) and the Milk Marketing Board of England and Wales has recently implemented a cow index which enables the farmer to assess the relative merit of all the cows in the herd.

Statistical analysis of the lactation curve has also shown that the peak or maximal daily yield of the cow has 3–4 times the influence of persistency (or rate of decline in daily yield) on total yield and this indeed is the justification for some patterns of cow feeding. Moreover the successful fitting of prediction equations of the form:

$$Y_n = a n^b e^{-cn}$$

[where $Y_n$ = daily yield in week n, e is the base of natural logarithms and a, b and c are constants measuring average yield level, initial rise in yield and persistency respectively] by Wood (1969) of the Milk Marketing Board, together with the availability of milk records on farms and computers for rapid calculation, has made it possible to forecast individual and herd milk yields, a valuable guide for more accurate feeding and management.

## Mastitis

Mastitis, an inflammation of the udder, has been a serious and chronic disease occurring in clinical form in about 10% of cows and in sub-clinical form (detectable only by biological or chemical examination of the milk) in about 50% of the cows in a herd. The milking machine which is used successively on 8–15 cows at each milking was obviously a potential vector. A range of chemicals and antibiotics which could control the bacteria (Streptococci and Staphylococci) generally responsible for mastitis, were introduced in the 1940s and 1950s but surveys have shown that their use resulted in no dramatic reduction in the incidence of mastitis although there was some change in the bacterial flora.

Dodd and his colleagues at Shinfield, together with the Central Veterinary Laboratory, began a comprehensive study of this problem, including large well-controlled farm experiments, in the late 1950s which led to the widespread application of a series of control measures. Unfortunately control is not attainable from a single treatment or injection. It requires consistent careful management by the stockmen to reduce the persistence of mastitis from one lactation to the next by the careful administration of long-lasting antibiotics to each cow as she is dried off, together with regular (14 times a week) treatment of the teats of each milking cow at the end of each milking to counteract the spread of bacteria by the milking machine. It is not surprising that complete control has not been achieved since, because of human failings, the measures are sometimes ineffective. In addition in some herds peculiar conditions or unusual organisms are responsible. These problems are now being investigated.

## Milk Hygiene

Milk as it comes from the cow, warm and with readily available nutrients is an excellent substrate for bacterial growth. Rapid cooling of the milk and maintenance of a high standard of hygiene in milking machinery and receptacles are therefore essential. Work at Shinfield and the Hannah Institute provided the technical background for recent developments. In the 1930s and 1940s thorough cleaning with hot water and detergents was practised and disinfection of milking machinery and equipment was done with steam or boiling water. These methods were costly and inconvenient and in the search for simpler procedures, immersion of rubbers in caustic soda solution, and the use of hypochlorites, and quaternary ammonium compounds have been investigated. For complex milking parlours, methods of cleaning and disinfecting in position, circulation cleaning, and disinfection of milk cooling equipment have been developed. Development and validation of improved methods depended on mechanical and bacteriological expertise and many of these studies were made at Shinfield. An example is the acidified boiling water technique which is now applied to recorder milking machines. A solution of nitric or sulphamic acid is added to boiling water and circulated at a temperature above 96°C through all the rubber, metal and glass components of the milking machine. The acid prevents the deposition of salts from hard waters and, provided all the surfaces reach 77°C, disinfection is achieved by the high temperature. The method makes little demand on labour and does not accelerate deterioration of rubber.

Although this aspect of dairy technology may seem far removed from animal husbandry the maintenance of a high standard of hygiene in milk production is vital and it is therefore an essential component of dairy husbandry.

## Animal Behaviour

Observation of animal behaviour has always been an important aspect of the stockman's art, enabling him to anticipate events such as oestrus, parturition and illness, and on occasion to avoid attack. Recently it has become a more or less objective scientific discipline providing a better understanding of the effects of modifications to normal husbandry, and, it is hoped, contributing to the improvement of animal welfare.

One aspect has been merely the accurate observation and recording of normal behaviour. A knowledge of the frequency of suckling of the baby piglet (approximately once per hour) or the lamb (5–6 times per day) in normal conditions was essential before accurate measurements of milk intake by these young could be recorded. Observation of grazing behaviour and of the normal pattern of grazing, showing that from six to eleven hours might be spent on grazing and that peak grazing times occurred at and just after dawn and for some time before dark, influenced the choice of grazing management procedures particularly for dairy cattle. Similarly a knowledge of the frequency of drinking stressed the importance of providing ample water for dairy cows after milking.

The Brambell Committee (HMSO 1965) focussed attention on the adverse effect which some systems of husbandry might have on animal welfare and on the lack of precise measures of the effects of stress on animal welfare or performance. The search for objective measures of stress continues, a difficulty being that some of the measures are themselves stress producing. However records of the effects of husbandry practices, show for example, that increased stocking density with chickens and pigs in particular, results in an increase in the number of aggressive encounters, a reduction in sleep (in pigs) and a decline in production per animal. Changes in group composition as when piglets are grouped after weaning into fattening pens or when cows are regrouped at intervals according to milk yield or stage of lactation, disturb the hierarchy which has been established and may temporarily at least, result in increase in adrenal size and a decline in production. The practical conclusions from these studies are that if at all possible groups of stock once assembled should not be changed. This applies particularly to pigs for fattening, bull beef and to dairy cows, loose housed in winter. In small groups there is an indication that even numbers are preferred.

Close confinement of stock may result in obvious damage, feather picking in chickens and tail biting in pigs being major examples, each attributable to a barren environment which together with close confinement, allows little opportunity for animals to escape from aggression. Improved pen layouts for chickens have been proposed. With pigs, providing straw (unfortunately inimical to some slurry disposal systems) has often alleviated the problem. Providing such materials also reduces the incidence of stress and "displacement activities" in stalled sows.

That transport of livestock can involve stress was demonstrated dramatically with the Pietrain breed of pigs introduced in Britain in the 1960s, which suffered a high proportion of fatalities in transit. The normal oestrus cycle of cattle has also been disturbed.

Finally of the examples of studies in animal behaviour are investigations at Babraham on "operant conditioning" where chickens are offered the opportunity to demonstrate their preference for floor covering, or chickens and pigs are trained to control temperature and air flow of their housing. These methods have been used in an attempt to discover the environment preferred by the animal. How truly they reflect the requirement as opposed to the preference of the animal is of course debatable.

The accumulation of ethological knowledge in research on animal production may assist in the development of a scientific basis for proper utilization of the productive potential of animals while animal welfare is not impaired, but it is a particularly difficult area for research.


## Animal Breeding

The term animal breeding refers both to the maintenance of the reproductive cycle, since meat and milk production both depend on the regular production of young, and to improving the productive potential of the species by applying genetic theory. The latter aspect is dealt with by Dr. King in this volume.

Maintenance of breeding females is a major cost in all forms of animal husbandry. With beef cattle and sheep which may produce one or rarely two young a year, avoiding barrenness and if possible, increasing the number of births per year could be worth while. With sheep for example doubling the present average of 1.4 lambs reared per ewe mated would result in an increase from 0.3 to 0.5 g protein produced per MJ of total gross energy consumed per year. With milk cows and sows, regular breeding with one birth per year for cows and at least two parturitions per year for sows are essential for profitable and efficient management.

Research workers with Hammond at Cambridge, at Babraham and at Nottingham University have investigated the hormonal interrelationships which affect the reproductive cycle. Aside from disease, reproductive failure may result from interrupting the oestrus cycle, failure to observe oestrus, failure of mating or failure of the zygote to implant in the placenta. When artificial insemination is used detection of oestrus is most important; various devices have been developed, but detailed observation of animal behaviour is still essential and it is recommended that stockmen should allot time at intervals throughout the day and evening for observation.

The attempt to over-ride the natural cycle by using prostaglandins, so that group matings can be organised according to a timetable, is an example of the application of new knowledge of endocrine control.

With cows and sheep inducing multiple ovulation by providing exogenous hormones at the appropriate point in the oestrus cycle has been investigated. Unfortunately the variability between individuals is such that precise dose levels have proved elusive. Longer term selection procedures, possibly with cross breeding to develop breeds or strains of high prolificacy, may prove more reliable. The possibility, developed at the Animal Research Station of the Institute of Animal Physiology, that fertilized ova may be transferred by non-surgical means to develop in recipient cows raises possibilities both of increases in biological efficiency, by implanting twins, and of increasing the proportion of stock of high genetic merit.

One of the functions of animal production research is to explore the limits of productivity since even if the methods are currently uneconomic they may reveal new opportunities for practical developments. Some such studies have been conducted with sheep at Hurley, the Rowett Institute and Reading University. These seasonally polyoestrus animals have a gestation length of about 5 months. Allowing for normal weaning, the production of three litters in two years instead of the normal one per year, is possible. Combinations of nutrition, control of day length and the use of hormones have enabled Rowett Institute workers to develop a select flock with a mean litter size of over two lambs per ewe producing over 3.5 lambs per ewe per year.

With milking cows accurate methods of pregnancy diagnosis and management control are valuable aids to management. The recent development of an assay of progesterone in the milk derives from basic studies on hormone levels in pregnancy made at the Royal Veterinary College, Babraham and Nottingham University. That such fundamental studies can be applied rapidly is shown by the provision by the Milk Marketing Board, within a year or so, of a diagnostic service, by which from a milk sample taken 24 days after insemination a clear indication of non-pregnancy and a reasonably accurate prediction of pregnancy can be given.

## Novel Meat Animals

To be an efficient food producer an animal must have a high reproductive rate and, or, attain high production (of meat, milk or eggs) relative to body size. It should also be well adapted to particular environments or satisfy a particular market demand. The number of domesticated animals normally used for food production is small and other possible animals have been considered from time to time. The red deer and the rabbit have been studied recently.

The normal domestic animals have been selected, possibly for winter survival in captivity, so that they now tend to contain large proportions of saturated fat in the carcass, a possible hazard to human health. Deer and rabbit, in contrast, provide carcasses low in fat content.

The red deer has been studied in detail by the Hill Farming Research Organisation in collaboration with the Rowett Research Institute (Plate 2). Its reproductive rate is low but it normally has a long life and hence a low replacement rate and its growth rate is comparable with sheep. However, although it may survive better than sheep in adverse conditions, it is probably at the limit of its climatic adaptation on the Scottish mountains and is better adapted to the open forests than the higher hills.

Rabbits are raised both for meat and for pelt production. Although the meat is low in fat content and the relative growth rate is similar to other domestic animals, the reproductive rate of the rabbit relative to the maintenance cost of the dam, is not exceptionally high. Moreover it has not responded to intensive management so readily as chickens and pigs and is best suited to small scale enterprises.

Deer and rabbit are both now exploited on a small scale, but they depend rather heavily on export prices for profitability.

*Plate 2* Mustering deer at the Hill Farming Research Organisation/Rowett Research Institute red deer research station.

## Research Management

There has been considerable expansion of the facilities for research in animal husbandry, both by an increase in the number of Institutes and in the numbers of animals and facilities within the Institutes. A recent estimate of the numbers of cattle, sheep and pigs available for research is in Table 3. Although these numbers appear to be large the design and analysis of animal experiments has become increasingly complex.

Table 3

Approximate numbers of animals available for experimentation in the Agricultural Research Service in 1980.

| Ruminants | | Non-ruminants | |
|---|---|---|---|
| Cows | 1 700 | Sows and gilts | 900 |
| Other cattle | 4 000 | Other pigs | 6 000 |
| Ewes | 13 500 | Laying poultry | 15 000 |
| Other sheep | 15 000 | Other poultry | 23 000 |
| Goats | 400 | | |
| Deer | 370 | | |

Moreover it has been increasingly realised that experiments which show no significant differences between treatments may be misleading if the experimental design is not sufficiently precise to measure as significant a difference which could be of economic importance. A difference in milk yield of only 1 kg per cow per day could be of considerable economic importance in a herd of 100 or more milk cows but to detect it as a significant effect in an experiment would require groups of about 100 cows on each treatment. The numbers of animals needed to establish significant differences in various circumstances are shown in Table 4.

Table 4

The numbers of animals required to detect treatment differences
of 5% and 10%.

| Coefficient of variation | Expected treatment difference | | | | | |
|---|---|---|---|---|---|---|
| | 10% | | | 5% | | |
| | 0.9* | 0.8* | 0.5* | 0.9* | 0.8* | 0.5* |
| 20% | 86 | 64 | 32 | 338 | 254 | 124 |
| 10% | 23 | 17 | 9 | 86 | 64 | 32 |

*probability of detecting a treatment difference; e.g. to ensure an 80%
chance of detecting a 5% difference in a character with 20% coefficient of
variation, 254 animals per group would be required.

A further difficulty is the major influence of the management and environment both
at a particular research centre and in practical farming. To overcome the requirements
for large numbers in some experiments and the possible variations between sites a
number of co-ordinated experiments have been conducted. Successful examples are the
ARC co-ordinated experiments on pigs initiated and co-ordinated by Braude and by
Greenhalgh. Such experiments can be effective only if the possibility of human error
is virtually eliminated, by for example, central formulation and labelling of test diets,
and preferably if the management environment is unlikely to influence the result. A
study which compared the effect of various growth substances, implanted in the animal,
by one operator is for example much more likely to succeed than one which involved
comparison of different teat dips applied by several operatives over long periods to
milking cows in a number of herds.

A disadvantage of the co-ordinated experiment is the logistic problem of assembling
the data, analysing them and presenting a report. In several instances many years
elapse before the final report and indeed events may by that time have changed the
situation.

The complexity of agricultural research, the observation that seldom did a new
treatment have a single easily identifiable effect on the farm organisation, and the
impossibility of conducting many massive experiments in the field, has encouraged the
application of the "systems approach" to agricultural experimentation. Work by
Spedding at Hurley and by Eadie at Hill Farming Research Organisation is particularly
relevant. In this approach, when a production system is to be investigated a list of the
contributory factors is made and a conceptual framework is developed in which the
known links of the various components are indicated. Where possible, quantitative
relationships between the components are derived from experimental data. When the
information does not exist (and one merit of such an approach is the identification of
areas of uncertainty) a best guess, or a series of values must be assumed. (It is however
important that these be validated as soon as possible.) From these data a mathematical
predictive model is formed and tested or validated against existing recorded data. It is
then possible to synthesise new systems, to explore novel approaches and gain an
indication of their likely outcome, their sensitivity to price changes or weather fluctuations. This approach will expand.

A major problem of research management in general and in the narrower field of
animal husbandry is resource allocation, the identification of the important research
areas, and those which will yield the best returns. Initially this depended largely on the
initiative of the research worker, the guidance given within his Institute and the advice,
formal and informal, which he could gain from advisers and farmers. The institution
in 1973 of the Joint Consultative Organisation for Research and Development in
Agriculture and Food (JCO), attempted to put this on a more formal basis, with the

Ministry of Agriculture, Fisheries and Food and other sponsors commissioning areas of more applied work on the basis of advice from the JCO Committees and from their own co-ordinating organisation. In theory a comprehensive systems approach would indicate the priorities unequivocally. But vital information may be lacking and technical possibilities are influenced by political and economic changes. So far therefore informed judgement appears to be the best available guideline. As in so many other affairs, complex organisation introduces delay and can stifle initiative. It remains important that the research worker and his own organisation should be aware of the problems of the industry but it is an increasing function of the ARC and its staff to maintain liaison, to encourage collaborative studies where this is appropriate, and to offer guidance on the direction of research.

## The Future

The impact of science on animal husbandry in the past 50 years has been dramatic. Whether progress could continue at recent rates is debatable, prediction is notoriously unreliable, and future developments are much affected by the political and economic situation. In the United Kingdom some 66% of all temperate food products are at present home produced. This could be increased to near 100% particularly if less emphasis was given to animal products in the diet. However, within the EEC, food production is already virtually equal to requirements and prices are likely to discourage expanded production.

Technical progress is likely to continue albeit at a less rapid rate. If increased production were required the most rapid increase would come from the application of existing knowledge to a greater proportion of the farming industry. This is a task which agricultural advisory services have found to be extremely difficult. Some progress may

*Plate 3* Clun Forest sheep from the Institute of Animal Physiology which won First Prizes at the Royal Show in 1979.

however be expected from the growing tendency for advisory targets, guidelines or blueprints to be provided, particularly where these can be combined with simple, or easily operated monitoring devices possibly effected by computer, as for example the comparison of pig performances with the Edinburgh Pig Model, or of dairy herd performances with the Milk Marketing Board's Herd Management Control.

If food production is judged to be sufficient, there remains a role for research to devise alternative simpler or less energy demanding methods of production. There is also growing public concern with aspects of animal welfare and of pollution associated with animal production and these will require continued attention.

Finally it may be suggested that animal husbandry is not suited to mass production methods and that medium scale enterprises which can enlist the interest, enthusiasm and enjoyment of the operator are more likely to provide human satisfaction and acceptable animal production than a continued increase in the scale of production. The intangible satisfactions in animal husbandry should not be ignored. It is rather pleasant that the Institute of Animal Physiology, concerned with some of the most fundamental aspects of animal science, should also maintain flocks and herds which win prizes at Agricultural Shows (Plate 3).

I am grateful to many colleagues past and present whose work has contributed to the formulation of this paper and to Dr. J. C. Tayler who read it in draft, made many helpful suggestions and assembled the data in Table 3.

## Poultry Production

by D. W. F. Shannon, ARC Poultry Research Centre, Edinburgh

The application of science and technology has had dramatic effects in poultry production. Methods of production have been revolutionised by the introduction of intensive environmentally controlled houses equipped with battery cages, in place of the extensive range system. Poultry meat has become established as a regular and cheap item of food rather than the luxury product it was 50 years ago. The changes in production methods which these developments entail have been made possible by increased knowledge (a) of the bird's nutritional requirements, (b) of poultry diseases and their control, as described by K. N. Burns in this volume, and (c) of the bird's environmental requirements for maximum productivity. Another dominating factor has been the provision of superior stock by commercial breeding companies through the application of the principles of quantitative genetics.

The denial of access to grass range and the limited scope for vitamin syntheses through microbial fermentation in the bird's digestive tract mean that modern poultry depend on the feed provided by man for their nutritional needs. The importance of poultry nutrition was recognised by the Council and this was to be one of the founding disciplines when the Poultry Research Centre (PRC) was established in 1947.

Two of the major contributions that nutritionists have made, have been in defining the specific nutrients required by the different classes of poultry and in developing the technology to allow these requirements to be met economically by blending the available feedingstuffs appropriately.

The inability of the chick to synthesise significant quantities of many of the vitamins it required, made it an ideal animal model for vitamin research. The vitamins required by poultry were established, but the need for continued vigilance was highlighted by recent research at the Poultry Research Centre on the biotin responsive condition Fatty Liver and Kidney Syndrome. Described in K. N. Burns' essay, this work showed how the greater biotin requirement of modern fast-growing birds and changes in feed ingredients combined to create an unexpected vitamin deficiency.

Efficient poultry production depends on making optimum use of the available feedingstuffs and poultry nutritionists have made a distinctive contribution to the technology of feed evaluation and economic diet formulation. The greater nutritive value of maize than oats was still a matter of doubt in the early 1930s. Through a series of digestibility experiments on the cereals and their by-products, Bolton, at the Poultry Research Centre, demonstrated that the system of feed evaluation used for ruminant feeds (proximate analysis) was inappropriate for poultry. He, and others working at Cambridge, recognised that the digestibility of certain carbohydrate fractions varied considerably from one feedingstuff to another. They proposed that the system of evaluation should emphasise the importance of the digestible fractions and developed improved techniques of feedingstuffs evaluation based on sugar analyses.

Modelling techniques, used notably at Reading University and subsequently at the Poultry Research Centre, have led to significant improvements in the assessment of nutrient requirements. It was recognised that the production response of the bird was directly related to the amount of the nutrient ingested and that for animals with free access to feed, this was only indirectly related to the concentration of nutrient in the feed. Moreover, although the production response of birds was the summation of the responses of individuals within the flock, the shape of the flock response curve was distinctly different from that of an individual. The integration of information on flock responses to nutrient intake with data on the nutrient content of feeds, allows the economic optimisation of the feeding process.

Concern about the dependence of poultry on feeds that might also be eaten by humans has prompted research at the Poultry Research Centre and elsewhere to establish the potential value of unconventional feedstuffs, including the microbial protein produced by biotechnology.

The introduction of intensive husbandry methods in the 1950s permitted closer control of a number of important environmental factors. It had been recognised many years earlier that the increase of day-length during the winter months by artificial lighting reduced the magnitude of the seasonal decline in egg production. The introduction of windowless houses allowed much greater control of day-length. Research, particularly at Reading University, on the response of the bird to varying day-lengths and on the effect of day-length on sexual maturity laid the foundations for current lighting practice. Work is continuing at a number of centres to elucidate the hormonal control mechanisms.

Control of environmental temperature has helped to improve the utilisation of feed by laying birds. Research at Nottingham University and Queen's University, Belfast, had shown that the heat production and hence feed intake of birds decreased as house temperature was increased above that commonly used in practice. Refinement of the minimum ventilation requirements and the demonstration that the higher temperatures could be achieved without supplementary heating (at Gleadthorpe Experimental Husbandry Farm), led to the widespread use of higher, and hence more economical, poultry house temperatures, e.g. 21°C. The success of modern husbandry and housing methods owes much to the developments in knowledge of poultry diseases and their control (described in K. N. Burns' essay).

The development of improved lines of growing and laying stock by the poultry breeding companies has been an important factor in improving the efficiency of poultry production. The development of artificial insemination and long-term semen storage techniques at the Poultry Research Centre are likely to contribute to the efficiency of future breeding programmes.

In this short review, it has been possible to mention only some of the developments which have contributed to the advances in poultry production. Many others, such as the development of complete feeds, the elucidation of the role of calcium and other minerals in poultry nutrition, and husbandry and engineering developments, have also been important.

Finally, not all the developments have the approval of all members of society. There is widespread debate about the welfare of farm animals housed in modern intensive systems. Whatever the outcome of this debate, many of the scientific and technological developments with poultry will be equally applicable under other systems of poultry housing.

## Further Reading

Baker, R. D., Kilkenny, J. B., Spedding, A. W. and Tayler, J. C. (1967) An intensive system of beef production from grassland using autumn born calves from the dairy herd. *Beef production Handbook. No. 1.* Beef Recording Association, Reading, UK

Blaxter, K. L. (1962) *The Energy Metabolism of Ruminants.* London: Hutchinson

Dodd, F. H. (1957). Factors affecting the rate of secretion of milk and lactation yield. Chap 20. In: *Progress in the Physiology of Farm Animals.* (pp. 962–1004). Ed. Hammond. London: Butterworth

Elsley, F. W. H., McDonald, I. and Fowler, V. R. (1964) The effect of plane of nutrition on the carcasses of pigs and lambs when variations in fat content are excluded. *Animal Production:* **6:** 141–154

Ely, F. and Petersen, W. E. (1941) Factors involved in the ejection of milk. *Journal of Dairy Science.* **24:** 211–223

HMSO (1965) *Report of the Technical Committee to enquire into the welfare of animals kept under intensive livestock husbandry systems.* Cmnd. 2836. London: HMSO

HFRO (1979) *Science and Hill Farming. 1954–1979.* Hill Farming Research Organisation: Edinburgh

Holmes, W. (1977). Choosing between animals. *Philosophical Transactions of the Royal Society London,* **B, 281:** 121–137

Leach, G. (1975). *Energy and food production.* 151 pp. International Institute for Environment and Development: London

Leitch, I. and Godden, W. (1942). The efficiency of farm animals in the conversion of feedingstuffs to food for men. Commonwealth Bureau of Animal Nutrition *Technical Communication No 14.* CAB: Farnham Royal, Bucks

MAFF (1975). *Energy allowances and feeding systems for ruminants.* Technical Bulletin No.33 London: HMSO

Michel, J. F. (1976). The epidemiology and control of some nematode infections in grazing animals. *Advances in Parasitology.* **14:** 365–397

Monteith, J. L. and Mount, L. E. (1974). (Eds). *Heat loss from animals and man.* Proceedings of 20th Easter School, University of Nottingham, London: Butterworth.

Roy, J. H. B. (1954, 1959, 1970, 1980). *The calf, management, feeding, nutrition and health.* 4th edition London: Butterworth

Thiel, C. C. and Dodd, F. H. (Eds) (1977, 1979). *Machine Milking.* The National Institute for Research in Dairying, Shinfield, Reading

Webster, A. J. F. (1977). Selection for leanness and the energetic efficiency of growth in meat animals. *Proceedings of the Nutrition Society,* **36:** 56–59.

Wood, P. D. P. (1969). Factors affecting the shape of the lactation curve in cattle. *Animal Production.* **11:** 307–316

# Grassland Research

## W. F. RAYMOND

Ministry of Agriculture, Fisheries and Food, London

In the maritime climate of the British Isles grassland forms the sub-climax vegetation; uncultivated arable land is rapidly colonised by herbaceous plants, mainly Gramineae, and by appropriate cutting or grazing the resulting "permanent pasture" can be prevented from further regression to shrub and woodland. These pastures formed the traditional grassland of Britain. On limited areas the system of "ley-farming" was adopted, in which grass seeds were sown to produce leys within an arable rotation. But most of the seeds sown were from hay meadows, were short-lived, and were rapidly replaced by more persistent but less productive species, mainly agrostis and fescue. Only under superb management, as on the Midland fattening pastures and Romney Marsh, did more productive species, in particular ryegrass and white clover, make a significant contribution.

## Early Research

During the last century a few farming "improvers", notably Elliot at Clifton Park, stressed the importance of better seeds and grassland management, and limited experimental work was done, as in the white clover/basic slag studies of Gilchrist and Somerville at Cockle Park, and the Park Grass Experiment at Rothamsted. Interest in grassland decreased during the agricultural Depression, and with good supplies of cheap imported cereals and oilcakes management and productivity of British grassland progressively deteriorated. This continued until the 1914–18 War. Then the derelict condition of most of the pastures, and the fertility released when they were ploughed for sowing to cereals, aroused the interest of a young botanist, George Stapledon (Plate 1), working in the Food Production Department of the Ministry of Agriculture. Stapledon became convinced that adopting the traditional system of ley farming, but with more persistent and productive grasses replacing the short-lived species of earlier rotations, would greatly improve British agricultural productivity. His enthusiasm led Lord Milford to support the setting up of the Welsh Plant Breeding Station at Aberystwyth in 1919: there Stapledon and his small team established the basis of modern grassland science. The first priority was for more productive and persistent strains of grasses and clovers, and Stapledon and Jenkin reasoned that the most likely sources of these were the small areas of first-class pasture that had survived the Depression. From these they selected seed from the most vigorous plants, developed novel methods for controlling the breeding of these cross-pollinated species, and organised the large-scale multiplication of the progeny. By 1936 the Station had released some dozen new varieties of grasses and legumes, notably more productive than existing commercial stocks; a measure of this achievement is that S23 and S24 ryegrass, S48 timothy, S37 cocksfoot and S100 white clover remain the standards against which the National Institute of Agricultural Botany at Cambridge tests newly-introduced varieties.

Stapledon also recognised the vital role of management in maintaining the productivity of these new "varieties", and his programme soon included work on pasture establishment and cutting and grazing management. Sward persistence was shown to

*Plate 1* Sir George Stapledon, CBE, FRS. Director of the Welsh Plant Breeding Station from 1919 to 1942 and then Director of the Grassland Improvement Station until 1945.

depend on the production of a succession of new tillers, tillering being stimulated by frequent defoliation to prevent flowering — the practice on the best fattening pastures compared with traditional meadows. These studies were supported by the fertilizer trials at Rothamsted, which foreshadowed the key role of N-fertilizers, and by the nutritional studies of Woodman at Cambridge and Watson at Jealott's Hill, which showed that nutritive value increases the more frequently that grass is harvested.

During these early years the Welsh Plant Breeding Station also established close working partnerships with leading farmers which have remained a notable feature of grassland research in UK. New grass varieties, before release, were tested on commercial farms, and farmers such as Bennett Evans played an important role in developing and testing new seeding and management techniques. A significant step was the appointment of William Davies as the Empire Grassland Investigator: from 1931 Davies expounded the Welsh Plant Breeding Station philosophy in New Zealand, Australia, Canada and South Africa and in Europe. The first fully-international grassland meeting was held in Aberystwyth in 1936, and later International Congresses have plotted, and often heralded, the continuing progress of grassland science — as well as hosting some notable controversies.

## Grassland Improvement in 1939–1945

By 1939 a range of improved grass and legume varieties was available to farmers, together with increasingly comprehensive advice on seeds mixtures, on establishment and manuring, and on grazing and cutting management. Yet they had had only minimal impact because British agriculture was again in the Depression of the inter-war years. The disastrous effect on grassland was shown by a survey which Stapledon organised in 1937/38; only a few percent of the total was fully productive and huge areas had reverted to scrub; much was not even tenanted. As a result of this survey, and with war now imminent, Stapledon was asked to initiate research on reclaiming this derelict land. He selected three farms typical of major soil-types to be reclaimed; at Colesbourne on limestone brash, at Mixon Hay on upland peats, and at a main centre at Dodwell-Drayton, on the Midland lias clays.

At these three farms of the Grassland Improvement Station the initial emphasis was on ploughing-up and exploiting the fertility under old grassland for crop production. But Stapledon could now really develop ley farming; in the following years thousands of trial plots were sown, both at Drayton and on commercial farms, and extensive measurements made both of grass produced and of output by grazing animals. Particularly important were the Royal Agricultural Society of England's sponsored trials, which compared live-weight gains by cattle grazing different grades of permanent pasture with gains by cattle grazing leys sown on adjacent fields; only on grade I permanent pasture (less than 1% of the total) did gains equal those from the ley (as at the famous Mill Field at Medbourne in Leicestershire).

## The Post-War Years

By 1946, when Stapledon retired, the basic principles of "ley farming" had been established — and his successor, William Davies, was not unopposed in his advocacy that further research on grassland was needed. But he was strongly supported by leading grassland farmers; the Grassland Improvement Station became the Grassland Research Station, and in 1949 was incorporated as the Grassland Research Institute within the Agricultural Research Service (ARS). By the 1950s the UK had a considerable capability in grassland research, in the Institutes of ARS, in the Experimental Husbandry Farms and Regional Experimental services of the Ministry of Agriculture, Fisheries and Food, at experimental farms run by industry, (in particular by ICI and Fisons), and at Universities and Colleges. Overseas there was increasing interest, stimulated by the first post-war International Grassland Congress in the Netherlands in 1949; grass and legume breeding had become very important.

In the progress of this research two particular features stand out. Firstly, grassland pioneered the interdisciplinary approach in agricultural research; at a time when academic success depended on specialisation, Stapledon, Martin Jones and William Davies were studying the inter-actions between soil, plant and animal, which are today widely accepted but which 40 years ago were viewed with suspicion. Secondly, grassland research, at least until 1970, was notable as much for controversy as for consensus, with grassland scientists adopting dogmatic positions on many subjects. In fact a survey of some of these controversies — on leys and permanent pasture; varieties and seeds mixtures; fertilizer-N and clovers; and on rotational and strip grazing — encompasses much of the contemporary development in grassland science.

## Leys and Permanent Pasture

By 1950 the inherent superiority of leys had become a basic tenet — despite the earlier Rothamsted work and the wartime Royal Agricultural Society trials which had shown that well-managed and fertilized permanent pasture could be as productive as leys. Thus when the Grassland Research Institute moved from Drayton in 1955 it was to an arable farm at Hurley in Berkshire, rather than to a traditional grassland area. The 1958 Caine Committee Report did draw attention to the potential of the millions of acres of under-used grassland in Britain which would never be ploughed. But the advice that the Institute should have a permanent grassland substation was not followed, and research continued to concentrate almost exclusively on sown grassland. It was not until 1971, stimulated by Woodford, that the Permanent Pasture Group, jointly established by the Grassland Research Institute and the Agricultural Development and Advisory Service, was set up — to study a resource which was not only underused but, almost unnoticed, was becoming more important. Or rather, leys were becoming less important as the cost of establishing them increased, and as the need for break-crops in arable farming decreased with advances in methods of cereal-growing; between 1960 and 1977 the area of temporary grassland in Britain decreased by 20%. But any improvement in permanent grass resulted more from the pressure of higher rents and other costs than from the results of research, and the overall improvement of the 5 M ha of lowland grass and the 6 M ha of upland and hill pastures remains a top priority for research in the 1980s.

## Grass and Legume Varieties

The grasses and clovers bred at Aberystwyth in the 1930s were much more persistent and productive than any other varieties then available. From this developed the concept of the inherent superiority of the S-varieties over commercial strains, which unfortunately was hardly questioned until the late 1950s, long after the methods of grass-breeding developed at Aberystwyth had been widely adopted by other breeders, both State and private. Thus a comparison was made at Hurley from 1959–64 of animal production from two "farmlets", sown respectively to "S" and "commercial" varieties of grasses and legumes. While output from the farmlet based on S-varieties was initially higher, by 1964, as a result of the progressive introduction of improved commercial varieties, production from the two farmlets was almost identical. Since then the rate of introduction of new varieties has quickened, further stimulated by the introduction of Plant Variety Rights in 1962; today there are some 80 grass and 40 legume varieties on the National Institute of Agricultural Botany's Recommended List, and the continuing influx of new material is creating problems both in variety testing, and in the profitability of breeding and certification of new varieties. S23 and S24 ryegrass and S100 white clover are still widely sown; but UK-bred varieties are increasingly challenged by European varieties, particularly from Belgium and the Netherlands, with their greater winter-hardiness, first apparent in the severe winter of 1962/63. A series of mild winters and early springs in the 1950s had encouraged the novel concept of all-the-year-round grazing, based on Italian ryegrass for early bite, late-applied nitrogen to encourage autumn growth, and new winter-growing ecotypes of tall fescue. Many

*Plate 2* Plots of perennial ryegrass in experiments at the Grassland Research Institute on long-term evaluation by grazing and cutting techniques (upper photograph) and maximising yield in mid-season (lower photograph).

of these were killed in that winter; with the subsequent more frequent hard winters and less reliable early spring growth, more attention is now paid to breeding and management for survival rather than production in the winter, and to the use of conserved forages rather than grazing for winter feed.

This has been reflected in a more rigorous cold-testing of new breeding material, and the introduction from the Welsh Plant Breeding Station of more winter-hardy varieties of ryegrass such as Mantilla and Augusta. However, despite much work, progress by conventional breeding is now less rapid in grass than in crops such as cereals and potatoes. Future progress will require more complex methods, including basic studies on photosynthesis and nutrient uptake, and for example the production of inter-specific hybrids — as in the Welsh programme to combine the palatability and high digestibility of ryegrass with the persistence of tall fescue. The problem remains that sward productivity depends greatly on sward management; in practice the grassland farmer's management decisions are based on grazing needs and on the weather as much as on the optimum treatment of the variety sown, and more attention is being given to grasses which withstand poor management; to improving digestibility and palatability; and to breeding varieties whose maximum growth is towards mid-summer, when sunshine is greatest.

There was less progress in legume-breeding, partly because legumes are difficult to manage, and can cause bloat in grazing cattle, but mainly because cheap N-fertilizers had made all-grass swards an easier alternative. However more expensive fertilizers, and recent recognition of the inherently high nutritive value of legumes, have revived interest in legume-breeding, with the search for white clovers with longer petioles, better able to compete with vigorous grasses, and for disease-resistant varieties of red clover and lucerne. Good progress has been made — the white clover Olwen from the Welsh Plant Breeding Station can fix up to 300 kg ha$^{-1}$ of N during the growing season — and forage legumes will become more important in the 1980s.

## Seeds Mixtures

Inextricably linked with grass-breeding was a major controversy of the 1950s, that of the composition of seeds mixtures and of simple versus complex mixtures. Again insufficient note was taken of the dominant effect of management on sward productivity. The Cockle Park mixture had been most commonly used as it withstood a wide range of management practices, and, as Martin Jones had shown, responded to different managements by becoming dominant in one of the 3 grass species. In contrast a sward sown to a single variety would need more well-defined management for optimum performance. Hence the profusion of advice on seed mixtures, some with many components, and serving as a main outlet for the new varieties emerging from breeding programmes. Yet, in practice, farmers found that ryegrass swards gave the highest and most reliable levels of animal output, and this has been the main species sown since 1960. A significant outcome was the marked decrease in the use of cocksfoot; its generally inferior animal production, evident from detailed on-farm recording by Rex Paterson in Hampshire, was confirmed by work at Hurley, showing that cocksfoot is inherently less digestible than most other grass species.

At the same time, the use of white clover declined, and, despite the introduction of tetraploid species with greater disease resistance, sowings of red clover also decreased markedly. The area of lucerne also remained small, despite its obvious advantages in drought resistance and N-fixing ability (up to 450 kg ha$^{-1}$ of N), because of difficulties in using the crop, and because few varieties were resistant to verticillium wilt.

## Clovers versus Nitrogen-Fertilizers

Argument first surfaced at the International Congress in the Netherlands in 1949, between scientists from New Zealand on the one hand, and from the Netherlands and

UK on the other, each unwilling to concede the other's case — that Europe had a relatively short growing season for legumes, coupled with an abundant supply of N-fertilizers, while in New Zealand clovers grew during most of the year, while N-fertilizers were expensive. Ryegrass responds well to N, but is then so competitive that white clover can make only a marginal contribution to yield. In contrast under intensive grazing in New Zealand clover makes a major contribution, both to total herbage yield and to symbiotic N-fixation, with much of this N being recycled via animal excreta.

Numerous experiments indicated that, under optimum management in Europe, a white clover/ryegrass sward would fix annually about 200 kg N with a yield potential of 7500 kg ha$^{-1}$ of dry matter. When N was applied to grass there was a linear response of 20–25 kg of dry matter per kg applied N, up to about 400 kg ha$^{-1}$ of N, with a potential yield over 11 000 kg ha$^{-1}$ of dry matter. Grass/nitrogen swards were also easier to manage. So N use in UK increased rapidly (though lagging well behind the Netherlands), and on many swards no clover was sown. In contrast New Zealand continued to exploit livestock production based on ryegrass and vigorous white clover.

Again new factors changed attitudes. Most earlier research had studied legumes primarily as a source of "free" N; little note was taken of their feed potential, until nutritional studies in the late 1960s showed that white clover is of consistently higher digestibility than the grasses, and that legumes have an intake potential much higher than would be expected from their digestibility. Soil fertility studies also showed that legume-rich swards increased subsequent cereal yields more than all-grass swards and this, coupled with better disease control, gives important gains from a legume break in the arable rotation. Finally the 1973 energy crisis led to marked increases in the cost of N-fertilizer (which are likely to continue) and this is leading to a reappraisal of the role of legumes in UK agriculture. Animal production experiments, following the nutritional studies, confirmed that white clover, in particular, gives higher weight gains per unit of dry matter eaten than ryegrass. This could partly redress the lower yield of the ryegrass/clover sward, and has further encouraged the search for management systems which maintain clover in swards fertilized with N. Detailed studies have shown that clover is inhibited not by N-fertilizer *per se*, but by competition for light and water from the grass; clover is encouraged by frequent defoliation, and by avoiding growing large crops for conservation. The new clover varieties with longer petioles are also likely to be more competitive.

The forage legumes red clover, lucerne and sainfoin could also be more widely used, both in improving soil fertility and for their contribution to ruminant diets. They still present problems in management; but, for example, the potential of lucerne silage, as a complement to maize silage in the feeding system developed at Compton, strongly supports further research.

## Grazing Management

The early cutting experiments showed that annual herbage dry-matter yield increased with increase in the period between harvests. It was therefore argued that animal output should be higher from a sward grazed intermittently (paddock or strip grazing) than from the same sward grazed continuously; this proposition was tested, and confirmed, in numerous grazing experiments during the 1950s. So there was some consternation at the International Congress in New Zealand in 1956 when McMeekan reported almost identical levels of milk yield from a 3-year comparison of rotational grazing and set-stocking of dairy cows at Ruakura.

The cause of this divergence was analysed in a key paper presented by Mott of USA at the Eighth International Congress held at Reading in 1960. Using the model of Fig. 1, Mott examined the inter-relationship between outputs per animal and per hectare

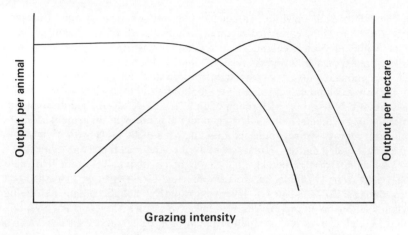

*Figure 1* The effect of grazing intensity on levels of animal output, per animal and per hectare (Mott, 1960).

at different animal stocking rates (equivalent over short periods to different grazing intensities); output per hectare continues to increase well beyond the stocking rate at which individual animal performance begins to decrease. In most earlier grazing experiments it had been assumed that more grass would be grown on the rotational treatment than under set-stocking, so that more stock were allocated to the former; thus the experimental design had ensured that animal output per hectare would be higher on this treatment. Fig. 1 also indicates that this might have been associated with some decrease in per-animal output; the experiments showed this had generally happened.

Mott's paper led to a major reappraisal of grazing management, and to a gradual move towards greater simplicity and flexibility. Set-stocking poses the basic problem of dealing with the natural seasonal growth rhythm of grass. On the best Midland pastures this was dealt with by drafting in additional young stock during the Spring flush of growth, to maintain the dense leafy sward needed by the fattening cattle. With rotational grazing some paddocks, set aside and cut for conservation at the end of May, can be brought into the grazing rotation when herbage growth slackens in June and July; this concept has been further simplified in the 3-paddock system developed by ICI. Detailed botanical studies also identified that under continuous grazing the individual grass plant is in fact only grazed intermittently, and develops a prostrate tillering habit, so that total herbage grown over the year is similar to that under rotational grazing.

These developments had an important practical effect. Management systems by the 1960s were becoming too complex to be adopted by most farmers; the more recent simplified systems must take at least some of the credit for better pasture management in the 1970s.

## Forage Conservation: Hay

Good supplies of cheap imported feedstuffs during the 1930s led to "hay and cake" forming the basic winter feed of productive livestock, with little attention given to the "quality" of the hay. This lack of interest continued into the 1950s; concentrates again bore a favourable price relation to milk, grassland research was mainly aimed at extending the grazing season, and the limited research on conservation was mostly concerned with reducing losses. Then in 1957 Hampshire farmer Sam Cray queried why hay and silage gave lower levels of animal production than when the field from which they were cut was grazed; the Hurley work on digestibility patterns, which had just begun, indicated that this might be because forage was generally cut for conservation at a more mature, and so less digestible, stage than when it was grazed. Joint work with the National Institute of Agricultural Engineering at Silsoe showed that the digestibility of hay was closely related to the digestibility of the herbage from which it was made, and that early-cut hay gave much higher rates of gains by cattle than mature hay (long known by observant stockmen).

The unreliability of systems based on an extended grazing season was also becoming evident and a major research effort on improved conservation methods began about 1960. Barn-drying of hay, though highly effective, proved difficult to mechanise; the main approach with hay has been through better cutting and conditioning equipment to speed up rate of moisture loss during field-wilting and more recently through the application of fungistats to hay to allow baling and storage at higher moisture contents and so reduce risks from weather damage and losses in the field. There have also been improvements in handling hay from field to barn, in particular by automatic bale-handling systems and by the introduction of big-bales; the first effective machine was designed and constructed by a farmer, Pat Murray, in Gloucestershire.

## Forage Conservation: Silage

More progress has been made with silage, defined in 1865 as "green crop kept in the complete absence of air", a prescription lacking in the advice of the 1950s that cut grass should be allowed to heat up in the silo before filling proceeded — leading to air convection through the mass, and ensuring overheating and high nutrient losses.

Work at Hurley confirming the vital importance of the anaerobic condition was combined with the practical experience of a farmer, Richard Waltham, to develop the Dorset Wedge silage system, which was widely adopted. Young wet high-protein crops however remained difficult to ensile. Earlier research, indicating that this should be overcome by using chemical additives, had not been effective in practice. The reason became evident when Naerling, in Norway, developed a simple method of applying additives directly to the cut crop as it passed through the forage harvester, so that it was mixed uniformly with the forage — solving the problem of scaling-up from test-tube to farm, which few earlier experimenters had recognised. This equipment, used to apply formic acid, and introduced into UK by British Petroleum in 1967, was rapidly incorporated into the Dorset Wedge system. It was this total "package" which underpinned the increase in silage making in the UK, from less than 10% of the total forage conserved in the late 1960s to over 35% a decade later. Research also showed the benefits of wilting and chopping before ensiling, in reducing dry-matter losses and increasing silage feeding value, and research has continued on improved additives and on combinations of silage with other feeds in diets for high-producing animals. Silage is now used on 80% of dairy farms; further improvement in its production potential could play an important role in reducing feed costs, still some two-thirds of the cost of producing milk.

## Forage Nutritive Value

Interacting with all these aspects of grassland research are the factors determining the nutritive value of forages. The classical studies of Woodman and Watson established several important factors, in particular the decrease in forage digestibility with increasing maturity. But animal digestibility experiments are too complex for routine evaluation, and relationships were sought between the chemical composition and the digestibility of the forages fed in these early experiments. A positive correlation between digestibility and forage crude protein content was reported by Watson in 1936. However the errors were not random; "Watson's regression equation" in fact comprised a series of relationships which differed between spring and autumn grass, between grasses and legumes, and between the same grass receiving low and high levels of N-fertilizer. This was not recognised until the early 1950s, and it was perhaps unfortunate that the equation was so widely used by other experimenters, for example in grass breeding, where high protein content, adopted as a selection index, was almost inevitably linked with limited yield potential (for at a given input of N-fertilizer, grass yield is likely to be inversely related to protein content).

Extensive facilities for research on digestibility with sheep were set up at Hurley and some 1000 different samples of forage were fed during the 1950s. The results, together with those from similar studies at the West of Scotland College and the Rowett Institute provided a basis for the study of new methods of laboratory evaluation. No single chemical component proved adequate to predict forage digestibility, but multiple relationships, based on work by van Soest at Cornell, proved more precise. The most significant advance was the *in vitro* digestibility technique, reported from Hurley by Tilley and Terry at the International Congress in 1960; in this a sample of dried forage is treated successively with rumen liquor, to simulate rumen digestion, and with acid pepsin, to simulate hind-tract digestion. This technique was subsequently validated in both temperate and tropical laboratories and, although rather complex, has been extensively used during the last 2 decades. A particularly valuable application has been in estimating the digestibility of different fractions, e.g. leaves and stems, of forage plants. This has greatly increased the understanding (as opposed to the description) of factors determining forage digestibility; thus immature stem was shown to be more digestible than leaf, and this aided the breeding of new high-yielding grass varieties which, although "stemmy", are of high digestibility when harvested at a relatively immature stage.

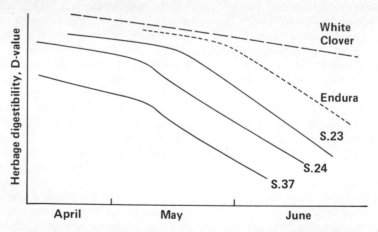

*Figure 2* Changes in digestibility of first-growth during spring, S24, S23 and Endura ryegrass; S37 cocksfoot. (Data from the Grassland Research Institute).

More detailed examination of the Hurley data was stimulated by the proposal by Reid, at Cornell, that the digestibility of first-growth forages could be predicted from the calendar date (an index of maturity). At the 1960 Congress Hurley workers reported that, within an overall general relationship, there were highly significant differences between grass species and varieties; S23 (late) ryegrass showed an identical time/digestibility relationship to that from S24 (early) ryegrass but with a lag of about 10 days; cocksfoot was consistently lower in digestibility than ryegrass; in contrast the digestibility of white clover decreased little as it matured (Fig. 2). Similar, though less precise relationships were found for regrowth herbage later in the season. These relationships were critically tested at other centres and in different years; the relationship for each grass variety was found to be reproducible, but with the date of inflexion (Fig. 2) closely related to the date of first ear-emergence and so delayed in a "late" season. By identifying this date on standard grass plots the current season can be "calibrated". The farming press now publishes in May and June each year the dates on which different grass varieties will reach particular levels of digestibility (D-values) — so allowing the farmer to cut each field at a predictable level.

## The Digestibility of Conserved Forages

This information is important practically because of the close relationship between forage digestibility and the digestibility of the conserved product made from it. Work by Hurley and Silsoe had shown the digestibility of barn-dried hay to be somewhat lower than that of the herbage cut, with the digestibility of field-made hay being lower, depending on the extent of losses in the field. Many animal experiments have since shown higher levels of milk and meat production from barn-hay than from field-made hay (e.g. at Drayton Experimental Husbandry Farm), and from early compared with late-cut (less digestible) hay. Other studies have shown that the digestibility of well-made silage is similar to that of the crop cut, again with some reduction if field-wilting or effluent flow from the silo have led to significant losses. Thus information on the species and date of cutting allows the farmer to estimate the productive value of his hay and silage.

## The Voluntary Intake of Forages

Until 1939 ruminant production in UK depended largely on concentrates, with little attention paid to how much forage animals would eat. With more interest in forages after 1945, investigators in UK and Canada, in particular, studying the voluntary intake of feeds, showed that the more digestible forage is the more of it animals will eat; as total nutrient intake is the product of intake and digestibility, this emphasised further the importance of forage being of high digestibility. However the relationship between intake and digestibility was perhaps over-simplified; thus the concept of "palatability" was dismissed, despite the common observation that some feeds are clearly "unpalatable"; at a given level of digestibility the voluntary intake of legumes is much higher than of grasses; and intake is increased when hay is milled before feeding. Analysis of these observations has greatly clarified understanding of the factors determining forage intake and has, for example, aided the selection at the Welsh Plant Breeding Station of grass varieties of higher intake potential. A notable exception was silage, the voluntary intake of which was generally less than of the original grass, often with little relation to its digestibility. Analysis of experimental results showed that intake was depressed in silage which had suffered protein degradation (indicated by a high ammonia level); degradation could be prevented by rapid acidification, but intake might then be limited by high acid content. This indicated that silage intake should be increased by wilting and by additives which preserve with limited fermentation; the application of these methods has markedly improved silage intake both in experiments and under farm conditions. Other work examined intake interactions *between* feeds. Cereal supplements decrease the voluntary intake of forages with which they are fed, at least partly because they make the rumen contents acid, and so less efficient at digesting fibre; when the supplement is fed frequently, as in "complete diet" systems, rumen pH is higher, and forage intake is increased.

The application of these ideas, coupled with the concept of lead-feeding of dairy cows developed at Shinfield, has done much to clarify another controversy of the 1950s — that of grass-versus-concentrates — itself perhaps an over-reaction to the earlier reliance on concentrate feeds. By using forages and concentrates as complementary feeds in a total ration (in contrast to the earlier division into maintenance and production feeding) high output per animal can be combined with high output per hectare, solving the problem posed by Fig. 1 of efficiently using grass grown without sacrificing individual animal performance. Similarly "barley-beef" feeding, developed at the Rowett Institute, stimulated new systems of grass beef production, in which the tactical use of cereal supplements avoids periods of low productivity, such as the winter "store" period, typical of earlier grass sytems.

## The Protein Value of Forages

Protein nutrition is dealt with elsewhere in this volume; but it is worth noting that while forage, except when mature, generally contains an apparent excess of crude protein, animal production responses to protein supplementation are often found. Workers at the Australian Prospect Laboratory in the 1960s confirmed earlier work at Cambridge that this was because forage protein may be too rapidly deaminated in the rumen; deamination could be reduced by "protecting" the protein by heating, with increased protein gains by sheep fed the heated forage. Work at Hurley showed that the protein value of forage is markedly improved by high-temperature drying; that in some forages, e.g. sainfoin and lotus, the protein is "protected" by naturally-occurring tannins; and that "protection" can also be achieved by use of chemicals such as formaldehyde. This information is incorporated in the latest ARC system of Protein Evaluation based on the "degradability" of protein — a less descriptive term than the original "protected" protein — and its application could lead to significant economies in protein feeding in the next decade.

## Grassland Research and Practice

This essay has been mainly concerned with research to increase the productivity of grassland and to improve the conversion of grass into meat and milk. But a recurring theme has been of the need to translate the results of this research into farm practice — and the farmer is concerned with economic and management factors, as well as the biological factors which have been the traditional concern of the research worker. Grassland research workers were among the first to recognise that a formal process of synthesis and economic evaluation is needed before results from discrete experiments can be applied, and the farmer advised on the complex economic interactions between different fertilizer inputs, grazing systems, supplementary feeding levels, conservation systems and levels of animal output. The need for this link between research and practice had been implicit in Stapledon's original concern with grassland, and the link has been immeasurably strengthened by the activities of the British Grassland Society, which he helped to found in 1945, with membership equally from the research and advisory services, from industry, and from practical farming, and by over 60 Local Grassland Societies which have developed from the parent Society. Grassland research is a complex subject; so also is grassland farming, which must combine the management of soil, plant and animal. By bringing together research workers, advisers and farmers the Grassland Societies have played a key role in helping the application into practice of the ARC's first half century of endeavour.

## Further Reading

Cooper, M. McG and Morris, D. W. (1977). *Grass Farming*. 4th Revised Edition. Ipswich: Farming Press Ltd.

Davies, William (1960). *The Grass Crop*. 2nd Edition revised. London: Spon Ltd.

Elliot, R. H. (1943). Introduction by Sir R. George Stapledon. *The Clifton Park System of Farming and Laying Down Land to Grass*. London: Faber and Faber.

Nash, M. J. (1978). *Crop Conservation and Storage in Cool Temperate Climates*. London: Pergamon Press.

Raymond, W. F., Shepperson, G. and Waltham, R. W. (1978). *Forage Conservation and Feeding*, 3rd Edition. Ipswich: Farming Press Ltd.

Stapledon, R. G. and Davies, William (1948). *Ley Farming*. London: Faber and Faber.

Spedding, C. R. W. (1965). *Sheep Production and Grazing Management*. London: Bailliere, Tindall and Cox.

Spedding, C. R. W. (1971). *Grassland Ecology*. Oxford: Clarendon Press.

Watkins, P. (1968). *Grass and the Dairy Cow*. London: Faber and Faber.

Watson, S. J. and Nash, M. J. (1960). *The Conservation of Grass and Forage Crops*, 2nd Enlarged Edition. Edinburgh: Oliver and Boyd.

Wilkinson, J. M. and Tayler, J. C. (1973). *Beef Production from Grassland*. London: Butterworth.

British Grassland Society (1946–1979). *Journal of the British Grassland Society* Vol. 1–33, continued as *Grass and Forage Science* Vol. 34.

# Milk and Milk Products

## J. A. F. ROOK

Hannah Research Institute, Ayr, Scotland

By the end of the 19th century, trade in butter and cheese was well established but the market for liquid milk was restricted. There was a lack of consistent standards of hygiene, a substantial risk from milk-borne disease, a poor understanding of human nutrition and of the contribution that milk could make to it, and an absence of a satisfactory transport and marketing system. The first legislation relating specifically to the sale of milk was enacted in 1901 and since then much has been done to improve the hygienic and compositional quality of milk as a marketable commodity. The consumption per capita of liquid milk in the United Kingdom before the Second World War was probably less than 0.2 litre per day but post-war the figure has been close to 0.4 litre, and currently within the European Economic Community (EEC) is second only to that of Eire. Many factors contributed to the development of the market — notable historical events were the formation of the National Milk Publicity Council in 1920 and of the Milk Marketing Boards in 1933, and the establishment at the beginning of the Second World War of a Ministry of Food whose policy gave high priority to milk consumption, but success would not have been possible without research and investigation into milk production and milk use, much of which was done within the public sector.

The sale of liquid milk became the dominant market for home-produced milk. From 1940 to 1950 it accounted for about 90% of total production, and the United Kingdom depended heavily on imports of butter and cheese from the Commonwealth countries in particular. From 1950, however, home-production of milk increased more rapidly than liquid sales and in 1977–78 47% of the milk produced went for manufacture. Entry into the EEC led to the phasing out of imports of dairy products from non-EEC countries but introduced strong competition from member countries of the Community. If the present scale of milk production is to be sustained, every effort will need to be made not only to maintain markets for conventional products, through improving quality, nutritive appeal, storage life and the economics of production, but also to create new outlets for milk and its constituents. To meet this challenge, the dairy trade will have to rely more heavily than in the recent past on support through research and development, and if that support is to be provided through the public sector a change in direction, with a greater emphasis on milk use, and possibly also in the style of publicly-funded research and development will be called for.

## Publicly-Funded Research and Development Work

In 1888, the British Dairy Farmers' Association established the British Dairy Institute to provide practical and scientific education in dairying but at that time there was no nationally-organized research into the problems of the dairying industry and heavy reliance had to be placed on the results of foreign research. The Institute was subsequently moved to the campus of the University College (later University) of Reading where better teaching facilities were available and there became the nucleus for the first United Kingdom centre for investigation into milk and milk products. A University

Department of Dairying was created in 1902 and when, in 1912, the Development Commission established the first British dairy research institute, the National Institute for Research in Dairying, it too was located within the University. Transfer to the present site at Shinfield took place in 1922 but the close links with the University remain.

A second, smaller institute, the Hannah Dairy Research Institute (now the Hannah Research Institute), was established in 1928 in south-west Scotland. One factor influencing the choice of site was the earlier existence of a dairy school in Kilmarnock and adjacent sites were found for the Institute and for the re-location of the dairy school as part of the West of Scotland Agricultural College, on the Auchincruive estate, near Ayr. The common links of the two institutions have been greatly strengthened through affiliations with the University of Glasgow.

In the period between the two world wars, universities and some of the larger agricultural colleges made distinctive contributions to research and development in dairying, especially dairy technology, and one or two centres remained eminent in the years after the Second World War. The University research contribution diminished, however, with the transfer of responsibility for the teaching of dairy technology to departments of food science and with the rapid expansion of the Agricultural Research Service in the 1950s and 1960s. The focus within the United Kingdom for research into milk production and milk use is now strongly within the Research Service. The institutes most fully involved are inevitably the two dairy research institutes but as the service expanded, specialist aspects of dairying, breeding and disease in particular, became the prime responsibility of other institutes. Those topics fall naturally into other contributions to this volume and this essay will concentrate on some of the contributions of the two dairy research institutes, with only occasional reference to work from elsewhere.

## Contributions of the Dairy Research Institutes

### Hygiene

When the National Institute for Research in Dairying was established in 1912, spoilage of milk and its products was extensive but the causes were unknown. A committee appointed by R. Stenhouse-Williams, the first Director, to assist the work of the Institute, instigated an inquiry that identified bad hygiene during production and handling as a major factor. Work was undertaken which demonstrated the profound effect of cleanliness and sterilization of utensils on bacteriological and keeping quality, and the benefits of good working conditions for the efficient production of clean milk. Later, the importance of time and temperature of storage for keeping quality was assessed and the need for adequate refrigeration identified. During the 1920s hygiene control schemes were introduced in England and Wales and Shinfield involved itself vigorously, through demonstrations and advice, in publicising clean milk production, in support of the efforts of the Ministry of Agriculture and the larger dairy firms. A specific research contribution was the improvement of the plate-counting technique by the inclusion of 1% milk in the agar medium which gave more consistent and higher counts, especially when the milk under test was of poor bacteriolgical quality or had been pasteurised.

The need for a rapid, objective assessment of keeping quality led to an extensive evaluation of dye-reduction tests. Methylene blue reduction time at 15°C was shown to correlate well with keeping quality, as judged by taste, but had the limitation that it was insensitive to the presence of mastitis streptococci but affected by somatic cells. Resazurin was found to be more easily reduced by somatic cells than was methylene blue, and could be used as an indicator of mastitis, and a rapid 10-min test was devised for the detection of poor quality milk, which, in spite of its known shortcomings, is still

*Plate 1* Cleaning by immersion in caustic soda solution; the basket containing the milking components is being drained (1955).

in use in England and Wales today. Both a 2 h and the 10-min resazurin test were incorporated into a National Milk Testing and Advisory Scheme in England and Wales, which brought some order into the control of the bacteriological quality of raw milk.

The National Institute continued to work on the assessment and improvement of hygiene tests, as did the Hannah Institute in relation to the different statutory requirements that existed in Scotland, and in the 1950s detailed study was made of mastitic organisms and of the development of improved methods of cleaning milking equipment — immersion cleaning for example (Plate 1) and later the acid-boiling water method. Work at Shinfield on milking routines, the factors influencing the milking rates of cows and the mechanical properties of milking machines had started earlier, but the greatest impact of that work was on the development of effective pipeline milking systems, approached on the premise that research on pipeline layout, farm use and cleaning methods was inseparable. Pipelines and machines were devised that met the user's requirements and had simpler and more effective in-line cleaning methods that formed the basis for United Kingdom codes of practice. The importance of testing detergent/disinfectants was also emphasized and this led to the introduction of an Approval Scheme, based on Shinfield testing until 1973 but now done in the Laboratories of the Government Chemist.

The limitations of the objective dye-reduction tests were recognized from the outset but the basis of the tests became less relevant following the widespread introduction of refrigerated bulk farm storage and collection, which reduced the importance of the lactic-acid producing (souring) bacteria but enhanced that of the psychrotrophic bacteria. Satisfactory replacement tests have yet to be developed but Shinfield has recently devised a rapid method of counting bacteria in milk which is currently being evaluated in commercial laboratories.

The change in type of contaminating organism has important implications for the quality of milk and its products. The psychrotrophs cause proteolytic and lipolytic changes that induce off-flavour and though the organisms are destroyed by heat treatment, the proteolytic and lipolytic enzymes are not completely inactivated and long-life products may deteriorate during storage. There is a renewed interest in the assessment of the nature and extent of contaminating organisms, and of changes in composition and somatic cell count originating from mastitis, and of the consequences for milk processing.

## Milk-borne disease

Pasteurisation, (as originally applied to milk, raising the temperature to between 62.8°C and 65.1°C for 30 min) was introduced at the turn of the century for the improvement of the keeping quality of milk but later it was recognised that holding milk for 10 min at 62.8°C also killed all the common pathogens. An important step in its effective application was the development of the phosphatase test by H. D. Kay, Director of Shinfield from Stenhouse-Williams's retirement in 1933 until 1958. The enzyme phosphatase is always present in raw milk but is destroyed by the time-temperature combination for efficient pasteurisation.

The most dangerous common pathogen, and the most heat-resistant, was the tubercle bacillus (man is susceptible to bovine tuberculosis). In the 1920s and 30s, as only a proportion of milk was heat-treated and some of that was underheated or contaminated later by unsterile plant, the consumption of infected milk was an important source of tuberculosis in children; about 3000 fresh cases were reported annually. There was additionally a direct economic loss due to deterioration in the health of cattle.

In 1929 the Medical Research Council instigated an investigation into the feasibility of eradicating bovine tuberculosis from dairy herds. Ayrshire, a county with a high population of dairy cattle and an established nucleus of tuberculin-tested herds was selected as a suitable location for the study and staff were appointed to the Hannah Institute to undertake the work. A collection of 30 typical herds in an area bounded by public roads was chosen and by repairing and renovating existing premises, thorough disinfection, isolation of reactors at pasture and in the byre, the rearing of young stock away from adult stock and the eventual replacement of adult stock with home-bred heifers, the herds were progressively freed from tuberculosis and the practices adopted were taken up by neighbouring farms. The final outcome was that the county of Ayr became the first tuberculosis-free area in the country. The Attested Herd Scheme, which was introduced by the Ministry of Agriculture in 1937 and based on compensation for slaughtered animals and payment of a bonus on milk produced by attested herds, was only partially successful in the eradication of tuberculosis but the introduction in 1950 of an Area Eradication Plan which embodied the principles of free testing and advice to the farmer of the Hannah investigation led to the virtual elimination of bovine tuberculosis by 1960. A comparable scheme for the elimination of brucellosis was begun in 1964.

## Bovine mastitis

Mastitis, apart from affecting hygienic quality, was, and still is, an important source of economic loss to the milk producer, through reduction of milk yield or more general effects on health of stock. Early in 1934 the Hannah Institute was asked by local farmers for assistance in dealing with mastitis and a scheme was introduced on local farms which put into practice recommendations on hygienic measures at milking that had emerged from studies at the Royal Veterinary College, London. Some success was achieved in controlling the spread of infection, and this success stimulated a wider interest in research into mastitis, which was further encouraged by the introduction during wartime of effective therapeutic substances for the control of clinical infection. Subsequent research at the Institute for Research on Animal Diseases, the Animal Diseases Research Association, Shinfield and the Hannah Institute, some of it in collaboration with the Central Veterinary Laboratory, made major contributions to the aetiology and pathology of mastitis and to improved diagnosis and antibiotic therapy; an account of some of this work appears in the essay on Diseases (pages 258–9).

## Compositional quality

The Sale of Milk Regulations, 1901, identified presumptive minimum standards for genuine milk of 3.0% fat and 8.5% solids-not-fat but these were introduced in relation to the detection of added water or the removal of fat. The only reliable basis for the detection of added water is the freezing-point test and definitive work on the use and limitations of the Hortvet test was undertaken in the Chemistry Department at Shinfield in the 1940s. Recently, Shinfield and the Hannah Institute, in collaboration with public analysts and trade laboratories, have developed an improved Hortvet test and introduced a thermistor cryoscope method, both of which will appear shortly in a revised BSI Standard for "Determination of the freezing-point depresssion of milk". They have also undertaken a survey of bulk farm milks in England, Wales and Scotland to establish average values for the freezing point of milk, as a basis for recommendations on the interpretation of the freezing-point test.

The composition of milk and the factors that influence it are matters of great scientific interest. Numerous contributions to these subjects have been made by both institutes over the years and work continues to the present day. All aspects of composition have been studied, from gross composition, to the detailed amino acid or fatty acid composition of milk proteins and fat respectively, to inter-relationships between ionic and other water-soluble constituents, and the influence on composition of such factors as breed, individuality, age, stage of lactation, udder disease and nutrition has been investigated. Recent work has included the controlled modification of milk-fat composition to give butter of improved physical and nutritional characteristics. Of critical importance in many of the studies has been the availability of suitable methods for the separation and measurement of the individual milk components and the institutes have made distinguished contributions to methodology. An example is the progressive improvement in methods for the separation of milk proteins. Important steps were the publication in 1938 from Shinfield of a now classical method based on salt and acid precipitation, the later application at Shinfield of paper chromatography to the separation of the whey proteins which provided the first evidence for the existence of genetic variants of milk proteins, and more recently at the Hannah the development of methods of high resolution based on ion-exchange chromatography for the fractionation of the caseinate complex and on gel filtration for the fractionation of the whey proteins.

Information on milk composition and its variations stimulated research into biochemistry and physiology of milk secretion but has not been fully applied in practice. For many years the dominant concern of the industry was to meet the presumptive minimum compositional standards, and advice was offered to farmers on methods of improving compositional quality to meet that limited objective, but even today there is a failure on the part of the industry to appreciate fully the commercial importance of variations in the composition of bulk milk. The recent introduction by the Milk Marketing Board of England and Wales of a scheme of payment related to the market value of the main components is a welcome development but more comprehensive schemes will emerge in the future. The full value of past work will then be realised and more rewarding research opportunities will become available for the study of the manipulation of milk composition according to market need.

Of more immediate benefit to the trade has been improvement in methods of analysis, especially those that have found application in rapid, routine tests suitable for control procedures. An apparently trivial development, the introduction by Shinfield of the aluminium foil milk-bottle cap into a scaled-down, more rapid gravimetric procedure for the determination of the total solids content of milk, did much to promote the frequent testing of milk for solids-not-fat content and an appreciation of the commercial importance of that fraction. Of comparable significance was the later development, also at Shinfield, of the Infra Red Milk Analyser for the routine measurement of the fat, protein and lactose contents of milk, which is now widely used in research and control laboratories but, for reasons of cost, has not proved suitable for routine testing in creameries. Less spectacular but of equal importance has been the work of the institutes in support of standard analytical procedures for milk and its products published by the British Standards Institute and the International Standards Organisation.

## Nutritive value of milk

The National Institute was founded at the time of the discovery of vitamins in milk and, appropriately, it, and later on a more limited scale the Hannah Institute also, has contributed to the study of the vitamins and their metabolism. Of special interest was the origin of the vitamins of milk, in particular the role of rumen microbes in B vitamin synthesis, and their nutritional significance. Gut microbes were shown to be important to the vitamin nutrition of simple-stomached animals also, and interest in this topic led to the development at Shinfield of facilities for gnotobiotic work.

An early controversial issue was the influence of pasteurisation of raw milk on its nutritive value. With the exception of the heat-labile vitamins, certain of the B vitamins and vitamin C in particular, no important chemical change could be demonstrated but a considerable prejudice against pasteurisation persisted. More direct assessments of the effects of heat treatment on nutritive value were made with a variety of species — the first study with calves was done at the Hannah Institute, and these failed to identify adverse effects providing pasteurisation was carried out efficiently. The most convincing demonstration, however, was a comprehensive study planned by the Milk Nutrition Committee in 1934–35, and undertaken in collaboration with the staff of Shinfield and the Rowett Research Institute, which sought to compare the nutritive value of raw and pasteurised milk and to assess the benefit to children of including milk in the diet. No distinction between pasteurised and raw milk was identified and, in common with observations elsewhere, the provision of milk, as an addition to prevailing diets, was shown to give improvements in physique, general appearance, scholastic ability and, to a lesser extent, muscular strength, observations that influenced profoundly the decisions of Government on the role of milk in the national diet during and after the Second World War.

Severe heat treatment may affect nutritive value, and S. K. Kon and his colleagues at Shinfield undertook an extensive investigation using rats as the experimental animal, of the biological value of milk protein and the extent to which it may be modified by heat. Carefully controlled heat-treatment followed by good storage led to no loss of biological value, and any damage appeared to be dependent more on the duration of the heat treatment than on the temperature employed. Ultra-heat treatment (UHT) (the holding of milk at not less than 132.2°C for not less than 1 second), a process that was studied in detail by Shinfield, had no effect on biological value. The same group of workers demonstrated also the high availability of the calcium of milk and milk products; milk is a major source of dietary calcium, one-half litre of milk supplying about two-thirds of the daily requirement of the child and adult.

Improvement in the food supply has diverted public and medical interest from the need to meet nutritional requirements to the possible adverse effects of dietary constituents. Cow's milk and its products, as common components of the diet, especially of the young, have inevitably been a focus of interest as possible causal factors in such topical disorders as coronary heart disease and food allergies. The prime responsibility of the Medical Research Council for matters concerning human nutrition has limited the role of the Agricultural Research Service in the study of these problems but work at Shinfield with laboratory animals provided the first experimental demonstration of the importance of calorie intake, as opposed simply to the intake of saturated fatty acids in the development of aortic atherosis. (Ruminant fats, including butter, are highly saturated and deficient in polyunsaturated fatty acids.) The complex aetiology of these disorders, and the lack of suitable animal models for man, restricted further direct study but investigations at the institutes contributed significantly to general knowledge of the metabolism of lipids; at the Hannah Institute research was done on the polyunsaturated (essential) fatty acids, and at Shinfield the immunological properties of milk proteins were investigated recently.

Physiological studies offer the best prospect for providing direct and unequivocal evidence on the possible causal role of milk and its constituents in nutritional disorders. An important need is still, however, the identification of a satisfactory animal model. Pigs were introduced at Shinfield in the 1920s for the study of the nutritional role of the vitamins but have been used since mainly for investigation of the nutritional requirements of pigs themselves — the traditional primary outlet for waste products of the dairy industry was in pig feeding. As a more fundamental approach to studies on pig nutrition has developed, metabolic studies have become commonplace and the pig now offers good prospects as an experimental model for many studies relating to human needs.

## Milk processing

An early interest of the National Institute was in discolouration of Stilton cheese, at the time a source of serious loss in cheese factories. The fault was shown to be due primarily to dirt organisms in the milk supplied to the factory but it could be prevented by the development of acidity. This discovery was seen to be of great practical importance as the use of clean milk could not be recommended since there was no assurance that satisfactory Stilton could be prepared from clean milk and that the dirty milk might not contain organisms that were beneficial! The work led to a recommendation that factory managers should make use of starter (a culture of one or more lactic-acid producing organisms, used to assist the regular development of acidity) in the manufacture of the cheese and initiated a research interest in starters, and their inhibition by bacteriophage, that continues to the present day. There has also been a wider interest in the cheese-making process. A notable contribution was the development in 1960 of a system of continuous cheese-making that was never taken up by industry. When equipment for such systems of cheese-making was eventually introduced, it had to be imported from the Antipodes. An incidental discovery was the isolation from *Streptococcus lactis* of the antibiotic nisin, now a permitted additive for certain foodstuffs.

On the establishment of the Hannah Institute, there was an informal agreement with the National Institute that the new Institute would specialise in research into the condensing and drying of milk, a major outlet for surplus milk. The first bulletin issued by the Hannah in 1929, was entitled "Surplus milk and milk residues" and this led to the commissioning by N. C. Wright, the first Director, of two further bulletins dealing respectively with the chemical and bacteriological and with the engineering aspects of milk-powder production. Research into numerous aspects of the production of milk powders and their properties followed. Attention was given to the development of suitable tests for the effect of drying on the solubility of milk powder and then to the storage properties of full-cream, spray-dried powder, an interest stimulated by the need to stockpile essential foodstuffs in the immediate pre-war period. The normal storage life of the powder was typically about 6 months and the problem was how to increase that appreciably. A major cause of spoilage was the formation of peroxides due to the oxidation of trace amounts of unsaturated fatty acids in milk fat, and this was overcome by a simplified gas packing system of 1 cycle of vacuum followed by the introduction of a mixture of 95% nitrogen and 5% hydrogen. The inclusion in the can of a pellet of palladium catalysed the reduction of the remaining oxygen and maintained an oxygen content of less than 0.1% which inhibited peroxide formation. The possibility of increasing the production of natural antioxidant from the sulphur-containing proteins during the preheating stage of spray-dried powder manufacture was then investigated, together with the importance of the cleanliness of the milk supply, in collaboration with Shinfield and the Low Temperature Research Station at Cambridge. Raw milk of poor hygienic quality had a slight adverse effect on the keeping quality of the resulting powder when the milk was preheated at the usual temperature of 74°C but none when it was preheated to 88°C at which temperature the resistance of the powder to oxidation was also improved.

Also in collaboration with Reading and Cambridge, work was done on the influence of moisture content on the nutritive value of skim milk powder. Storage at 37°C of powders with a moisture content above 5% caused, over a period of months, a darkening of colour, a decrease in solubility and a decrease in free amino-N associated with a fall in the biological value of the protein. These effects were attributed mainly to the reaction of $\epsilon$-amino groups of lysine residues with the aldehyde group of lactose. The work reinforced the view that for efficient transport and storage, milk powder should be produced with a low moisture content and packed to prevent absorption of atmospheric moisture.

The early work on milk products identified the need for a better knowledge of the physics and physical chemistry of milk and its constituents. At both institutes, effort was put into describing various phenomena of importance in milk processing; the micellar form of casein in liquid milk, the foaming properties of whey proteins, the action of rennet in the formation of curd, the rheological properties of milk products, homogenisation, the heat denaturation of milk proteins and sediment formation in heat-treatment plants, for example. Useful background information was acquired but only recently, because of more general advances in science, has it become possible to begin to study these phenomena in molecular terms. The opportunity for a more systematic approach to many aspects of milk processing comes fortuitously at a time when applied research into milk utilization is being expanded. There is current research into the relation between milk fat composition and the physical properties of butter, into the process of cheese making and the factors that affect the efficiency of conversion of milk solids to cheese, into the characterisation and manipulation of the properties of milk powder in relation to use, and into the utilization of whey constituents. Invariably, the approach involves a combination of empirical work, more systematic studies and fundamental investigations of the processes involved and also encompasses the use of new technologies. An example is the use of ultrafiltration and reverse osmosis for concentration of milk prior to further processing, either in the production of Cheddar cheese as studied recently at Shinfield or at the Hannah of protein-rich concentrates which have been found to be very stable at sterilisation temperatures.

## Dairy cattle feeding

Feed accounts for about half the costs of milk production and the price of milk as a raw material is an important limitation to its use. Early work on cattle feeding undertaken by the institutes was on the characterisation of feeds, in terms of their production and potential as a crop, and the evaluation of their use for milk production. The growth and use of crops for milk production continued as a major research interest, Shinfield including arable crops in its studies — the recent extensive work on maize is a good example, whereas the Hannah Institute from its inception, because of its location on the west coast, concentrated mainly on grass. At the Hannah, plot trials were introduced in pre-war days and are currently being used to assess possible economies in the use of nitrogenous fertilizer offered by the inclusion in a sward of the recently developed vigorous, broad-leaved clovers. In 1940 a ten-year study of "self-sufficiency" was started on the initiative of N. C. Wright, which relied heavily for its success on the efficient use of grassland. That work was followed by systematic investigations of the production and use of dried grass, of simplified systems of grazing management and more recently of the production and use of high-quality silage.

Alongside the empirical studies, more systematic approaches emerged, exemplified by the work of K. L. Blaxter on energy metabolism of ruminants at the Hannah Institute, which was to form the basis of the Agricultural Research Council's metabolizable energy system of feed evaluation (described in the essay on Animal Nutrition), and the work at Shinfield on feeding systems for dairy cattle. A wholly rational approach to the feeding of dairy cattle has been prevented by the lack of knowledge of the ruminant system of food digestion and of the metabolism of the digestion products in their use for milk formation. There was an early scientific interest in the mammary gland and its development — the mammary gland is in many ways a unique tissue, in terms of the details of its metabolism and its ease of access for experimental study, and this interest was greatly strengthened and broadened with the recognition of the importance of diet for mammary gland metabolism and milk secretion; in particular the demonstration that the products of fermentation in the rumen are important sources of nutrients for the host animal and have detailed, individual effects on tissue metabolism and milk secretion.

These topics have commanded world-wide interest and attention but the two institutes have themselves made notable contributions. Historically important were the early studies at the Hannah of J. A. B. Smith on diet in relation to milk fat secretion and later on non-protein nitrogen utilization in the rumen and of S. J. Folley and his colleagues at Shinfield on many aspects of the physiology and endocrinology of lactation. In collaboration with G. Popják of the National Institute for Medical Research, Folley's group identified the use of acetate for milk fat synthesis in the ruminant several years before the discovery of the role of acetate, in the form of its coenzyme-A derivative, as an intermediate in the malonyl pathway of fatty acid synthesis. At a later stage, following a report by G. L. McClymont from Australia of a depression in the milk fat content of cows grazing young oat plants, an extended study was begun at Shinfield of the influence of the physical form of the diet on milk-fat secretion in the cow and subsequently of the qualitative relationships between the composition and amount of diet, the products of rumen fermentation and milk secretion.

The two institutes made surprisingly little contribution to the study of the quantitative metabolism of the mammary gland during the 1960s when, largely through the efforts and inspiration of the late J. L. Linzell and his colleagues at the Institute of Animal Physiology at Babraham (near Cambridge), the subject was expanded rapidly. Following the introduction of satisfactory techniques for the cannulation of the intestine of sheep and cattle, however, work was begun at both institutes on quantitative aspects of ruminant digestion and later on the role of nutrient uptake in the regulation of tissue metabolism and on the hormonal modulation of substrate supply and utilization by the mammary gland. Recently, a group has been established at the Hannah Institute to study the mechanisms and control of milk secretion and the efforts of the two institutes should, in the next decade, contribute greatly to knowledge of the fundamental control of metabolism in relation to lactation and reproduction. Identification of key periods in the reproductive/lactational cycle when nutritional and also non-nutritional factors can influence milk secretion and the partition of nutrients between body tissues, and definition of the maximum extent of variation in the synthetic and secretory pathways of the various milk components, will permit the formulation of new strategies for milk production. The production of milk of a more standard composition throughout lactation may become a practical possibility and the scope for the manipulation of milk composition according to market requirements should be enhanced. Empirical approaches to the study of the influence of production conditions, feeding in particular, on the manufacturing properties of milk have already begun, heralding a much closer future interdependence of research into milk production and milk use.

## Research Perspective

Initially, the dairy research institutes involved themselves directly in the identification and investigation of industrial problems and some of the early findings were of immediate and obvious benefit to the farmer, the milk distributor, the dairy manufacturer and the consumer. Many of the problems that were identified, however, proved intractable and information and advice were sought on matters where, through lack of scientific knowledge, there was difficulty in formulating precisely the requirements or objectives. If progress was to be made, effort had to be put into establishing a sound scientific base in the many areas of biology and technology relevant to dairying.

In the rapid, post-war expansion of the institutes, many new appointments were of persons who had specialised in a narrow scientific discipline and who were highly motivated by scientific curiosity. This policy led to a rewarding expansion of fundamental knowledge in the several areas of dairy science, particularly within the fields of biochemistry and physiology that were subject more generally to rapid growth. Progress in applied research was more limited, however; the physical resources necessary were not available on an appropriate scale, and the work, by its nature less definitive, was judged to offer poorer prospects for scientific advancement and proved unattractive to many of the more able scientists.

Within the last decade the climate has changed. There is now a greater readiness on the part of the scientists to see the wider relevance of applied research, and public-funding authorities are more conscious of the need to exploit to the full new scientific knowledge. In the institutes themselves, the same importance as in the past is attached to basic research but there is a greater concern about its effective co-ordination and the links with applied research. More of the applied research is into problems identified by industry and the balance of effort has changed towards milk use rather than milk production, in response to the changed marketing situation. There has also been a welcome improvement in liaison with industry, both formal and informal, but the need exists for still closer working arrangements. The application of the results of research is extremely dependent on the translation of research findings into a form that can be understood and developed by industry, and this is achieved most readily where there is an efficient working collaboration with industry.

I am grateful to several colleagues at the National Institute for Research in Dairying and the Hannah Research Institute, and to Dr. J. A. B. Smith, former Director of the Hannah, for help and advice.

## Further Reading

The National Institute for Research in Dairying 1912–1937. Twenty-fifth anniversary review by the staff of the Institute. 1937.

The National Institute for Research in Dairying. 1970, 1972, 1974, 1976, 1978. Biennial Reviews.

The Hannah Research Institute 1928–1978. Essays on the scientific work of the Institute. 1978. (ed. J. H. Moore and J. A. F. Rook), Hannah Research Institute.

# Appendix 1

## Charter of the Agricultural Research Council, 1931

𝔊𝔢𝔬𝔯𝔤𝔢 𝔱𝔥𝔢 𝔉𝔦𝔣𝔱𝔥, by the Grace of God of Great Britain, Ireland and the British Dominions beyond the Seas King, Defender of the Faith, Emperor of India.

To all to whom these Presents shall come, Greeting !

𝔚𝔥𝔢𝔯𝔢𝔞𝔰 We were pleased by Our Order in Council dated the 28th day of July, 1930, to appoint the Lord President of the Council, the Minister for Agriculture and Fisheries, the Secretary of State for Home Affairs, the Secretary of State for Scotland and the President of the Board of Education, respectively, for the time being, to be a Committee of Our Privy Council for the organisation and development of agricultural research :

AND WHEREAS the said Committee of Our Privy Council has represented to Us that for the purpose of furthering the objects of the said Committee of Our Council and with a view to facilitating the holding of and dealing with any money provided by Parliament and any other property real or personal available for those objects and with a view, further, to encouraging the making of gifts and bequests in aid of the said objects it is expedient that there should be constituted a body under the name of the Agricultural Research Council which should be responsible to the said Committee of Our Privy Council and should act under its directions, and that the members of the Agricultural Research Council should be created a Body Corporate :

𝔑𝔬𝔴, 𝔱𝔥𝔢𝔯𝔢𝔣𝔬𝔯𝔢, 𝔨𝔫𝔬𝔴 𝔶𝔢 that We, by virtue of Our Royal Prerogative and of all other powers enabling Us in that behalf, do, of Our special grace, certain knowledge and mere motion by these Presents for Us Our Heirs and Successors *grant, will, direct, ordain, constitute and declare as follows :—*

1. That the first members of the Agricultural Research Council shall be J. A. Arkwright, Esq., F.R.S., M.A., M.D., F.R.C.P. ; Sir Merrik Burrell, Baronet, C.B.E., J.P. ; E. J. Butler, Esq., C.I.E., D.Sc., M.B., F.R.S. ; Professor E. P. Cathcart, C.B.E., M.D., D.Sc., LL.D., F.R.S. ; The Right Honourable Lord Richard Cavendish, C.B., C.M.G. ; Joseph F. Duncan, Esq. ; Sir John B. Farmer, Knight, M.A., D.Sc., LL.D., F.R.S. ; Sir A. Daniel Hall, K.C.B., LL.D., F.R.S. ; Professor Sir F. Gowland Hopkins, Knight, M.A., M.B., D.Sc., LL.D., F.R.C.P., F.R.S. ; Professor T. J. Mackie, M.D., D.P.H., M.R.C.P.E., F.R.S.E. ; Sir Thomas Middleton, K.C.I.E., K.B.E., C.B., LL.D.; Spencer Mount, Esq. ; Professor D. M. S. Watson, F.R.S.

2. That all those persons who shall, pursuant to this Our Charter, be members for the time being of the Agricultural Research Council be one Body Corporate under the name of " The Agricultural Research

A 2

2

Council," having a perpetual succession and a Common Seal with full power by and in such name :—

    (*a*) To sue and be sued ;

    (*b*) To enter into contracts or agreements in furtherance of the objects of the said Committee of Our Privy Council ;

    (*c*) To accept, hold, and dispose of, money or other personal property in furtherance of the said objects, including sums voted by Parliament for those objects ;

    (*d*) To accept any trusts, whether subject to special conditions or not, in furtherance of the said objects ; and

    (*e*) Generally to do all other lawful acts whatsoever that may be conducive or incidental to the attainment of the objects for which the said Committee of Our Privy Council has been appointed and the said Agricultural Research Council is hereby established.

3. And We do hereby for Us, Our Heirs and Successors, license, authorise and for ever hereafter enable the Agricultural Research Council to purchase take on lease or otherwise acquire any lands tenements or hereditaments within Our United Kingdom of Great Britain and Northern Ireland not exceeding in the whole the annual value of £50,000 to be determined according to the value thereof at the time when the same are respectively acquired and to hold all or any lands tenements or hereditaments, in perpetuity or on lease or otherwise and from time to time to grant demise alienate or otherwise dispose of the same or any part thereof, or of any interest in or over the same.

4. And We do hereby also for Ourselves, Our Heirs and Successors give and grant Our licence to any person or persons and any Body politic or corporate to assure in perpetuity or otherwise or to demise to or for the benefit of the Agricultural Research Council any lands tenements or hereditaments whatsoever within Our United Kingdom of Great Britain and Northern Ireland within the limits of value aforesaid, hereby nevertheless declaring that it shall not be incumbent upon any person or persons or Body to enquire as to the annual value of the property which may have been previously acquired by the Council.

5. The number of members of the Agricultural Research Council shall on the occurence of a vacancy be reduced to twelve, and thereafter the said Council shall consist of twelve members of whom eight shall at all times be persons appointed after consultation with the President for the time being of the Royal Society, on account of their qualifications in one or other of the basic sciences underlying agriculture and four shall be persons appointed on account of their general experience of and interest in agriculture.

6.—(1) The members of the Agricultural Research Council shall retire in rotation, but any member so retiring shall be eligible for re-appointment.

3

(2) On the first day of July, 1933, and on the same date in each subsequent year two members appointed as aforesaid on account of their scientific qualifications, and one other member, shall retire.

(3) The members so to retire shall be determined in such manner as the said Committee of Our Privy Council may from time to time prescribe.

7. Any vacancy, whether casual or otherwise, which may hereafter occur among members of the Agricultural Research Council shall be filled by appointment by the said Committee of Our Privy Council provided, however, that the number of members shall not thereby be increased to more than twelve ; but any person appointed to fill a casual vacancy shall only hold office for the remainder of the period of office of the member in whose place he is appointed.

8. In the appointment of persons to be members of the Agricultural Research Council regard shall be had to the desirability of securing at all times that, so far as possible, one member shall be a person who is also a member of the Medical Research Council, and one other member shall be a person who is also a member of the Advisory Council for Scientific and Industrial Research.

9. The said Committee of Our Privy Council shall, after consultation with the members of the Agricultural Research Council and the President of the Royal Society, appoint one of the members of the Agricultural Research Council to be Chairman thereof.

10. The Agricultural Research Council shall with the approval of the Lord President of the Council and after consultation with the President of the Royal Society appoint a Secretary of the Council and may pay to him such remuneration as the said Committee of Our Privy Council may, with the approval of the Lords Commissioners of Our Treasury, from time to time determine.

11. The Agricultural Research Council may also appoint such other officers and servants as they think fit, but the number of such officers and servants and their remuneration shall be subject to the approval of the said Committee of Our Privy Council and of the Lords Commissioners of Our Treasury.

12. There may be paid as honoraria to members of the Agricultural Research Council such sums as the said Committee of Our Privy Council may, with the approval of the Lords Commissioners of Our Treasury, from time to time direct, and the Council may also expend such sums for the administrative purposes of the Council, including travelling expenses and subsistence allowances for members and staff, as the said Committee of Our Privy Council may with the like approval from time to time determine.

13. The Agricultural Research Council shall at all times be responsible to and shall, subject to the provisions of this Our Charter, comply with such directions as may from time to time be given to them by the said Committee of Our Privy Council.

4

14. All property for the time being vested in the Agricultural Research Council or the proceeds of sale thereof shall be held by them for the purposes of the Council and in such manner as the said Committee of Our Privy Council, subject to the provisions of this Our Charter or of any trust affecting such property, may approve.

15. The accounts of the Agricultural Research Council shall be made up for each financial year ending the 31st day of March and shall be prepared and audited in such manner as the Lords Commissioners of Our Treasury may from time to time direct.

16. The Agricultural Research Council shall in every year prepare and submit a report to the said Committee of Our Privy Council.

17. It shall be lawful for Us, Our Heirs and Successors by Supplemental Charter to add to amend or repeal the provisions of this Our Charter or any of them.

**In Witness** whereof We have caused these Our Letters to be made Patent.

**Witness** Ourself at Westminster the *twenty-third* day of *July* in the *twenty-second* year of Our Reign.

**By Warrant** under the King's Sign Manual.

*Schuster.*

# Chairmen and Members of the Agricultural Research Council, 1931–1980

## The Original Council

| | |
|---|---|
| 1931–38 | **Cavendish, the Rt. Hon. Lord Richard, CB, CMG** (Chairman). |
| 1931–43† | **Middleton, Sir Thomas H., KCIE, KBE, CB, LLD, FRS** (Chairman 1938–43). |
| 1931–40 | Arkwright, J. A. (later Sir Joseph) MD, FRCP, FRS. |
| 1931–42 | Burrell, Sir Merrik Bt, CBE, JP. |
| 1931–35* | Butler, E. J. (later Sir Edwin) CMG, CIE, DSc, MB, FRS (resigned to become Secretary). |
| 1931–40 | Cathcart, Professor E. P., CBE, MD, FRS. |
| 1931–35 | Duncan, Joseph F., LLD. |
| 1946–52 | ,, |
| 1931–35 | Farmer, Sir John B., DSc, FRS. |
| 1931–39 | Hall, Sir A. Daniel, KCB, LLD, FRS. |
| 1931–38 | Hopkins, Professor Sir Frederick Gowland, OM, DSc, FRCP, FRS. |
| 1931–39 | Mackie, Professor T. J., CBE, MD, FRSE. |
| 1944–45 | ,, |
| 1946–51 | ,, |
| 1931–41 | Mount, Spencer, W. |
| 1931–42 | Watson, Professor D. M. S., DSc, FRS. |

## Later Members of Council

| | |
|---|---|
| 1935–45 | Dampier, Sir William C., ScD, FRS (previously served as Secretary). |
| 1936–43 | Robertson, Sir Robert, KBE, DSc, FRS. |
| 1936–45 | Smith, John, OBE, MRCVS. |
| 1936–41 | Smith, Professor Sir William Wright, DesSc, FRSE. |
| 1938–43 | Barcroft, Sir Joseph, CBE, DSc, FRS. |
| 1938–39* | Radnor, The Rt. Hon. the Earl of. |
| 1940–44 | Greig, Sir Robert, MC, LLD, DSc. |
| 1940–41* | Topley, Professor W. W. C., MD, FRCP, FRS (resigned to become Secretary). |
| 1941–52† | Brooks, Professor F. T., CBE, LLD, FRS. |

---

*Notes*

1. The list is complete at the end of 1980.
2. Titles, honours and distinctions are complete for the member's term of service, and as far as possible for afterwards.
3. For terms of service known to have been terminated otherwise than by normal retirement, resignations are marked * and deaths in office †. Members appointed by the Agricultural Ministers, marked **, are not appointed for fixed terms but serve at the discretion of Ministers. Sir John Ritchie and Lord Trenchard were initially appointed by the Minister of Agriculture Fisheries and Food, but were reappointed by the Secretary of State for Education and Science.
4. Two or more terms of service with no interval between them are treated as a single term.
5. Members are listed in order of the date of their first appointment to Council. Among members appointed in the same year a Chairman (name in **bold type**) is listed first, then others in alphabetical order.

| | |
|---|---|
| 1941–45* | Harington, Professor C. R. (later Sir Charles), PhD, FRS. |
| 1941–46 | Keilin, Professor D., ScD, FRS. |
| 1941–46 | Keith, Major J., CBE. |
| 1941–44* | Salisbury, Professor E. J. (later Sir Edward), CBE, DSc, FRS. |
| 1941–55 | Watson, Professor J. A. Scott (later Sir James), CBE, MC, MA. |
| 1942–47 | Engledow, Professor F. L. (later Sir Frank), CMG, MA, FRS. |
| 1942–47 | Gray, Professor J. (later Sir James), CBE, ScD, FRS. |
| 1949–50* | ,, |
| 1943–48 | **De La Warr, The Rt. Hon. the Earl of** (Chairman) |
| 1943–48* | Daly, Professor I. de Burgh, CBE, MD, FRS (resigned to become Director, Institute of Animal Physiology). |
| 1945–52 | Dalling, T. (later Sir Thomas), DSc, FRCVS, FRSE. |
| 1945–49 | Osborn, Professor T. G. B., DSc. |
| 1945–49 | Simonsen, J. L. (later Sir John), DSc, FRS. |
| 1945–49 | Wright, William J. |
| 1946–52* | Drury, A. N. (later Sir Alan), CBE, MD, FRS (resigned on appointment to Institute of Animal Physiology). |
| 1947–50* | Brunt, Professor D. (later Sir David), ScD, FRS. |
| 1947–56* | Cameron, Professor G. R. (later Sir Roy), DSc, FRCP, FRS. |
| 1947–52 | Chibnall, Professor A. C., ScD, FRS. |
| 1947–57 | Turner, James (later Sir James, later The Rt. Hon. Lord Netherthorpe). |
| 1959–64 | ,, |
| 1948–58 | **Rothschild, The Rt. Hon. Lord, GM, ScD, FRS** (Chairman). |
| 1949–50* | Marrian, Professor G. F., DSc, FRS. |
| 1949–54 | Mather, Professor K. (later Sir Kenneth), CBE, DSc, FRS. |
| 1955–60 | ,, |
| 1969–79 | ,, |
| 1949–59 | Zuckerman, Professor S. (later Sir Solly, later The Rt. Hon. Lord), OM, KCB, MD, DSc, FRS. |
| 1950–55 | Harland, Professor S. C., DSc, FRSE, FRS. |
| 1950–55 | Wright, N. C. (later Sir Norman), CB, DSc, FRIC. |
| 1951–61 | Watson, Professor S. J. (later Sir Stephen), CBE, DSc, FRIC, FRSE. (Deputy Chairman, 1953–58). |
| 1952–57 | Maskell, Professor E. J., PhD, FRS. |
| 1952–62 | Medawar, Professor P. B. (later Sir Peter), CBE, DSc, FRS. |
| 1952–57 | Pugh, Professor L. P., CBE, MA, FRCVS. |
| 1952–57* | Young, Professor J. S., MC, MD. |
| 1954–64 | Lowe, D. (later Sir David), CBE, FRSE (Deputy Chairman 1958–64). |
| 1954–59 | Rayns, F., CBE, ScD. |
| 1954–65** | Ritchie, J. N. (later Sir John), CB, FRCVS, FRSE. |
| 1965–73 | ,, |
| 1955–60 | Krebs, Professor H. A. (later Sir Hans), MD, DSc, FRCP, FRS. |
| 1956–58** | Davidson, L. G., CB. |
| 1956–66 | Glover, R. E., CBE, DSc, FRCVS. |
| 1956–64** | Sanders, Professor H. G. (later Sir Harold), PhD. |
| 1956–58** | Tame, W. C., CB, BA. |
| 1957–67 | Bennet-Clark, Professor T. A., CBE, PhD, FRS. |
| 1957–60* | Cox, Professor E. G. (later Sir Gordon, KBE), TD, DSc, FInstP, FRIC, FRS (resigned to become Secretary). |
| 1957–58** | Hensley, J., MA. |
| 1957–63* | Howie, Professor J. W. (later Sir James), MD, FRCP. |
| 1957–62 | Jones, Elwyn, OBE, JP. |
| 1958–68 | **Northumberland, His Grace the Duke of, KG, FRS** (Chairman). |
| 1958–68 | Alston, J. D., CBE, JP. |

| 1958–66** | Senior, W. H., CB, MSc, FRSE. |
|---|---|
| 1959–69 | Brambell, Professor F. W. Rogers, CBE, DSc, FRS. |
| 1959–60** | Engholm, B. C. (later Sir Basil, KCB). |
| 1960–62** | Button, H. G. |
| 1960–65 | Robertson, Professor Alexander, MA, PhD, LLD, FRS. |
| 1961–69† | Frazer, Professor A. C., CBE, MD, DSc, FRCP. |
| 1961–66* | Williams, Professor W. T., DSc, ARCS, DIC. |
| 1962–72 | Dugdale, Major J. E. M., TD, DL, JP. |
| 1962–68† | Harris, Professor J. E., CBE, PhD, FRS. |
| 1962–65** | Wilcox, C. H. M., MA. |
| 1963–73 | Oakley, Professor C. L., CBE, MD, DSc, FRS. |
| 1965–74 | Addington, The Hon. J. (later The Rt. Hon. Viscount Sidmouth). |
| 1964–70† | Watherston, R. H., CBE. |
| 1965–70 | Heath, Professor O. V. S., DSc, FRS. |
| 1965–73** | Jones, W. Emrys (later Sir Emrys), BSc, LLD. |
| 1965–70** | Reid, John, CB, MRCVS. |
| 1966–75 | Ubbelohde, Professor A. R. J. P., CBE, DSc, FRS. |
| 1966–76 | Brian, Professor P. W., CBE, ScD, FRS. |
| 1966–67**† | Law, R. H., MA. |
| 1967–77 | Katz, Professor B. (later Sir Bernard), MD, DSc, FRS. |
| 1968–78 | **Astor, The Hon. J. J. (later Sir John), MBE, DL.** (Chairman). |
| 1968–78 | Harris, Professor Henry, MB, DPhil, FRS. |
| 1968–78 | Martin, J. S., CBE, MA. |
| 1968–72** | Smith, J. Ian, MA. |
| 1969–79 | Neuberger, Professor A., CBE, MD, PhD, FRCP, FRS. |
| 1970–73** | Beynon, A. G., CB, MRCVS. |
| 1970–80 | Biggar, W. A., CBE, MC, BSc. |
| 1970–80 | Harley, Professor J. A., CBE, DPhil, FRS. |
| 1970–73** | Trenchard, The Rt. Hon. Viscount, MC. |
| 1973–79* | „ |
| | (Resigned on being appointed Minister of State, Department of Industry). |
| 1972–79** | Gauld, W. W., MA. |
| 1972– | Griffith, E. M. W. |
| 1973–80** | Brown, A. C. L., CB, FRCVS. |
| 1973–75** | Dobb, E. S., CB, TD, FRICS. |
| 1973– | Hughes, Professor D. L., CBE, PhD, FRCVS. |
| 1973–78 | Hutchison, J. S., CBE, MC, TD. |
| 1973– | Mandelstam, Professor J., PhD, FRS. |
| 1973–78** | Maude, E., CB. |
| 1973–77** | Pereira, H. C. (later Sir Charles), DSc, FRS. |
| 1975–** | Dexter, K., CB, PhD. |
| 1974–** | Mackay, C., MSc. |
| 1974– | Selborne, The Rt. Hon. the Earl of, MA, JP. |
| 1976– | Ford, Professor Sir Hugh, DSc, FIMechE, FICE, FIM, FRS. |
| 1977– | Heslop-Harrison, Professor J., DSc, MRIA, FRSE, FRS. |
| 1977– | Huxley, Professor Sir Andrew, DSc, MD, FRS. |
| 1977–** | Weitz, Professor B. G. F., OBE, DSc, MRCVS. |
| 1978– | **Porchester, The Rt. Hon. Lord, KBE, DL** (Chairman). |
| 1978– | Cross, J. E. |
| 1978– | Halstead, R., CBE, MA, FRSC. |
| 1978– | McLaren, Anne, DPhil, FRS. |
| 1979–** | Gibson, J. S. |
| 1979– | Jinks, Professor J. L., DSc, FRS. |
| 1979– | Kornberg, Professor Sir Hans, ScD, FRS. |

1979–**    Smith, E. J. G., MA.
1980–      Harper, Professor J. L., MA, DPhil, FRS.
1980–      John, G.
1980–      Maitland Mackie (Junior), J., MA.
1980–**    Rees, W. H. G., BSc, MRCVS.

# Appendix 3

## Officers of the Council

From the establishment of the Council until 1950 its only full-time Headquarters officer was the Secretary. Staff as well as accommodation for the Council's work was provided on repayment terms by the Development Commission. Thus Mr. Havelock who was appointed by the Council first as its interim Secretary, then Assistant Secretary, and eventually Administrative Secretary, was at the same time an officer of the Development Commission — for most of the time its Secretary. Mr. (later Brigadier) F. R. W. Jameson DSO, MC and Mr. S. Stagg OBE, named by the Council as Assistant Secretaries in 1934 and 1937 respectively, were also officers of the Commission.

In 1950 the Council established its own Secretariat, taking into its service a number of officers formerly employed by the Development Commission. Since then Secretaries, Second Secretaries, Deputy Secretaries and Clerks to the Council have been appointed by resolution of Council. Other staff have been appointed by the Secretary.

Deaths in office are marked †.

**Secretaries to the Council** (from 1931)

| | |
|---|---|
| 1931 | Havelock, E. H. E., CB, FRSE (interim Secretary). |
| 1931–35 | Dampier, Sir William, ScD, FRS. |
| 1935–41 | Butler, Sir Edwin J., CMG, CIE, DSc, MB, FRS. |
| 1941–44† | Topley, Professor W. W. C., MD, FRCP, FRS. |
| 1944–49† | Fryer, Sir John C. F., KBE, MA, LLD, FRSE, FRS. |
| 1949–60 | Slater, Sir William K., KBE, DSc, FRIC, FRS. |
| 1960–71 | Cox, Sir E. Gordon, KBE, TD, DSc, FInstP, FRIC, FRS. |
| 1971–72† | Baskett, Professor Sir Ronald G., OBE, DSc, FRIC. |
| 1972–78 | Henderson, Sir William M., DSc, FRCVS, FRSE, FRS. |
| 1978– | Riley, R., DSc, FRS. |

**Second Secretaries to the Council**

| | |
|---|---|
| 1968–71 | Porter, Professor Helen K., DSc, FRSE, FRS. |
| 1981– | Rook, J. A. F., DSc, FRSE. |

**Deputy Secretaries to the Council**

| | |
|---|---|
| 1952–71† | Alexander, W. G., CBE, MA, FRSE. |
| 1971 | Berry, W. E., CBE, PhD. |

**Under Secretaries**

| | |
|---|---|
| 1971–73 | Parkinson, D. J., OBE, BA. |
| 1973– | Myers, G. M. P., MSc. |

**Chief Scientific Officers**

| | |
|---|---|
| 1971–75 | Webster, C. C., CMG, PhD, AICTA. |
| 1975–80 | Cooke, G. W., CBE, PhD, FRSC, FRS. |

**Assistant Secretaries**

This list includes all who have served the Council in that office since the establishment of the separate secretariat in 1950. Names are listed in order of appointment as Assistant Secretary.

| | |
|---|---|
| 1947–52 | Alexander, W. G., CBE, MA, FRSE. |
| 1950–60 | Thorne, P. A. C. |
| 1951–61 | Ness, W., CBE. |
| 1957–59 | Woods, A. J. D., CBE. |
| 1959–67† | Jourdain, E. D. T. |
| 1960–65 | Oates, A., LLM. |
| 1961–71 | Berry, W. E., CBE, PhD. |
| 1965–71 | Parkinson, D. J., OBE, BA. |
| 1967–75 | Culley, F. J. S., BSc, LLB. |
| 1971–73 | Myers, G. M. P., MSc. |
| 1971–73 | Shimwell, J. H. |
| 1973–77 | Bird, F. V., OBE. |
| 1973–76 | Lester, E., BSc. |
| 1976– | Harris, R. J., BSc. |
| 1976–78 | Lake, J. V., PhD. |
| 1977–79 | Beauchamp, M. R. |
| 1977– | Croker, E. E. |
| 1978– | Jamieson, B. G., PhD. |
| 1979– | Coles, J. C. F. |

**Clerks to the Council**

| | |
|---|---|
| 1971–77 | Porter, L. S., OBE, MA, BSc. |
| 1977– | Coltman, E. S. |

# Appendix 4

## Assessors to the Council

From its first establishment the Council called officers of the Agricultural Departments into consultation from time to time. In 1941 it first formally appointed assessors from the Ministry of Agriculture and Fisheries and the Department of Agriculture for Scotland; these received papers, were free to attend all meetings except when confidential matters were under discussion, and could speak but not vote. In 1942 the Technical Secretary of the Agricultural Improvement Council for England and Wales was added as an Assessor, in 1944 a representative of the Ministry of Agriculture for Northern Ireland, and in 1946 one from the Scottish Agricultural Advisory Council.

Following the Agricultural Research Act 1956 and a consequential modification of the Council's Charter, the Secretary of State for Scotland was empowered to appoint a Member of Council, and the Minister of Agriculture, Fisheries and Food two Members, plus the Chief Veterinary Officer who was a member *ex officio*. These two Departments and the technical advisory bodies then ceased to appoint Assessors, but the Ministry of Agriculture for Northern Ireland has continued to do so. In addition it was agreed in 1962 that the Council of the Royal Society should appoint an Assessor from amongst its membership. Death in office is marked †.

**Ministry of Agriculture and Fisheries**

| | |
|---|---|
| 1942–43 | Wilkins, V. E., OBE, PhD. |
| 1944–45 | Nathan, C., CB, MA. |
| 1946–51 | Wall, R. G. R., CB, MA. |
| 1951–56 | Bartlett, A. B., MA. |

**Agricultural Improvement Council for England and Wales**

| | |
|---|---|
| 1942–44 | Fryer, Sir John C. F., KBE, MA, LLD, FRSE, FRS. |
| 1942–49 | Slater, Sir William K., KBE, DSc, FRIC, FRS. |
| 1949–56 | Morley Davies, W., CBE, MA, BSc, FRIC. |

**Department of Agriculture for Scotland**

| | |
|---|---|
| 1942–46 | Caie, J. M., CB, MA, LLD, BSc, FRSE. |
| 1946–52 | Senior, W. H., CB, MSc, FRSE. |
| 1951–54 | McCallum, J. R., MC, BSc. |
| 1955–56 | Sharman, G. D. |

**Scottish Agricultural Advisory Council**

| | |
|---|---|
| 1946–50† | Caie, J. M., CB, MA, LLD, BSc, FRSE (Dr. Caie was not replaced after his death). |

**Ministry of Agriculture for Northern Ireland**

| | |
|---|---|
| 1944–47 | Scott Robertson, G., DSc, FRIC. |
| 1947–50 | Baskett, Professor Sir Ronald G., OBE, DSc, FRIC. |
| 1953–59 | ,, |
| 1951–53 | Magowan, J. I. |
| 1959–66 | Lamont, Professor H. G., CBE, DSc, ScD, MRCVS. |
| 1966 | Young, J. A., BAgr (Mr. Young was appointed but did not attend a meeting). |
| 1966–70 | Woods, J.C.H., ISO, BAgr. |
| 1970– | Brown, W. O., MAgr, DSc, FRIC. |

**Royal Society**

| | |
|---|---|
| 1962–65 | Morgan, Professor W. T. J., CBE, DSc, FRIC, FRS. |
| 1965–66 | Katz, Professor Sir Bernard, MD, DSc, FRS. |
| 1966–67 | Krebs, Professor Sir Hans, MD, DSc, FRCP, FRS (previously a Member of Council). |
| 1967–68 | Blackman, Professor G. E., MA, FRS. |
| 1968–76 | Katz, Professor Sir Bernard, MD, DSc, FRS. (also a Member of Council during this term). |
| 1976–78 | Bell, G. D. H., CBE, DSc, FRS. |
| 1978– | Smith, Professor D. C., MA, DPhil, FRS. |

# Appendix 5

## Scientific Assistants/Advisers to the Secretary

The first full-time appointments of scientists to assist the Secretary to the Council were made before the establishment of the Council's separate office in 1950. Originally the title "Scientific Assistant to the Secretary" was used, but starting about 1960 the title "Scientific *Adviser*" gradually replaced it.

These officers are here listed in order of their dates of appointment. Death in office is marked †.

| | |
|---|---|
| 1948–62 | Samuel, G. G., MSc. |
| 1949–65 | Cheesman, E. E., CBE, DSc. |
| 1954–76 | Scarisbrick, R., PhD, MRCVS. |
| 1959–71 | Rudd-Jones, D., PhD. |
| 1959–66† | Moult, F. H., MSc. |
| 1961–64 | Lamb, J., OBE, MSc, FRIC. |
| 1963–71 | Gunn, D. L., CBE, DSc. |
| 1964–74 | Stevenson, G. C., BA. |
| 1965–71 | Webster, C. C., CMG, PhD, AICTA. |
| 1966– | Burns, K. N., BSc, MRCVS. |
| 1967–77 | Robinson, K. L., DSc, FRIC. |
| 1971– | Gasser, J. K. R., PhD, FRSC. |
| 1971–73 | Lester, E., BSc. |
| 1971–72 | Porter, Professor Helen K., DSc, FRSE, FRS (previously Second Secretary). |
| 1972–76 | Lake, J. V., PhD. |
| 1974– | Corbett, D. C. M., BSc. |
| 1974– | Fore, H., PhD, FRSC. |
| 1974–77 | Pritchard, A. J., PhD. |
| 1976– | Ingle, J., PhD. |
| 1976– | Perry, J. S., DSc. |
| 1976– | Ulbricht, T. L. V., DSc, FRSC. |
| 1977–79 | Hayes, J. D., PhD. |
| 1977– | Tayler, J. C., PhD. |
| 1977–78 | Vince-Prue, Daphne, PhD. |
| 1979– | Jenkins, G., BSc. |
| 1979– | Moorby, J., PhD. |

### Planning and Programmes Sections

In 1971 a small Planning Section was established, and included officers seconded from Research Institutes for limited periods. In 1976 the Head of Section became a Scientific Adviser (Special Duties) and the other staff then in post were transferred to a Programmes Section. The staff involved (in order of appointment) were as follows:

| | |
|---|---|
| 1971–76 | Ulbricht, T. L. V., DSc, FRSC (Head of Section). |
| 1971– | Wise, W. S., BSc, FRSC (Head of Section from 1976). |
| 1971–73 | Dodd, F. H., PhD (seconded from National Institute for Research in Dairying). |
| 1973–75 | Hance, R. J., PhD (seconded from Weed Research Organisation). |
| 1973–75 | McKay, A. D., BSc. |
| 1975– | Fell, Miss H., BSc. |

# Appendix 6

## The Directors of the Agricultural Research Institutes

# I  Council Institutes

**Animal Breeding Research Organisation**
(Animal Breeding and Genetics Research Organisation until 1951)
1945–50     White, Professor R. G., CBE, MSc, FRSE (1950–58 Consultant
                    Director).
1951–73     Donald, H. P., CBE, DSc, PhD, FRSE (later Professor).
1974–         King, J. W. B., MA, PhD, FIBiol, FRSE.

**Food Research Institute**
1965–77     Elsden, Professor S. R., PhD.
1977–         Curtis, Professor R. F., DSc.

**Institute of Animal Physiology**
1948–58     de Burgh Daly, I., CBE, MD, FRS.
1958–65     Gaddum, J. H., ScD, MRCS, LRCP, FRS.
1965–73     Keynes, R. D., ScD, FRS.
1973–74     Dawson, R. M. C., DSc, (Acting).
1974–         Cross, B. A., ScD, MRCVS, FRS.

**Institute for Research on Animal Diseases**
(Field Station, Compton, until 1961–62)
1937–42     Dunkin, Major G. W., MRCVS.
1942–67     Gordon, W. S., CBE, PhD, MRCVS, FRSE.
1967–72     Henderson, W. M., DSc, MRCVS (later Sir William).
1972–73     Pattison, I. H., BSc, FRCVS (Acting).
1973–         Payne, Professor J. M., PhD, MRCVS.

**Letcombe Laboratory**
(Radiobiological Laboratory until 1968)
1957–78     Scott Russell, R., CBE, DSc.
1978–         Lake, J. V., PhD.

**Meat Research Institute**
1963–73     Ingram, Professor M., CBE, MA, PhD, FIBiol, FIFST.
1973–79     Norris, Professor J. R., PhD, FIBiol.
1979–         Bailey, A. J., MA, PhD, ScD.

**Poultry Research Centre**
1947–62     Greenwood, A. W., CBE, DSc, FRSE.
1962–78     Carter, T. C., OBE, MA, PhD, DSc, FIBiol, FRSE.
1978–         Shannon, D. W. F., BAgr, PhD, DMS.

**Weed Research Organisation**
1960–64     Woodford, E. K., OBE, PhD.
1964–         Fryer, J. D., CBE, MA.

**Institutes taken over in 1959 by ARC from DSIR**

**Ditton Laboratory**
1959–69        Tomkins, R. G., PhD.

**Low Temperature Research Station**
1947–65        Bate-Smith, E. C., CBE, ScD.

**Pest Infestation Laboratory**
1940–68        Herford, G. V. B., CBE, MSc.
1968–70        Parkin, E. A., DSc.

# II  Grant-Aided Institutes (England and Wales)

**Animal Virus Research Institute**
Originally the Pirbright Experimental Station of the Foot-and-Mouth Disease Research
Committee, commonly known as the Foot-and-Mouth Disease Research Institute. From
1924 to 1939 the work was supervised on behalf of the Committee by the Director of
the Ministry of Agriculture and Fisheries' Veterinary Laboratory at Weybridge.

1951–63        Galloway, I. A., DSc, MRCVS (previously Scientific Superintendent,
               1939–51).
1964–79        Brooksby, J. B., CBE, DSc, PhD, FRCVS, FRSE, FRS.
1979–          Sellers, R. F., MA, ScD, PhD, BSc, MRCVS.

**East Malling Research Station**
1913–19        Wellington, Captain R., MC (War Service 1914–19).
1919–48        Hatton, R. G., CBE, DSc, FRS (later Sir Ronald) (Acting 1914–19).
1949–69        Tubbs, F. R., CBE, PhD.
1969–72        Pereira, H. C., DSc, FRS (later Sir Charles).
1972–79        Posnette, Professor A. F., CBE, ScD, FRS.
1979–          Graham-Bryce, I. J., DPhil.

**Glasshouse Crops Research Institute, Littlehampton**
The Institute was continued in 1953 from the Experimental and Research Station at
Cheshunt, which had been founded in 1914.

*Cheshunt*
1914–20        Lister, A. B., BSc.
1921–53        Bewley, W. F., CBE, DSc, VMH.

*Littlehampton*
1953–56        Bewley, W. F., CBE, DSc, VMH.
1956–71        Toovey, F. W., OBE, BSc, FIBiol.
1971–          Rudd-Jones, D., CBE, MA, PhD, FIBiol.

**Grassland Research Institute**
(Grassland Improvement Station, Drayton, 1940–45. Grassland Research Station, Drayton, 1946–49.)
1940–45     Stapledon, Professor Sir George, CBE, FRS.
1945–64     Davies, William, CBE, DSc.
1964–77     Woodford, Professor E. K., OBE, PhD.
1977–        Lazenby, Professor A., PhD.

**Houghton Poultry Research Station**
1948–73     Gordon, R. F., CBE, DSc, FRCVS.
1974–        Biggs, P. M., DSc, FRCVS, FIBiol, FRS.

**John Innes Institute**
1910–26     Bateson, Professor W., FRS.
1926–39     Hall, Sir A. Daniel, KCB, FRS.
1939–53     Darlington, Professor C. D., FRS.
1953–54     Lawrence, W. J. C., (Acting).
1954–66     Dodds, K. S., DSc.
1966–67     Cheesman, E. E., CBE, DSc. (Acting).
1967–79     Markham, Professor R., PhD, FRS.
1979–80     Davies, Professor D. R., PhD. (Acting).
1980–        Woolhouse, Professor H. W., PhD.

**Long Ashton Research Station**
1903–05     Lloyd, F. J., FIC, FCS.
1905–43     Barker, Professor B. T. P., CBE, MA.
1943–57     Wallace, Professor T., CBE, MC, DSc, FRIC, VMH, FRS.
1957–67     Kearns, Professor H. G. H., OBE, PhD, DSc, FIBiol.
1967–75     Hudson, Professor J. P., CBE, MBE(Mil); GM, PhD, VMH, NDH, FIBiol.
1975–        Hirst, Professor J. M., DSC, PhD, FIBiol, FRS.

**National Institute of Agricultural Engineering**
(Continuing the work of the Institute for Research in Agricultural Engineering (IRAE), University of Oxford, 1924–42)
1924–31     Owen, B. J., MSc, MEng.
1931–42     Denham, H. J., MA, DSc, FInstP } Directors, IRAE
1942–47     Wright, S. J., MA.
1947–63     Cashmore, W. H., CBE, BA, MIAgrE.
1963–77     Moss, Professor C. J., CBE, BSc, CEng, FIMechE, FIAgrE.
1977–        Bell, Professor R. L., BSc, PhD, CEng, FIM, FInstP.

**National Institute for Research in Dairying**
1912–32     Stenhouse Williams, Professor R., MB.
1933–58     Kay, Professor H. D., CBE, DSc, FRS.
1958–59     Mattick, A. T. R., CBE, PhD. (Acting).
1959–67     Baskett, Professor Sir Ronald, OBE, DSc, FRIC.
1967–77     Weitz, Professor B. G. F., OBE DSc, MRCVS.
1978–        Porter, Professor J. W. G., PhD.

**National Vegetable Research Station**
1948–67     Philp, J., CBE, PhD.
1967–77     Wright, Professor D. W., CBE, MA.
1977–        Bleasdale, Professor J. K. A., PhD, FIBiol.

**Plant Breeding Institute**
(University of Cambridge 1912–52)
1912–36        Biffen, Professor R. H., FRS (later Sir Rowland).
1936–46        Hunter, H., DSc.
1948–71        Bell, G. D. H., CBE, DSc, FRS. (Acting, 1946–48).
1971–78        Riley, R., DSc, FRS.
1978–79        Rogers, H. H., BSc, FIBiol. (Acting).
1979–          Day, P. R., PhD.

**Rothamsted Experimental Station**
1843–1900      Lawes, Sir John B., Bt, FRS.
1843–1901      Gilbert, Sir Joseph H., FRS.
1902–12        Hall, Sir A. Daniel, FRS.
1912–43        Russell, Sir E. John, FRS.
1943–58        Ogg, Sir William G., FRSE.
1958–72        Bawden, Sir Frederick C., FRS.
1972–73        Cooke, Dr. G. W., CBE, FRS. (Acting).
1973–          Fowden, Dr. L., FRS.

**Welsh Plant Breeding Station**
1919–42        Stapledon, Professor R. G., CBE, FRS (later Sir George).
1942–50        Jenkin, Professor T. J., CBE, DSc.
1950–58        Jones, Professor E. T., MSc.
1958–74        Thomas, Professor P. T., CBE, PhD.
1975–          Cooper, Professor J. P., DSc, FRS.

**Wye College, Department of Hop Research**
1947–52        Burgess, A. H., DSc.
1953–54        Thompson, F. C. (Acting).
1954–62        Darling, H. S., CBE, DSc.
1962–63        Thompson, F. C. (Acting).
1963–          Neve, R. A., OBE, PhD.

# III   Grant-Aided Institutes (Scotland)

**Animal Diseases Research Association**
1921–25        Gaiger, Professor S. H., MRCVS.
1926–29        Poole, W. A., MRCVS.
1930–54        Russell Greig, J., CBE, PhD, MRCVS, FRSE.
1954–77        Stamp, J. T., CBE, DSc, FRCVS, FRSE.
1977–          Martin, W. B., PhD, MRCVS, DVSM.

**Hannah Research Institute**
(Hannah Dairy Research Institute, 1928–71)
1928–30        Cathcart, Professor E. P., CBE, MD, FRS. (Interim Director 1928–29,
                   Hon. Director 1929–30).
1930–50        Wright, N.C., (later Sir Norman) CB, DSc. (Seconded to Ministry of
                   Food 1947–50).
1950–70        Smith, J. A. B., CBE, DSc, FRSE. (Acting 1947–50).
1971–80        Rook, Professor J. A. F., DSc, FRSE.

**Hill Farming Research Organisation**
1953–65     Wannop, A. R., OBE, BSc(Agr), BEng, FRSE.
1965–68     Reid, R. L., PhD. (Associate Director 1964–65).
1968–80     Cunningham, Professor J. M. M., CBE, PhD, FRSE.
1980–       Eadie, J., BSc(Agric).

**Macaulay Institute for Soil Research**
1930–43     Ogg, W. G., PhD, FRSE (later Sir William) (Honorary Director, 1943–45).
1945–58     McArthur, D. N., CBE, DSc, FRSE.
1958–68     Stewart, A. B., CBE, PhD, FRSE.
1968–75     Mitchell, R. L., PhD, FRSE.
1975–       West, Professor T. S., DSc, FRSE.

**Rowett Research Institute**
1914–45     Boyd Orr, J. MD, DSc, FRS (later Sir John, later Lord Boyd Orr).
1945–65     Cuthbertson, Sir David P., CBE, MD, DSc, FRSE.
1965–       Blaxter, Sir Kenneth L., DSc, FRSE, FRS.

**Scottish Horticultural Research Institute***
1953–65     Swarbrick, T., CBE, PhD, SHM.
1965–71     Cadman, C. H., PhD, FIBiol, FRSE, SHM.
1972–81     Taylor, C. E., PhD, FIBiol, FRSE.

**Scottish Institute of Agricultural Engineering***
(Formerly Scottish Machinery Testing Station 1946–49: National Institute of Agricultural Engineering Scottish Station, 1949–75)
1946–77     West, W. J., CBE, BA, FIAgrE, FRAgS, FRSE.
1977–       Blight, D. P., MSc(AgrEng), PhD, CEng, FIMechE.

**Scottish Plant Breeding Station***
1921–25     Drummond, M., FRSE.
1925–50     Robb, W.
1950–65     Gregor, J. W., CBE, DSc, FRSE.
1965–76     Simmonds, N. W., ScD, FRSE.
1976–81     Macer, Professor R. C. F., PhD., FIBiol.

***Scottish Crop Research Institute**
The Scottish Crop Research Institute was formed on 1 February 1981 by the amalgamation on the site at Mylnefield, Dundee, of the former Scottish Plant Breeding Station and the former Scottish Horticultural Research Institute. Dr. Charles E. Taylor was appointed Director of the Combined Institute.
1981–       Taylor, C. E., Ph.D, FIBiol, FRSE.

# Appendix 7

# The Recognition of Trade Unions by the Agricultural Research Council and the Establishment of a Consultative Machinery in the Agricultural Research Service

E. E. Croker, Chief Personnel Officer, Agricultural Research Council

(a)  *The non-industrial unions and the Whitley Council of the Agricultural Research Service*

Apart from ARC Headquarters, where a Whitley Council has been in existence for more than a quarter of a century, trade union organisation in the ARS is of relatively recent growth. With a few exceptions at local level, some of which are mentioned below, dealings with the unions, eg between ARC management on the one side and the Association of Scientific Workers and The Society of Technical Civil Servants on the other, were quite informal before 1966. In that year the Institution of Professional Civil Servants (IPCS) and the Society of Civil Servants (SCS) (now the Society of Civil and Public Servants — SCPS) became the first unions to achieve recognition by the ARC.

IPCS was recognised as the sole negotiating body for scientific, technical and professional classes. A negotiating procedure was agreed which made provision for central negotiation on matters of common interest to the Institutes, including hours, pay, leave, promotion, recruitment and redundancy, staff relations, superannuation, training and travel and subsistence, although in matters of hours, pay and leave, the ARC has, in fact followed the Civil Service. Questions arising from the application of the agreements were to be discussed locally between the IPCS and the Institutes concerned. Of the potential membership of 4 500 in the Agricultural Research Service (ARS), IPCS in 1980 has a membership of some 3 700.

The SCS gained recognition for executive grades. No formal negotiating procedure was agreed but in practice the same areas for central negotiation applied as for the IPCS. Potential membership for the Society is very much smaller than for the IPCS (about 200) but a high proportion of those eligible are members of this union.

In 1969 the Civil Service Union was granted sole recognition for laboratory attendants, stores supervisors, telephonists, non-industrial cleaners and messengers, and similar non-industrial grades.

The Civil and Public Services Association was initially slow to gain members, and was not recognised by the ARC until 1974. Grades covered are secretaries, clerical workers and machine operators. Other unions, such as the Association of Government Supervisors and Radio Officers, have attracted a small local membership from time to time, and in some cases local, but not national, recognition.

In large parts of the public service joint consultation between management on one side, and unions representing all the non-industrial staff on the other, is conducted through Whitley Councils (named after the chairman of the Committee which proposed the method during the First World War). A proposal to set up a Whitley Council covering all the Institutes and Units in the ARS, including the Scottish Agricultural Research Institutes, was first mooted in 1971. The question remained in abeyance until 1973, when a formal request for the formation of a Whitley Council was received from the four major non-industrial unions. The Agricultural Research Council agreed to this in principle at a meeting on 19 June 1973, and consideration of a draft constitution followed. The first meeting of the Whitley Council was held on 22 April 1974, and the constitution was put into operation for the ARS, with the exception of ARC Headquarters staff who preferred to retain their own Whitley Council. This division persisted until 1980 when the Headquarters Whitley Council was disbanded and the constituent unions agreed to join the ARS Whitley Council, the constitution of which was centrally ratified at the annual meeting in April 1980.

The ARS Whitley Council consists of up to 28 members, 14 of whom are appointed by ARC and the Department of Agriculture and Fisheries for Scotland (DAFS) and 14 by the constituent unions. The Secretary to the Council is Chairman, and the Vice-Chairman is the elected Chairman of the Staff Side. Since the inception of the Whitley Council in 1974 there have been two Vice-Chairmen — Mr. P. Richardson and Dr. P. J. Welbank. The full Council normally meets once a year, and most of the business is transacted within sub-committees, usually under the chairmanship of the Chief Personnel Officer of ARC.

The first local Whitley Committee was set up at the Meat Research Institute when that institute was formed in 1968, at the time when the Low Temperature Research Station of the Department of Scientific and Industrial Research was disbanded. Other institutes followed, and eleven now have their own local Whitley committees, for which a model constitution was agreed in 1976. Industrial unions may join local Whitley Committees, subject to local agreement.

(b)   *The industrial unions and the Joint Industrial Council*
Industrial unions were somewhat slower than the non-industrial to gain recognition. An Industrial Whitley Committee came into being as long ago as 1963 at the National Institute for Agricultural Engineering. Its membership, on the staff side, was formed from the traditional industrial unions. Elsewhere progress was slower. Although the Civil Service Union was recognised for ARS non-industrial grades in 1969, recognition for industrial unions was for a long time in doubt. The CSU attracted industrial members and local recognition at several institutes. Other unions which achieved local recognition were the National Union for Agricultural and Allied Workers (NUAAW), the Electrical, Electronic and Plumbing Trades Union (EEPTU), the Transport and General Workers Union (TGWU), the General and Municipal Workers Union (GMWU), the Union of Construction Allied Trades and Technicians (UCATT) and the Amalgamated Union of Engineering Workers (AUEW). In some cases grades are covered by more than one union.

A joint request for recognition and for the establishment of negotiating machinery for the ARS was received from NUAAW and CSU in 1974. EEPTU, TGWU and GMWU subsequently also asked for recognition and representation, and AUEW declared an interest. Formation of negotiating machinery was approved in principle in 1974 and a constitution for a Joint Industrial Council (JIC) was drafted. AUEW did not become a constituent union of the JIC, but receives relevant papers from the trade union side.

The constitution of the JIC was adopted at the first meeting in January 1977. The JIC consists of up to 18 members, 9 appointed by the ARC and DAFS and 9 by the unions. The Council is chaired by the Chief Personnel Officer of ARC, and the present Vice-Chairman is Mr. R. Pierson, a full time officer of the NUAAW. Industrial conditions of service have for some time been moving towards equality with the non-industrial, and the Whitley Council and JIC have agreed that it is in their interest to work together in matters of common concern.

(c)   *The operation of the negotiating machinery*
Within the negotiating machinery described above, the unions are consulted about all matters concerning the terms and conditions of employment of the staff. The Agricultural Research Service has 23 employers; the Agricultural Research Council, which is the employer of the staff in its own eight institutes and five units, and 22 separate employing bodies at the Institutes grant-aided by ARC or DAFS. There was close liaison with the Grant-aided Institutes at all stages in setting up the Whitley Council

and the Joint Industrial Council, and when the Whitley Council was established they all agreed to be bound by the agreements reached under the auspices of that body. Similarly, resolutions were passed by the Governing Bodies accepting the Joint Industrial Council as a negotiating forum on their behalf and recognising agreements reached in the JIC as operating in their institutes.

A somewhat unwieldy structure for coordinating management practices is created by there being 23 separate employers in the Service. However, serious difficulties have been avoided; there have been constructive discussions with the joint unions in the Committees of the Whitley Council and in the Joint Industrial Council and with individual unions where appropriate, on a wide range of topics relating to the terms and conditions of employment of the staff. An important part was played in the introduction of the new superannuation schemes for the Service in 1975 and many service-wide agreements have been entered into, including those on appointment and promotion, training, disciplinary procedure and redundancy procedure.

# Index

NOTES

NOTES

**NOTES**

NOTES

# Contents